Emma

Emma is the story of the eponymous Miss Woodhouse who, having lost her close companion Anne Taylor to marriage, sets out on an ill-fated career of match-making in the town of Highbury. Taking as her subject the pretty but dreary Harriet Smith, she manages to cause misunderstandings with every new tactic she employs. Though precious and spoilt, Emma is charming to all around her and so it takes her some time to learn her lesson and profit from spending less time worrying about how other people should live their lives.

Jane Austen was born in 1775. The seventh child of a country rector, she lived at Steventon in Hampshire until 1801, when she moved first to Bath, then to Southampton. Her father died in 1805, and from that time the Austens settled at nearby Chawton. From a young age Jane entertained her family with stories and plays; by 23 she had written early versions of her first three major novels, *Sense and Sensibility*, *Pride and Prejudice* and *Northanger Abbey*, though they were not published for several years. Twelve years later she started work on *Mansfield Park*; *Emma* and *Persuasion*, her last complete novel, soon followed. Jane Austen died at Winchester in 1817.

Emma

Jane Austen

THE WINCHESTER AUSTEN

Concept, design, introduction text and treatment
© Worth Press Ltd 2007

Introductions by Maggie Lane, John Wiltshire, Josephine Ross and
Caroline Sanderson ©Worth Press Ltd 2007

First published 2007 by Worth Press Limited, Cambridge, UK
www.worthpress.co.uk

British Library Publication Data
A catalogue record for this book is available from the British Library.

ISBN: 978-1-903025-59-8 (jacketed edition)
ISBN: 978-1-903025-65-9 (Skivertex edition)

Every effort has been made to ensure the accuracy of the information
presented in this book. The publisher will not assume liability for damages
caused by inaccuracies in the data and makes no warranty whatsoever express
or implied.

The images used in this book come from the public domain or
are public commons.

Designed, edited and typeset by Bookcraft Limited, Stroud, UK
Printed and bound in China by Imago

This series is named after the English city of Winchester, the county town of
Hampshire, where Jane Austen spent most of her life. She is buried in the
north aisle of the nave of Winchester Cathedral.

The endpaper image is 'The Cloakroom of the Clifton Assembly Rooms',
a painting by Rolina Sharples.

Contents

Maggie Lane is the author of *Jane Austen's World* and *Jane Austen and Food*, and a former Honorary Secretary of the Jane Austen Society. Her introductions to *The Winchester Austen* cover aspects of Jane Austen's social and economic world, including religion and food.

Dr John Wiltshire is Reader in the School of Communication, Arts and Critical Enquiry, La Trobe University in Australia, and is one of the world's leading Austen scholars. He has published three books on Austen, including *Recreating Jane Austen*, and is presently working on *Austen and England: Critical Politics*. His introductions to *The Winchester Austen* look at modern ways of understanding and interpreting the novels.

Josephine Ross is the author of *The Men Who Would be King*, and has written television drama scripts and a number of histories and biographies, including *The Winter Queen* and *The Tudors*. Her most recent publication is *Jane Austen: A Companion*. Her introductions to *The Winchester Austen* cover the historical and social context, including the role of women and women and fashion.

Caroline Sanderson is a devotee of Jane Austen and has made many trips visiting the locations of various periods in Austen's life and the possible basis of the places in her novels. Caroline's journey in search of Jane Austen is recounted in her latest book *A Rambling Fancy*. She is also a writer and reviewer for Bookseller magazine, and has written a travel book for children called *Pick Your Brains About Greece*. Her introductions to *The Winchester Austen* explore the geographical settings of the novels.

Emma

Modern Interpretations

John Wiltshire

Austen's *Emma*, gladsome, clever, and rich, seems to unite the comedy of *Pride and Prejudice* with the complexity of *Mansfield Park*, and has been read for nearly two centuries with very few to dispute its place as its author's greatest achievement. It was the second work to be completed in Jane Austen's Chawton period, which saw her living in a village, perhaps not unlike the Highbury of the novel, surrounded and supported by a family of unattached ladies. It is in fact the depth and complexity of Emma's rendering of a compact, rather isolated community, and its combining of this tight focus with immense narrative ingenuity, that has provided readers with great amusement, endless opportunities for explication, and faced film-makers with insuperable challenges.

Emma Woodhouse, with her delight in schemes and scheming of all kinds and her pleasure in contradiction for its own sake, is the motor force of the novel, a character whose energy and imaginative gusto runs headlong into the cramped and routine ways of a world only as large as the village, and always threatening to shrink to the size of her invalid father's drawing room. *Emma* is told from the point of view of its heroine, though slyly enough managing to suggest that she sees with the eyes of prejudice, and even occasionally delighting to trick the reader by blending its own narrative 'voice' with her own inner thoughts. Full of references to deceptions and games, and itself gaily teasing the reader, the novel is also at times surprisingly touching and even painful. Reginald Farrer wrote as far back as 1917 that even 'twelve readings' of *Emma* would give pleasure 'not repeated only, but squared and squared again with each perusal,' indicating that, on each re-reading, one finds more and more to enjoy and discover. So it is no surprise to find that critics – who usually offer, perforce, only one 'reading' of the novel – offer diverse interpretations that often complement rather than oppose each other. And the criticism of *Emma,* more than any other of the novels, tends towards delighted appreciation, and increasingly towards wonderment at its technical skill and artifice.

The most discussed technical achievement of *Emma* has been its employment of 'free indirect speech.' This is the mode (or trope) by which the thoughts of the character through whom the reader receives most of his or her information, Emma herself, are simultaneously represented and critiqued. 'When free indirect style mimics Emma's thoughts and feelings, it simultaneously inflects them into keener observations of its own; for our benefit, if never for hers, it identifies, ridicules, corrects all the secret vanities and self-deceptions of which Emma, pleased as Punch, remains comically unconscious' (D. A. Miller offers a penetrating discussion in *Jane Austen and the Secret of Style,* 2003). Earlier critics used this as a cue for the sternly moralistic view that Emma's character faults are continually being exposed. Thus Marilyn Butler in *Jane Austen and the War of Ideas* (1975) argued that 'The novel's attitude to the workings of Emma's consciousness is steadily critical. Although so much of the action takes place in the inner life, the theme of the novel is scepticism about the qualities that make it up – intuition, imagination, original insight.' Free indirect speech, in A. Walton Litz's words, made certain 'that we would understand and criticize every aspect of Emma's self-deception by establishing a context of ironic qualifications and explicit judgements' (*Jane Austen: A Study of her Artistic Development,* 1965). Later critics have argued rather that 'the authorial relation to character in free indirect speech' mitigates against just such judgements – such a 'composite narrative' connecting the reader with the character, not detaching us from her. In Frances Ferguson's words, 'the novel is hard on Emma to exactly the same extent that it is committed to her' (Jane Austen, *Emma*, and the Impact of Form,' *Modern Language Quarterly*, March 2000).

If, according to the earlier criticism, the novel exposed Emma's self-deceptions, Mr Knightley embodied the standard by which they were to be measured. 'The reader always knows when [Emma] is wrong, because the novel's other style ['manly and direct'] has given him the unmistakable note of simplicity and sincerity,' Butler claimed, a point re-fashioned in Roger Gard's *Jane Austen's Novels: the Art of Clarity* (1992) so that it applies to Emma and Knightley when they act in concert: 'This clear-headed efficiency is a kind of moral pointer. Clear speech is always indicative in Jane Austen.' 'Knightley is established early as completely reliable,' declared Wayne Booth in his influential *The Rhetoric of Fiction* of 1961. Many interpretations of the novel in the later twentieth century therefore considered Knightley a version of the 'mentor-lover,' familiar to readers of eighteenth-century fiction in such incarnations as Sir Charles Grandison, Lord Orville (in Frances Burney's *Evelina*) or even Mr Darcy. This is the male who is at one and the same time both the heroine's love interest, and in a position to teach her the truth about herself and the world she lives in. Such readings considered the book to be about the dangers of Emma's erring imagination, and focused on the progression of incidents in the novel that educate and eventually, perhaps, reform her. Though there is something very unfashionable about this approach, which Eve Sedgwick famously labelled 'the spectacle of a girl being taught a lesson' in her essay 'Jane Austen and the Masturbating Girl' (*Tendencies*, 1993), it points to an important aspect of the novel's narrative structure. Its comedy does turn on the fact that Emma is first egregiously mistaken about Mr Elton's intentions, then about Frank Churchill and Jane Fairfax, then (whilst thinking she won't commit the same error again) about Harriet and Frank – and that the reader must at least half suspect this. What Sedgwick derided as a lesson is largely inseparable from the reader enjoying the joke.

Mr Knightley's position as custodian of good sense, though, can certainly be questioned and qualified. In *Jane Austen and the Fiction of her Time* (1999) Mary Waldron re-reads one of the novel's most famous set-pieces, the first big quarrel between Emma and Knightley over Harriet's refusal of Robert Martin's proposal. Waldron argues that Knightley is 'complacent' and 'smug' in his advocacy of Robert Martin's courtship, joining with his socially inferior 'friend' in 'a male conspiracy to trap Harriet before she has time to protest.' She suggests that Knightley's arguments are partisan, and when challenged by Emma, contradictory. Waldron's Emma, on the other hand, is 'rational' and 'cogent.' Knightley's arguments 'are a mass of ill-thought notions, which he is quite prepared to reverse in the interests of getting his own way.' It is interesting when a critic starts to sound like Emma herself, and useful to be reminded that Knightley is not always right, and that Emma does scent a male conspiracy. But is he really smug? 'I praised the fair lady too, and altogether sent [Martin] away very happy. If he had not esteemed my opinion before, he would have thought highly of me then; and, I dare say, left the house thinking me the best friend and counsellor man ever had.' His attitude is one of irony at his own role; and the phrase 'fair lady,' which Waldron finds 'diminishes' Harriet, typifies his benevolent amusement at the whole transaction. 'The problem with such arguments,' as Terry Castle remarks in her 'Introduction' to the Oxford World's Classics edition of the novel (1998), 'is how deeply they betray the experience of reading.' A first reader of *Emma* will probably, following Austen's clues, side with Mr Knightley, and events in the novel certainly prove him to be usually correct. Another reading though, might produce another version – perhaps one in which the reader finds both participants in this quarrel making sweeping generalisations and assertions as they set to in a confrontation that provides the reader with the enjoyable spectacle of two very intelligent people crossing swords and losing their heads. And this is a variety of several different scenes between them that in Castle's words 'fairly buzz with sexual tension.'

Criticism of *Emma,* though continuing to focus on the Emma/Knightley relationship, has increasingly acknowledged the importance of the matrix of village life, and its network of relationships and dependencies in which they live. 'The predicted responses of dull Highbury are not just a comic background for the main protagonists' lives,' comments Roger Gard, 'They are interactive with those lives, and each depends intimately on each.' Gard shows, for example, how a moment in which Mr Knightley's love for Emma is hinted at occurs in the midst of the neighbourly conspiracy to chide Jane Fairfax for walking in the rain; and how Miss Bates's long speeches during the ball at the Crown are full of amusing information hinting at Frank Churchill's constant attendance on Jane. So that Miss Bates's chatter is important to what Castle calls 'the illusion of being included in a palpably human world.' 'We feel ourselves profoundly involved in Emma's destiny and that of the little community in which she lives and moves.' Miss Bates's ramblings, besides conveying important clues to the hidden romantic plot, give us – with their familiar references to figures who never appear in the novel, like Patty, John Saunders, Mrs Wallis at the bakery, William Larkins, Mr Perry – a feeling of depth and intricacy, the pulse of a living community formed by gifts, charity, neighbourliness and gossip. 'Her talk is a constant validation of others, concern for others, and applause for others' concern for her,' Isobel Grundy writes; 'Miss Bates's talk weaves a web of interdependence, of reciprocity.' ('Why do they talk so much? How can we stand it?' in *The Talk in Jane Austen,* 2002).

Miss Bates is invited to all the festivities of the gentry, but she also pays charity visits to her father's old groom, gossips to Patty, and is familiar with Larkins, Mr Knightley's agent. The apothecary Mr Perry calls her his 'very old friend.' The word friend is ubiquitous in this novel, just as the notion of friendship is essential to its ethical world. The generalised benevolence that is characteristic of Highbury means different things between different people, but, as William Deresiewitz argues, this 'old style of Highbury friendship create[s] the conditions of its own transcendence', when the word 'friend' assumes a potent meaning between John Knightley and Jane Fairfax, and, ultimately between Emma and Frank Churchill (*Jane Austen and the Romantic Poets*, 2004). It is also a pivotal word in the later encounters between Emma and Knightley. From this point of view *Emma* presents an apparently classless society, in which neighbourliness and benevolence can seem to override and subsume the still salient distinctions of wealth and status.

More recently, critics have understood *Emma* as a contribution to national consciousness in the closing year of the Napoleonic Wars. Roger Sales, in his chapter on the novel in *Jane Austen and Representations of Regency England* (1994), argues that 'the differences between English and French values,' are a recurrent motif of the text, and that they are 'embodied respectively by the village and the watering place' (Frank Churchill is associated with Weymouth, Mrs Elton with Bath). However, Sales suggests, Mr Knightley's 'Francophobia' is not necessarily shared by the novel. Others have disagreed. Claudia Johnson's 'Remaking English Manhood in *Emma*,' in her *Equivocal Beings* (1995), argues that the novel creates a new plain style of manliness which 'is a matter of national import.' *Emma* 'persistently asks how a man should behave and what he ought to do.' It 'works ... to redefine masculinity.' Mr Knightley's manliness is contrasted both with Mr Woodhouse's old-fashioned courtesy and sentimentality, and Frank Churchill's modern gallantry. Situating the novel after Burkean sentiment had had its day Johnson argues that *Emma* seeks 'to recover a native tradition of gentry liberty, which valued its manly independence from tyrannical rule, where that rule is figured as courtly, feminine, and feminizing ... – a tradition which the French Revolution made dangerous by fulfilling.' In valuing the 'manly' it also valued the 'manliness' in women like Emma herself, so that the concept is both re-invented and cleansed of its sexist implications.

Mr Knightley's contrast of the amiable, 'the true English style,' which is sincere and direct, with the 'aimable,' gallant and dissembling, French version, is important too in Brian Southam's 'Emma: England, Peace and Patriotism' in *Jane Austen and the Navy* (2000). Southam's point is that *Emma* 'is the only novel in which Jane Austen examines the ideas of Englishness and patriotism', and where 'the traditional enmity of England and France is played out in the antipathy between George Knightley, a gentlemanly John Bull, and the Frenchified Frank Churchill.' Frank's 'patriotism,' exercised in purchasing gloves at Ford's shop, is the 'refuge of a scoundrel' (to use Samuel Johnson's John Bullish phrase): whilst the Donwell Abbey estate, home of the Knightleys for centuries, is celebrated as both ancient and functional, and 'identified as being quintessentially English.' Thus this apparently parochial novel, with its very confined setting, reverberates with political and historical implications.

Modern criticism of the novel, then, has progressed from a focus on Emma and Mr Knightley, to an interest in the community in which their relationship is set, and thence outwards further, to England in 1815. This recognition that the novel is a deep and intricate work of art, and a contribution to national culture, is hardly reflected in the two films released in 1996. The British film directed by Dairmuid Lawrence (1997) reminds the viewer of the class society that accords Emma and Knightley their privileges, but fails to capture the depth of the local community. The Hollywood film, written and directed by Douglas McGrath (1996), is more interested in comedy than romance, and in creating a nostalgic world, to carry any of the import of the novel. In both films the role of Miss Bates, such a key to the novel's own world, is only focused on at the Box Hill picnic.

The British *Emma,* with script by Andrew Davies, does try to place Emma's story within a social setting. But rather than the tightly-knit, and seemingly classless community of the novel (in which Miss Bates interacts with everyone in the village) it presents a Marxist sense of this as a class society. (David Monaghan in *Jane Austen on Screen* (2003) however, gives a cogent account of the film as a demonstration of the conservative

'Burke's organicist social theories.') The labour of servants is as conspicuous here as it is inconspicuous in the novel. Those scenes in *Emma* which suggest so amusingly and at the same time so gratifyingly how deeply runs the notion of kindness in Highbury (as Deresiewitz notes) are omitted. The film replaces the novel's sense of a functional, integrated community with a hierarchical one. The invented final scene, in which Emma and Knightley address the labourers and servants, and Emma shakes hands with Robert Martin, seeks to present a reconciliation, to make a final comedic resolution of these divisions, but the effect is really to underscore the hierarchy, rather than to dissolve it.

The Miramax film is a star vehicle for Gwyneth Paltrow, which alludes to the 1940 *Pride and Prejudice*. Both begin with a credit sequence that emphasises the distance of its action from the contemporary world. 'It happened in Old England' in the earlier film is now 'A time when one's town was one's world' and both title sequences are accompanied by drawings of villages and great houses. Though the film credits state that it was filmed 'on location in Dorset and London,' the effect is consciously to imitate the artificial studio-world of the forties film. In *Emma*, the cycle of the seasons – beginning with approaching winter, moving through spring to mid-summer – is integral to its realism, but in this film there is no sense of seasonal development; instead there is a wildly pastoral effect, as Paltrow, always hatless and clad in flimsy Grecian-style gowns, meets Frank Churchill outdoors in February. The curious tent under which Emma and Harriet exchange confidences reproduces a similar one in *Pride and Prejudice*, with the same quaintly period touch. And the archery scene between Garson and Olivier (itself derived from the nineteenth-century illustrated editions of Austen) is archly recreated in an exchange of barbs between Paltrow and Jeremy Northam's Mr Knightley. The film includes moments of latter-day screwball comedy, with a clumsy Harriet dropping her basket, and running jokes – such as Emma's attempts to get away from Mr Elton's attentions – that turn Austen's comedy into farce. The gardens over-bloom fantastically, the settings are grandiose and Victorian (rather than modest and Regency) and filmed in syrupy amber light. This film is not about Old England, it is about Old Hollywood.

Both movies try to reproduce the novel's illusion of delightful intimacy with the imaginative inner life of Emma Woodhouse. The McGrath film intermittently uses the voice-over and has Emma confiding her thoughts to her 'Dear Diary'(!) or praying aloud in a chapel. These are deliberately old-fashioned strategies, but there is some clever modern editing through which Emma's inward thoughts segue into her spoken words. The Davies script uses fantasy or dream-sequences, in the manner of the older British *Northanger Abbey*, to represent Emma's imagination. Some of these are plausible visual parallels to Emma's thoughts in the novel (such as her idea that Jane Fairfax was rescued from drowning by Mr Dixon), others are more interventionist. Emma looks at a portrait of Frank Churchill and he, amazingly, steps forward and kisses her hand. But the film does at least attempt to reproduce the comic play between Emma's inner life and the actuality that surrrounds her.

Neither version has the secure artistic purpose of *Clueless* (1995), the relatively modest teen comedy that captures more of *Emma*'s warmth and appeal than either. But *Clueless* imitates only the first third of the novel closely, and is a fantasy, whereas Jane Austen's *Emma*, whilst presenting a wholly enjoyable experience, and employing techniques of consummate artistry, somehow, as so many critics agree, convinces the reader that the world it presents is real.

Emma

Regency Life

Maggie Lane

Food and Farming

Jane Austen grew up in a household that was virtually self-sufficient in food. Her father, besides being a clergyman, was a gentleman farmer, renting a 200-acre farm and employing a bailiff to oversee its working. It was a mixed farm, producing cereal crops and meat. The surplus not required by the household – and it was a large household, comprising not only the seven children but the servants and a number of boarding pupils – was sold for profit. Farming talk – the state of the harvest, the effect of the weather, prices at market – was familiar to Jane from an early age.

Her mother looked after the poultry yard, dairy, beehives and kitchen garden, as well as overseeing the cookery and planning of menus. Only citrus fruits, spices, tea, coffee and sugar had to be purchased, and these commodities were valued accordingly.

Jane and her sister Cassandra were trained by their mother in all the arts of housekeeping, for even having a number of servants left the mistress of the house with the task of directing them in their work. Jane's letters are full of remarks about the provision of food and drink. Interestingly, however, she gives her heroines very little concern with such matters. In *Pride and Prejudice*, Mrs Bennet remarks indignantly that *her* daughters have nothing to do in the kitchen; it is fortunate indeed that Jane and Elizabeth both marry wealthy husbands. How the untrained, feckless Lydia will run her house is another matter – probably with as much lack of method and comfort as the slatternly Mrs Price in *Mansfield Park*. Mrs Bennet has done her daughters – and her putative grandchildren – no favours.

It is in the novel *Emma* that food production and consumption are most conspicuous. This is partly because Emma Woodhouse herself is already mistress of a household, keeping house for her father even before her marriage, and partly because the hero is a gentleman farmer who takes an active interest in the cultivation of his land. Food, which most frequently appears in the guise of a gift from one person who has plenty to others who are without, runs through *Emma* like a metaphor for the spiritual nourishment and interdependence of a community. In this sense, it is the novel most rooted in the fundamentals of life. Tied firmly to the seasons, there is a solidity about the world of *Emma* that generations of readers have found deeply satisfying.

Not that Emma herself ever thinks or talks about food in the sense of a meal anticipated or enjoyed. None of the heroines is allowed to have the natural relish for food that Jane Austen's own letters evince. In fiction, she regards preoccupation with food as vulgar, shallow or greedy, and only the most unworthy characters are guilty of it. No, Emma's relationship with food is that of the lady bountiful. Suiting her own notions of herself as principal lady in the community, she takes pride in providing exquisite dishes for her guests and charity to her neighbours. Housekeeping comes easily to Emma, she has been doing it since she was sixteen, and the comfortable income of her father supports a housekeeper and a cook as well as numerous under-servants at Hartfield. All Emma has to do is give orders.

Emma's gifts of food range from soup for poor cottagers, through a hind-quarter of pork for the impoverished but still genteel Mrs and Miss Bates (widow and spinster daughter of a former vicar of Highbury, in rather similar circumstances to Jane, Cassandra and their mother) and the offer, not taken up, of arrowroot for the sick Jane Fairfax. As a hostess, Emma provides delicacies like fricassee of sweetbreads, minced chicken and scalloped oysters to the old ladies who play cards with her father and who, having dined unfashionably early, appreciate a good supper at the end of the evening. These dishes, we understand, are more refined than their own humble kitchens can produce, and eating such food at Hartfield comprises one of the pleasures that make turning out on a cold winter evening worthwhile.

The joke is that Emma's father, though full of benevolence and courtesy to his old neighbours, is so frightened of indigestion that he discourages them from eating what Emma has provided. 'His own stomach could bear nothing rich, and he could never believe other people to be different from himself. What was unwholesome to him, he regarded as unfit for anybody.' His attitude to food is the opposite of life-enhancing, as he tries to stop everybody eating anything good, including the wedding-cake that joyously makes the rounds of the village at the beginning of the story – and even worse, as he tries to force on everybody his own favourite 'basin of gruel, thin but not too thin.' There is no more comic scene in Jane Austen than that in which, 'while the ladies were comfortably clearing the nicer things,' Mr Woodhouse gently harangues them:

'Mrs Bates, let me propose your venturing on one of these eggs. An egg boiled very soft is not unwholesome. Serle understands boiling an egg better than anybody. I would not recommend an egg boiled by anybody else – but you need not be afraid – they are very small, you see – one of our small eggs will not hurt you,' and so on.

Emma is not the only food-giver in the neighbourhood of Highbury. Mr Knightley gives the last of his apples to the Bates household, and invites all his friends to pick and eat his strawberries in season. The tenant farmer Robert Martin's courtship of Harriet Smith includes gathering walnuts for her, going three miles out of his way. His mother, Mrs Martin, sends Harriet back to Mrs Goddard's school, where she is a parlour-boarder, with a goose, 'a beautiful goose, the finest goose Mrs Goddard had ever seen.' Mrs Goddard then shares this treat with her employees; she 'had dressed it on a Sunday and asked all three teachers, Miss Nash, Miss Prince and Miss Richardson, to sup with her.' The net result is a picture of a community where food is abundant and where the producers of food – Mr Knightley and the Martins on their respective farms, and the Woodhouses who evidently keep pigs ('our Hartfield pork') and hens ('one of our small eggs') make sure the fruits of the soil are shared fairly with those whose lack of land mean they cannot produce food for themselves.

The good management of his farm is the all-absorbing interest in Mr Knightley's life, coupled with doing right by his neighbours and – despite her faults – falling in love with Emma. He eagerly discusses with his brother the disposition of various fields for wheat, turnips or spring corn, and even when entertaining guests at Donwell keeps an eye on the clover to see if it is ready for cutting. Mr Knightley farms the Donwell Abbey home farm with the help of a bailiff, William Larkins, and rents out his other farm, Abbey Mill, to Robert Martin. As men engaged in the same business, though of different social standing, Mr Knightley and Mr Martin hold each other in high esteem personally and professionally. 'I never hear better sense from anyone than Robert Martin,' says Mr Knightley, while his contentment in William Larkins' company is a standing joke in the novel.

Even the pleasure-grounds at Donwell Abbey are characterised not by elegant improvements, as in some of Jane Austen's other great houses, but by productive orchards, strawberry beds and 'the old Abbey fish-ponds.' From here too can be viewed the 'rich pastures' and 'spreading flocks' of Abbey Mill Farm: what Jane Austen calls its 'appendages of prosperity and beauty.' For her, the English landscape is never more beautiful than when it is also productive, and kept in good trim. The prosperity of Abbey Mill Farm is the achievement of Robert Martin, a new breed of tenant farmer, better educated than his forbears, reading the *Agricultural Reports* to keep up with the latest ideas in farming.

This was the age of agricultural reform. Large farms were more economical. The old system of open fields cultivated in strips by peasant proprietors, with everyone having rights to common and waste land, had almost disappeared in favour of the kind of fields we know today, bordered by hedges and in the ownership of a few individuals. Enclosure of this kind, which required individual Acts of Parliament, and which had far-reaching effects on the population, turning the majority into agricultural labourers rather than their own masters, but producing enough food to sustain a rising population, including those in the burgeoning towns, had been taking place for a century and was now almost complete, the wars with Revolutionary and Napoleonic France providing the final impetus. The appearance of the countryside was transformed into the lovely patchwork we think of as quintessentially English. Other reforms included crop rotation, so that no field need lie fallow, the cultivation of turnips as cattle-fodder, enabling them to be over-wintered, and the invention of machinery such as seed-drills and threshing machines. All these modern methods are followed by Mr Knightley.

The success of Britain's farming community in adopting new ways is measured by the fact that by 1800 wool and mutton output had doubled compared with a century earlier, and grain production had kept pace with a population increase of some seventy per cent. It is this success, and the obligation to make sure everybody shares in it, that *Emma* celebrates.

The Role of Women

One person in Highbury who is *not* sustained by the abundance of food on offer is Jane Fairfax who, in her illness and secret misery, cannot be coaxed to eat: in her aunt's words, 'Jane would hardly eat anything; Mr Perry recommended nourishing food; but everything they could command (and never had anybody such good neighbours) was distasteful.' Jane Fairfax is one of three young women in Jane Austen's novels who, powerless and at the mercy of men, seek relief in one aspect of their lives that they *can* control, their personal consumption of food.

The other two are Marianne Dashwood in *Sense and Sensibility*, and Fanny Price in the Portsmouth scenes in *Mansfield Park*.

Though their stories are very different, all three are unfortunate in being desired and trifled with by young men of independent means who have been accustomed all their lives to having their own way. While these men come and go at will, Marianne, Fanny and Jane are immobile, constrained not only by an almost total lack of money that they can call their own, but by the type of behaviour their society authorises in respectable young women.

That Jane Austen was deeply and imaginatively engaged by the place of women in society, their constraints and their options, their advantages and their drawbacks, is indisputable. She is never strident on the subject of women's wrongs, and in general she shies away from advocating change, but there are plenty of comments in her letters and novels to show she was aware of imbalance between the sexes.

'Poor Woman! I shall support her as long as I can, because she *is* a Woman, & I hate her Husband,' she wrote of the suffering, though hardly admirable, Caroline, Princess of Wales, in a letter to a friend. In *Mansfield Park,* she questions the double standard that wreaks social ostracism on a female adulterer but lets her male co-offender off scot-free. In *Persuasion,* Anne Elliot, usually the mildest of heroines, protests that men have had the advantage in telling their own side of the story: 'Education has been theirs in so much higher a degree; the pen has been in their hands.' Anne acknowledges that women lead sheltered, protected lives in comparison to men, who often have hardships and dangers to contend with. But even that is not always in women's favour: 'we live at home, quiet, confined, and our feelings prey upon us,' while men always have some business or occupation to take them out into the world.

In the early novels, Jane Austen touches for the most part obliquely on the lack of opportunities for women; the heroines are concerned to marry the men they love, but are not concerned about what will happen to them if they do not marry at all. In *Pride and Prejudice* there is an insouciance about Elizabeth Bennet on this subject that probably reflects the youthful optimism of her creator. Mrs Bennet's famous obsession with finding husbands for her five daughters is mocked rather than applauded as proper maternal care for their futures. It is left to Charlotte Lucas to voice the fact that matrimony is 'the only honourable provision' for an educated woman of small fortune, and because she accepts the odious Mr Collins on that basis, her views, however realistic, are accorded no moral weight.

By the time she came to write *Emma,* however, Jane Austen was approaching forty years old. Her own youthful flirtations had come to nothing, and the one proposal of marriage she had received, at the age of twenty-seven, had come from a man she did not care for enough to marry. She had settled into a fairly contented early middle age (her niece thought she put on the garb of middle age unnecessarily early), sustained by her family relationships and rich creative life. Her novels were her 'darling' children, in some ways preferable to the real children who would almost certainly have followed marriage. 'Poor animal, she will be worn out before she is thirty,' she wrote of a niece who was producing a baby a year. Three of her sisters-in-law died in childbirth, two after giving birth to eleven children, another at the age of twenty-four leaving three tiny girls motherless.

Nevertheless, the passing years had taught her how financially precarious was the situation of most women of her class if they did not marry. Though a gentlewoman lost caste if she was known to do anything for money, Jane Austen rejoiced in her own modest (and anonymous) earnings in the last few years of her life. It irked her that she, her sister and their widowed mother had to rely on the charity of brothers. Had nothing been forthcoming from that quarter – and all the brothers had their own families or their own financial difficulties to contend with – how would Jane and her sister have lived? There were two answers, both of which she explores in *Emma.*

Like Miss Bates, she might have found herself devoting her middle years to the care of an elderly mother and the endeavour to make a small income go as far as possible. The Austen women must have been reduced to lodging in a cramped set of rooms (as they had in Bath, for some year and a half, before other arrangements were provided by the brothers). In depicting the Bates household, Jane Austen trains her clear vision on a situation perilously close to her own. 'A single woman, with a very narrow income, must be a ridiculous, disagreeable old maid!' thinks Emma herself. Another novelist of mature years might have made Miss Bates's predicament the focus of her novel. But Jane Austen is writing firmly within the courtship genre, and Miss Bates is presented as a comic character, albeit with some sympathy. The difference with her creator is one of intellect, not circumstance. Miss Bates 'had no intellectual superiority to make atonement to herself, or frighten those who might hate her, into outward respect.' It is not hard to read this remark of Jane Austen's autobiographically, and to guess at the moments of social pain that underlie it.

The other path open to educated women without fortune was governessing, about which *Emma* has much to say. Jane Fairfax, destined to be a governess, makes the comparison with slavery: 'widely different certainly as to the guilt of those who carry it on; but as to the greater misery of the victims, I do not know where it lies.' Jane Austen pitied the life of even a well-treated governess. She cultivated a friendship with Anne Sharp, the woman employed by her rich brother Edward to teach his large brood, and corresponded with her long after she had left his employment. (We do not know what Edward's wife thought of her sister-in-law treating a member of the household staff as an equal.) In *Emma* Miss Taylor has been almost one of the family at Hartfield, but it is not to be compared with having a home of her own.

Alternatively women could teach in a school, which avoids the servant stigma but brings its own difficulties. Mrs Goddard, the *proprietor* of a school, is mistress of her own fate and enjoys the rewards of her labours, but her three assistants, though presumably not unkindly treated, seem to have no possibility of life outside the school. They are included in none of the social activities of Highbury. Nobody thinks to invite them to the ball at the Crown. Their only connection with the village seems to be mooning through the windows at passing men . 'I would rather do anything than be teacher at a school,' says a character in Jane Austen's unfinished fragment 'The Watsons.' 'I have been to school, and know what a life they lead.' Jane Austen too had been to school.

And while the working matrons, Mrs Wallis the baker, Mrs Stokes the landlady and Mrs Ford the draper (we do not know whether they have husbands, or are widows, or have adopted the honorary title Mrs), like Mrs Goddard, are accorded the respect due to them in the community, all in all, earning one's own living does not seem particularly desirable in *Emma*. Miss Taylor and Miss Fairfax escape that fate with a relief that is shared by all their true friends; and while Miss Smith's unknown father supplies enough money to keep her in board and lodging, with nothing to occupy her time, there is no suggestion that she would be a better woman, or have a more fulfilled life, if she went out to work. Marriage is her only resource; and as she is pretty, she 'is a girl who will marry somebody or other,' in Mr Knightley's words.

Towards the end of the book, as Emma is learning to be more sympathetic to others, she sits 'musing on the difference of woman's destiny', struck by the contrast between the rich and capricious Mrs Churchill's 'importance in the world,' and Jane Fairfax's: 'one was everything, the other nothing.' Emma herself is an unusual heroine in that she possesses a comfortable home and fortune even without marriage, and consequently thinks that she has none of women's usual inducements to marry. The passage in which she explains this to Harriet is unique in Jane Austen's fiction, for Emma projects ahead as to what her life as a single woman of mature years might be – and while we are meant to smile at Emma's self-satisfaction and perhaps delusion, the actual picture she paints is not a bad one, thanks to a sufficiency of money.

But despite her advantages, Emma is not really free; she cannot walk far without a companion, has never fulfilled her wish to see the sea, and is as tied to her father as many a wife to her husband. Money makes a big difference to the women in Jane Austen's world, but even the comfortably-off have to accommodate their desires to the realities of a patriarchal society.

Emma

Geographical Settings

Caroline Sanderson

The English county of Surrey is the setting for Jane Austen's fourth published novel, *Emma*, a book featuring that heroine of whom Jane Austen once remarked 'no-one but myself will much like.' It is the most confined of her novels; all the action in the main narrative takes place within seven miles of the fictional village of Highbury. This localised setting reflects the fact that Emma herself has lived a relatively charmed life within comfortable surroundings and has never ventured far from them. She has thus remained blithely blind to the ways of the wider world; Highbury is her domain and she has reigned over it since she was a child.

Jane Austen stayed in Surrey on several occasions and regularly passed through the county on her way to and from the homes of her brothers Henry and Edward in London and Kent. A plausible model for Highbury, which is described as a 'large and populous village almost amounting to a town' is Great Bookham near Leatherhead, which was home to her mother's cousin, Cassandra and her husband, the Revd Samuel Cooke, who was also Jane's godfather. Cooke was vicar at Great Bookham for more than 50 years, from 1769 until his death in 1820. It seems that Jane may not have been keen on staying with the Cookes. In a letter of January 1799 she remarks to Cassandra: 'I can assure You (*sic*) that I dread the idea of going to Bookham as much as you can do.' Jane's godfather, however, was an admirer of her work, particularly *Mansfield Park*. According to Jane, in another of her letters, he proclaimed it 'the most sensible Novel he ever read, and the manner in which I treat the Clergy, delights them very much.'

Emma was written between January 1814 and March 1815, and as Jane is known to have stayed with the Cookes in 1814, it is possible that her visit provided her with much useful geographical material for her novel.

Great Bookham has another interesting literary association. Between 1793 and 1797 it was the home of the novelist Fanny Burney, and her husband General d'Arblay, a French aristocrat in exile. The d'Arblays encountered the Cookes on many occasions, but it is not known if they ever met Jane Austen. That Jane admired and learned from Fanny Burney's work is undeniable. Take the following amusing description from one of her letters of an acquaintance she met in Kent in 1796: 'Miss Fletcher and I were very thick, but I am the thinnest of the two – She wore her purple Muslin, which is pretty enough tho' it does not become her complexion. There are two Traits in her Character which are pleasing; namely, she admires *Camilla* [a novel by Fanny Burney], & drinks no cream in her Tea.' It is believed that Jane took the title *Pride and Prejudice* from the end of another of Burney's novels, *Cecilia*.

From her careful description of its location in the novel, it seems likely that Jane Austen had the area of Surrey around Cobham and Leatherhead in mind for Highbury, although no real town corresponds exactly with the place she pinpoints for us. Highbury is nine miles from Richmond-Upon-Thames, and seven from Box Hill. Kingston-Upon-Thames is also nearby; we are told that Robert Martin rides there every week for the market. The London home of Emma's sister, Isabella Knightley, her husband John and five children is sixteen miles away in Brunswick Square, a newly built residential area on what were then the northern outskirts of London. 'Our part of London is so very superior to most others! ... We are so very airy! Isabella remarks to reassure her father who is worried about the effect of living in the city on the family's health, and 'could not be induced to go to London, even for poor Isabella's sake.'

Jane Austen's very precise description of Highbury's relative location to other places mentioned in the novel is important because it emphasises the insular, static lives that Emma and her father lead. Because her father refuses to travel even very short distances, Emma has never seen the sea, and has never been to London. We also discover that she has never visited Box Hill, a renowned local beauty spot that lies only seven miles away. Her father's constant indisposition demands that she remains close to Hartfield at all times. She cannot contemplate leaving him even overnight, making a trip to London, for example, impossible. 'You, who know how very, very seldom I am ever two hours from Hartfield,' Emma remarks tellingly at one point to Mr Knightley. Prior to the strawberry-picking expedition, Mr Woodhouse – and presumably Emma too – have not visited Donwell Abbey, the home of Mr Knightley, for two years, despite it being only a mile or so to the south of Highbury.

By contrast, most of the other characters in the book have much wider horizons and are often away from Highbury. Frank Churchill spends much of the novel shuttling between his father, Mr Weston in Highbury, and his wealthy uncle and aunt, Mr and Mrs Churchill, who brought him up. Frank is at the beck and call of Mrs Churchill, whose health is as unpredictable as that of Mr Woodhouse. At first, when recalled to his grandmother's side, Frank must journey to their home in Enscombe, Yorkshire, 190 miles north of London. Later in the novel, the Churchills move south to stay in London, because Mrs Churchill 'takes it into her head' that Yorkshire is too cold for her, though Mr Weston has another theory. 'The fact is, I suppose, that she is tired of Enscombe. She has been a longer time stationary there than she ever was before, and she begins to want change. It is a retired place. A fine place, but very retired.' Mr and Mrs Churchill's move south makes it much easier for Frank to visit Highbury. We are told on one occasion that he is even able to ride down for 'a couple of hours.'

No sooner have Mr and Mrs Churchill arrived in London, however, than they are on the move again on account of Mrs Churchill's nerves being 'under continual irritation.' 'It soon appeared that London was not the place for her. She could not endure its noise.' The Churchills remove to Richmond where 'a ready-furnished house in a favourite spot was engaged, and much benefit expected from the change.' Frank is now within easy reach of Highbury, being only nine miles and 'an hour's ride' away. His father is delighted. 'There was no comfort in having him in London; he might as well be at Enscombe; but Richmond was the very distance for easy intercourse.' Though London seems a world away to Mr Weston, Frank Churchill thinks nothing of 'travelling sixteen miles twice over' just to get his hair cut there. 'A sudden freak seemed to have seized him at breakfast, and he had sent for a chaise and set off.' This notable incident is designed to show up Frank's frivolous tendencies against the steady and sensible temperament of Mr Knightley, who would never dream of doing such a thing. Emma's 'very good opinion of Frank Churchill' is 'a little shaken' by the incident: 'there was an air of foppery and nonsense in it which she could not approve.' Frank's apparent restlessness surfaces again during the visit to Donwell Abbey, in the course of which he quarrels with Jane Fairfax. 'I ought to travel. I am tired of doing nothing. I want a change ... I am sick of England and would leave it tomorrow, if I could.'

Another character in *Emma* who often talks of places away from Highbury is Mrs Elton. The erstwhile Miss Augusta Hawkins of Bristol, with ten thousand pounds, whom Mr Elton meets and proposes to in the space of four weeks in Bath is constantly making comparisons – usually unfavourable ones – between Highbury and the home of her sister, Selina, who is married to a Mr Suckling of Maple Grove. 'The rich brother-in-law near Bristol was the pride of the alliance, and his place and his carriages were the pride of him.' Ironically, Mrs Elton is the youngest of two daughters of a Bristol merchant ('Bristol was her home, the very heart of Bristol'), which was little recommendation at the time. Bristol was notorious as a squalid, unsavoury place, full of smoke from its sugar refineries, and other factories, and with strong links to the slave trade. The relatively low-born

Mrs Elton's constant lauding of Maple Grove, and her delusions of grandeur, which include referring to her husband as her '*caro sposo*' marks her out as a flashy woman lacking in refinement. However, since her elder sister's fortunate marriage to a wealthy man, she has acquired a taste for the good things in life. When Emma finally marries Mr Knightley at the end of the novel, her wedding is described as being 'very much like other weddings, where the parties have no taste for finery or parade.' Mrs Elton thinks it is all 'extremely shabby' however and 'very inferior to her own ... Selina would stare when she heard of it.'

Though Emma herself has never been to the seaside, several coastal towns receive a mention in the novel. During a visit to Hartfield by Emma's sister, Isabella Knightley and her family, the relative merits of various English seaside resorts are discussed. Isabella takes after her father in her preoccupation with her own health. She laments the inability of the cook she hired during their recent holiday by the sea in Southend to make 'a basin of nice smooth gruel.' Mr Woodhouse is appalled. 'Ah! there is no end to the sad consequences of your going to South End. It does not bear talking of ... moreover, if you must to the sea, it had better not have been to South End. South End is an unhealthy place.' Mr Woodhouse has had Cromer in Norfolk recommended to him ('very pure air'), but when John Knightley protests that it is a hundred miles away from their home in London (Southend is only forty), Mr Woodhouse counters with, 'Better not move at all, better stay in London altogether than travel forty miles to get into a worse air.'

Frank Churchill and Jane Fairfax first meet at the south coast resort of Weymouth in Dorset. Weymouth, which had the distinction of being frequented by King George III in the late eighteenth century, is jokingly described by Jane as 'altogether a shocking place ... without recommendation of any kind' in a letter she wrote in 1804 to her sister Cassandra who had been staying there with their brother Henry and his wife Eliza. Weymouth remained a fashionable resort into the early nineteenth century, and it is therefore plausible that Frank Churchill and Jane Fairfax should find themselves staying in the town at the same time, Jane in the company of her friends, Colonel and Mrs Campbell and Mr and Mrs Dixon.

Later, Emma, who has not yet met Frank Churchill but has heard a great deal about him, questions Jane closely as to what he is like. Was he handsome? Was he agreeable? Jane's evasive answers are a great disappointment. 'At a watering-place, or in a common London acquaintance, it was difficult to decide on such points.' Little does Emma guess at the truth, for it is also at Weymouth that Frank and Jane's secret engagement is embarked upon.

These are only short geographical diversions, however, from the main setting of *Emma* in the county of Surrey. In the two hundred years since *Emma* was written, Surrey has witnessed a great deal of development. Small country villages have mushroomed into commuter belt towns, and the northern half of the county now merges indistinguishably with the suburbs of Greater London. In places, however, it is still possible to find pockets of attractive, rural countryside, to remind us of what the whole county was once like; after all, Emma herself remarks to Mrs Elton that 'Surry (*sic*) is full of beauties.' One such place is Box Hill, a steep chalk escarpment in the North Downs near Dorking, which Jane Austen chose as the setting for one of the most memorable and telling episodes in *Emma*.

Now in the care of the National Trust, Box Hill has long been one of the best-known and most popular beauty spots in Southern England. At 600 feet, the summit affords spectacular views of the kind of pastoral, green rolling scenery for which England is renowned, and its slopes provide a habitat for a remarkable variety of flora and fauna, as well as the ancient box woodland that gives the hill its name.

Many writers have visited Box Hill. The nineteenth-century novelist and poet George Meredith lived at the bottom in a flint and brick house where he was visited by such literary luminaries of the time as J.M. Barrie, George Gissing, Henry James and

Robert Louis Stevenson. And ordinary tourists have been coming to Box Hill in search of recreation for centuries. In *A Tour Through the Whole Island of Great Britain* (1724–26) Daniel Defoe observed that, 'here every Sunday, during the summer season, there used to be a rendez-vous of coaches and horsemen, with abundance of gentleman and ladies from Epsome to take the air, and walk in the box-woods; and in a word, divert, or debauch, or perhaps both, as they thought fit.'

Box Hill is, of course, the scene of the fateful picnic in *Emma*, when Emma is rude to Miss Bates, much to the chagrin of Mr Knightley. When he reprimands her, it suddenly dawns on Emma how much she cares about having his good opinion, and this is the prelude to her realisation that she loves him. Though Emma is keen to visit Box Hill – 'she wished to see what every body found so well worth seeing' – the outing is somewhat ill-starred from the beginning. Emma, seeking as ever to avoid the vulgar Mrs Elton and her *caro sposo*, hopes that it will be done in a 'quiet, unpretending, elegant way, infinitely superior to the bustle and preparation, the regular eating and drinking, and picnic parade of the Eltons and Sucklings.' Mr Weston, however, invites all and sundry, maintaining that, 'One cannot have too large a party. A large party secures its own amusement.'

On the day of the excursion the weather is fine, and 'all other outward circumstances of arrangement, accommodation and punctuality were in favour of a pleasant party.' Despite a 'burst of admiration' on first arriving, however, there is something lacking: 'There was a languor, a want of spirits, a want of union, which could not be got over.' To fill the void Emma flirts outrageously with Frank Churchill, who responds enthusiastically and loudly: 'Let every body on the Hill hear me if they can. Let my accents swell to Mickleham on one side, and Dorking on the other.' In an attempt to rouse the other members of the party Frank proposes a game in which each person must say 'one thing very clever ... two things moderately clever ... or three things very dull indeed.' When Miss Bates opts for three things Emma cannot help herself: 'Ah! ma'am, but there may be a difficulty. Pardon me, but you will be limited as to number – only three at once.'

Jane Austen's novels contain very few topographical descriptions, and *Emma* is no exception. Even the spectacular view from Box Hill is only alluded to briefly, when Emma, growing 'tired at last of flattery and merriment' walks off alone 'in tranquil observation of the beautiful views beneath her.' The setting is just a backdrop to this pivotal chapter in which all Emma's plans and pretensions start to unravel, and she begins to understand her true feelings and pay proper attention to those of others. Nevertheless, Jane Austen must have chosen this location with care, and Box Hill remains one of the few places where we can still walk with certainty in the footsteps of her characters.

At the end of *Emma*, the characters disperse to begin new lives. Jane Fairfax and Frank Churchill leave Surrey to begin married life together in Yorkshire at Enscombe. Harriet is proposed to by Robert Martin whilst she is staying in London with the John Knightleys, and once married, goes to live at Abbey Mill Farm on Mr Knightley's Donwell Abbey estate.

And for a time anyway, it seems as if Emma may finally get to see the sea! She and Mr Knightley lay plans for their marriage to take place whilst John and Isabella are staying at Hartfield, 'to allow them the fortnight's absence in a tour to the sea-side.' But Mr Woodhouse has such difficulty in reconciling himself to the idea of his daughter being married, that in the end, Emma decides she cannot proceed with the honeymoon. So she remains at Hartfield after the wedding, and Mr Knightley takes up residence there with her. As we take our leave of the newly-weds, it seems that Emma's horizons are destined to remain confined to the small area of Surrey in and around Highbury.

And yet, perhaps not. In his 'Memoir of Jane Austen' published in 1870, Jane's nephew, J.E. Austen-Leigh reveals that his aunt 'would if asked, tell us many particulars about the subsequent careers of some of her people.' In this way, he learnt that 'Mr Woodhouse survived his daughter's marriage, and kept her and Mr Knightley from settling at Donwell, about two years.' So we can imagine Emma finally becoming mistress of Donwell Abbey and gazing on its 'sweet view – sweet to the eye and the mind. English verdure, English culture, English comfort, seen under a sun bright without being offensive.' And perhaps even tearing herself away from it for the occasional trip to London, or that long-awaited holiday by the sea.

Emma

A Modern Perspective

Josephine Ross

'The proportions must be preserved, you know'
Mr Elton in, *Emma*, Chapter 6

In the summer of 1814, a remarkable exchange of letters on the subject of writing fiction took place between Jane Austen and her eldest niece – lively, artistic Anna Austen, then aged just 21. Anna had embarked on a novel of her own, and naturally turned for advice and assistance to her literary aunt – the author of three modestly-successful published works: *Sense and Sensibility, Pride and Prejudice* and *Mansfield Park*. The correspondence thatensued would throw extraordinary light on Jane Austen's approach to the creative process. As successive instalments of Anna's manuscript were sent and returned, her Aunt Jane responded with detailed assessments, mixing praise and encouragement with constructive criticism and suggestions – whilst stressing, with fond concern for a would-be fellow-author's feelings, 'If *you* think differently, however, you need not not mind me.'

Among the points raised – the need for strict social accuracy, the importance of realistic characterisation and dialogue, the hazards of too much descriptive detail – one comment in partic-ular would stand out: after warning Anna not to venture into settings where she was not 'quite at home' (such as the world of Irish society) 'Aunt Jane' wrote approvingly, 'You are now collecting you.r People ... into such a spot as is the delight of my life; 3 or 4 Families in a Country Village is the very thing to work on.' What was not mentioned, in any surviving letter from this historic exchange, was the fact that, while assisting her niece with the never-to-be-published *Enthusiasm, or Which is the Man?* Jane Austen was herself at work on one of the greatest novels in the English language, *Emma*.

When she began to write *Emma*, in late January 1814, she was entering her thirty-ninth year. Settled contentedly, if modestly, at Chawton cottage in Hampshire, with her unmarried sister and widowed mother, she had achieved a certain critical reputation with her three previous novels, all published anonymously, by the middle-ranking London firm of T. Egerton; but her career to date had yet to earn her more than a few hundred pounds in profit; and as she confided in November of that year, 'Tho' I like praise ... I like what Edward calls *Pewter* too.' Beneath the teasing reference to her schoolboy nephew's Regency slang lay a painful truth: approaching middle age, as a single woman with almost no inherited wealth, Jane Austen was more than ever aware of the role played by 'Pewter' in defining social status, and ensuring domestic comfort – for women in particular. With this fourth novel, in which financial security (or the lack of it) in women's lives would be a central theme, she was determined to achieve commercial, as well as artistic, success. Once completed, *Emma* – the only one of her six novels to feature an independently-rich heroine – would be offered, not to Egerton, whose sales of her earlier works had proved so financially unrewarding, but to the most famous and fashionable 'Bookseller' of the day – John Murray of Albemarle Street, friend, patron and highly-lucrative publisher of bestselling authors from Lord Byron to Walter Scott.

'Mr Murray's letter is come. He is a rogue, of course, but a civil one,' Jane Austen reported to her sister Cassandra with mingled delight and deprecation, on 17 October 1815. She added, 'He sends more praise, however, than I expected.' The deal was eventually struck (handled somewhat ineptly by her businessman brother Henry) but brought no immediate remuneration. Having turned down an initial outright offer of £450 for *Emma*, to include the copyrights of *Mansfield Park* and *Sense and Sensibility*, she settled that *Emma* and a new edition of *Mansfield Park* should be published at her own expense, with 10% commission to Murray. It was a sign of her faith in *Emma*'s sales prospects that she opted for such a potentially risky arrangement; as matters turned out, it was an unwise decision. Nonetheless, becoming a John Murray author was in itself a mark of literary success, which could be expected to bring other benefits, from high production standards to favourable notices in the press through Murray's influence.

When *Emma* eventually appeared, at the end of December 1815 it was handsomely printed, in an edition of 2,000 3-volume copies, costing 21 shillings a set, and early sales were encouraging. What Jane Austen fortunately did not know was that, for all his civility and praise, John Murray had no great opinion of this latest novel by an obscure country gentlewoman. Sending a review copy to his friend (and most successful author) Walter Scott, he wrote cautiously 'Have you a fancy to dash off an article on *Emma*?,' adding 'It wants incident and romance, does it not?' Scott's response – a now-famous essay in the Murray-owned literary journal *The Quarterly Review* – would be eloquent in its praise for 'the Authoress's' merits, but the great Mr Murray himself had fallen into an all-too-familiar trap where Jane Austen's fiction is concerned: that of mistaking subtlety, delicacy and outward restraint for a lack of passion, drama and depth.

Certainly *Emma* can be read, on one level, as a mere light, enjoyable comedy of manners involving '3 or 4 Families in a Country Village' and the mishaps and misconceptions that befall them, written with a due attention to all the points of style and technique that the author had endeavoured to impress upon her protégée niece Anna. As Scott was one of the first to realise, however, it is also a masterpiece.

Unlike Anna's *Enthusiasm*, with its cast of implausible aristocrats, Jane Austen's *Emma* revolves around the lives of what Scott approvingly called the 'middling classes of society,' and reflects 'characters that the reader cannot fail to recognise,' 'common occurrences' and 'nature as she really exists.' Perhaps with

Murray's doubting comments in mind, Scott singled out for special praise the shift from 'romance' to 'real life' represented by *Emma;* and he emphasized that, while this novel might offer less 'story' than the writer's previous works, it had no lack of 'dramatic effect.' *Emma,* he wrote admiringly, was written by an author 'with a knowledge of the human heart.'

Scott compared Jane Austen's technique to the flawless Flemish school of painting; but to many readers in the twenty-first century the resemblance is more immediately to the art of Gainsborough, or Constable, in the delicacy of composition and deeply-felt connection with English pastoral society poised on the threshold of the Industrial Revolution. A telling passage in Chapter 42 of *Emma* evokes, lyrically, the ordered landscape in which this great novel is set: looking out from Donwell Abbey, the hero's ancestral home, across woods, fruitful meadows and a flourishing farm, embraced by the 'close and handsome curve' of a river, the heroine reflects, 'It was a sweet view – sweet to the eye and the mind. English verdure, English culture, English comfort, seen under a sun bright, without being oppressive.'

With the exception of the aristocracy (for whom Jane Austen's letters and novels generally show scant respect), the fictional 'Country Village' of Highbury contains a microcosm of early nineteenth-century rural English society, from the long-established Knightleys, squires of Donwell Abbey and its estate, through the gradations of military family, vicar, doctor, school-teachers and trades-people, right down to the gypsies who lurk on the outskirts, begging and alarming the more fortunate. It is a social order which – on balance – the heroine learns it is better not to disrupt, even with the best of intentions.

At the top of this village hierarchy are the true gentry headed by the novel's hero Mr Knightley, latest in a long line of benevolent owners of Donwell Abbey and its environs. On almost equal terms with him, by virtue of birth, good breeding and good manners, are the heroine Emma Woodhouse and her family, inheritors of 'elegant,' if less historic, Hartfield. Also part of their old, well-ordered world – though very differently circumstanced – are old Mrs Bates, a clergyman's widow, and her spinster daughter, the grandmother and aunt of beautiful, well-bred but penniless Jane Fairfax, orphaned daughter of an officer who has died fighting in the Napoleonic Wars. To the original Regency readers of *Emma* – published six months after the Battle of Waterloo had freed Europe from Napoleon Bonaparte and his Imperial ambitions – the plight of these impoverished gentle-women, reduced to living in rented lodgings, and grateful for the kindness (or charity) of their neighbours and local community, would have struck a special chord.

Chief among the newcomers to this society – newly-rich, upwardly-mobile products of the burgeoning worlds of industry and trade – are the Cole family ('only moderately genteel,' but 'very good sort of people'), and more prominently, the young vicar and his bride, the Eltons. Mrs Elton, affected, pretentious daughter of a Bristol merchant, is one of Jane Austen's great comic creations, on a par with – though very different from – Lady Catherine de Bourgh in *Pride and Prejudice*. Whereas domi-neering *grande dame* Lady Catherine derives her self-esteem from old birth and the supposed superiority of rank, Mrs Elton (née Miss Augusta Hawkins) bases hers on a recently-acquired fortune of £10,000, a veneer of 'elegance' and accomplishments, and her sister's marriage to a man with a large income, a country mansion ('Maple Grove ... A charming place!'), and every modern luxury, including the latest in expensive transport, a 'barouche-landau,' to which she refers at every opportunity.

Writing in an age of fast-expanding consumerism, Jane Austen makes exquisitely artful use in *Emma* of the significance of possessions, carriages in particular. When not bragging of the barouche-landau, Mrs Elton boasts of her own vehicle and its horse-power. 'I believe we drive faster than anybody!' To own a carriage required an income of at least £500; in one subtle plot-line there is talk of the local doctor 'setting up his carriage,' to his patients' gossiping interest. It is typical of down-to-earth, wholly unpretentious Mr Knightley that, for all his wealth and position, he rarely uses his, preferring to walk or ride whenever possible.

Musical instruments – another status symbol – are used to similar dramatic effect. Well-bred, but poor, Jane Fairfax, who is genuinely musical, does not possess a piano (until her secret fiancé, in another plot-twist, sends her one); the Coles, however – who are now in fortune and style of living, second only to the family at Hartfield – own a magnificent, brand-new grand pianoforte, although Mrs Cole cheerfully admits, 'I do not know one note from another.'

Property is always a guide to character in Jane Austen's fiction, and throughout *Emma* the Regency craze for 'improvements' to houses and grounds mirrors 'improvements' to characters' social status. Mr Knightley's Donwell Abbey, as befitting 'the residence of a family of such true gentility,' is 'rambling and irregular,' its grounds unaffected by 'fashion and extravagance.' The Coles, by contrast, have extended and aggrandised their house; while a strong hint as to Mr Elton's true nature is given early in the novel when his vicarage, 'with no advantage of situation,' is described as 'very much smartened up by the present proprietor.' Naive young Harriet Smith, the pretty, illegitimate schoolgirl whom Emma has taken as her protégée with a view to 'improving' her mind and marriage prospects, is especially struck by Mr Elton's yellow curtains – yellow being a fashionable and expensive feature of much modern Regency decor.

We may infer that there are no smart 'yellow curtains' in the mellow, rustic interiors of Abbey Mill Farm, on the Donwell estate, where Harriet's worthy, decent suitor Robert Martin lives and farms as Mr Knightley's tenant. Harriet's artless accounts of her visits to the family there are deeply touching: she speaks of 'moonlight walks and merry evening games'; of Mr Martin going 'three miles round one day, in order to bring her some walnuts, because she had said how fond she was of them'; of how he had brought his shepherd's son into the parlour one night to sing for her. 'I am going to take a heroine whom no-one but myself will much like,' Jane Austen reportedly told her family, when starting work on *Emma*; and the reader is never closer to detesting Emma and her misplaced, snobbish, bossy meddling than when she pressures Harriet into rejecting Robert Martin and the admirable rural lifestyle he represents, in favour of the sly, superficial pseudo-gentlemanly Mr Elton. 'For shame, Emma!' we want to cry – as her mild, indulgent former governess Mrs Weston does, albeit smilingly, over a less important offence.

And yet, unlike Mrs Elton, Emma is not in any sense hateful; only human. While showing us unsparingly her follies and errors, Jane Austen leaves us in no doubt as to her innate goodness of heart and moral worth, beneath the mistakes of judgement – the result of an over-privileged and indulged upbringing. She is seen taking comfort and food – unpatronisingly – to the local poor. She is not vain about her own beauty. She is endlessly patient with her kindly but self-centred father; she is a devoted sister and aunt; above all, she is stricken with remorse when made aware, finally, of her 'horrible blunders,' from insulting poor, foolish Miss Bates with a silly joke to interfering in others' lives for what she fondly believes is their benefit.

Self-deception is Emma's besetting flaw; and deception, whether of self or (more importantly) of others is at the heart of this sublime novel. The fashionable word-games, riddles and 'charades' with which the characters amuse themselves are echoed by the more serious and dramatic mind-games that they persistently play with one another. Charming Frank Churchill, adopted heir to a fortune, may be a 'gentleman' in rank, but he is wholly 'ungentlemanlike' (a favourite Jane Austen word) in his behaviour towards both Emma and Jane Fairfax, in pretending to pay court to one in order to conceal his secret engagement to the other. Emma deceives her protégée Harriet into believing that she is too good for Robert Martin, and that Mr Elton is courting her; Mr Elton deceives himself into believing that Emma is courting him; Harriet ultimately deceives herself into believing that Mr Knightley is courting her. Only on learning this does Emma, with pain, begin to understand what harm she may have done to herself, as well as others, by attempting to interfere in peoples' lives. As she acknowledges soberly, 'Mr Knightley is the last man in the world who would intentionally give any woman the idea of his feeling more for her than he really does.' It is at this point that she begins 'to understand, thoroughly understand, her own heart.'

Mr Knightley, the constant voice of sense and reason, deceives neither himself nor others. As eminent critics have pointed out, *Emma* is (among other things) a brilliantly-crafted detective novel, which requires at least a second reading for all the scrupulously-planted clues as to the real story that is unfolding to become apparent. Mr Knightley, through cool observation and a judgement unclouded by prejudice or conceit, sees below surfaces. He warns Emma of 'some double-dealing' on the part of Frank Churchill; he tells her of the risks she is taking in seeking to raise Harriet Smith out of her natural sphere, in which she is content; above all, he judges the inhabitants of what is essentially his domain, Highbury, on the basis of individual merit, not class or money. Emma initially declines even to be spoken to by Robert Martin; Mr Knightley says with pleasure, 'I believe he considers me as one of his best friends.'

The apparently stable Georgian world into which Jane Austen was born, in 1775, had set great store by the traditional principles of order, reason and proportion, in life as in art and architecture. (Watching Emma draw Harriet's portrait, early in the novel, Mr Elton observes fervently, 'The proportions must be preserved, you know.') By the time *Emma* appeared, in 1815, the author would seem to have come full circle in her attitude to these 'rules.' In *Pride and Prejudice*, published only two years earlier, the spirited, unconventional heroine Elizabeth Bennet is incensed at the notion that, just because she has some vulgar relations – including uncles 'in trade,' an embarrassing mother and an immoral sister – she is herself unworthy to marry Mr Darcy and become mistress of his ancestral home, Pemberley. When his snobbish aunt, Lady Catherine de Bourgh, exclaims indignantly, 'Are the shades of Pemberley to be thus polluted?' the reader responds with an unquestioning 'Yes!' on behalf of defiant, deserving Lizzy. Yet in *Emma* we are expected equally to endorse Emma's views as she reflects, with 'honest pride and complacency' that her sister's marriage to Mr Knightley's brother has 'given them neither men, nor names, nor places that could raise a blush,' by allying them 'unexceptionably,' to 'a family of such true gentility, untainted in blood.' On finding that Harriet Smith is the child, not of a gentleman but a tradesman, of only modest means, we share Emma's relief that 'the stain of illegitimacy, unbleached by nobility or wealth' has not been imposed, through marriage, on any leading Highbury family.

Fiction is, of course, a work of imagination not autobiography; nonetheless, Jane Austen's own deep concern with the need for 'Pewter' is unmistakably evident in *Emma*. Emma, her only independently rich heroine, is also the only one who declares at the outset that she plans never to marry. To Harriet's protest, 'You will be an old maid! and that's so dreadful!,' she replies with truth, 'It is poverty only which makes celibacy contemptible' since 'a single woman of good fortune is always respectable.' In *Pride and Prejudice*, homely Charlotte Lucas marries the repellent Mr Collins because marriage 'must be her pleasantest preservative from want'; in *Emma*, the full misery of the only other 'preservative from want' available to a woman of education but no money, is shown in the plight of Jane Fairfax, who seems fated to a life of underpaid, semi-drudgery as a governess. In a scene of raw, undisguised feeling, such as this character rarely displays, the references both to prostitution and the slave trade are stark.

By the time *Emma* was published, the slave trade had been abolished, under British law, for eight years, but the appalling suffering involved was far from ended. Jane Fairfax is scrupulous in separating her plight from that of the physically enslaved; but she is driven to muse, with pain, on the differing degrees of oppression which one human being may inflict on another. Mrs

Elton – aware of the suspicions which her father's description as a 'Bristol —merchant' may arouse, bridles that her brother-in-law was always 'rather a friend to the abolition'. There is a subtle ambiguity in that 'rather.' The author's own views on the 'sale ... of human flesh,' from the ghastly traffic in slaves abroad to the social and economic oppression of women at home, can, however, be in no doubt.

Jane Austen's hopes that *Emma* might prove to be her own 'preservative from want' in later life were not fulfilled. Though early sales were brisk, the earnings had to be offset against losses on the John Murray reprint of *Mansfield Park*, and by the time she died in 1817, aged only 41, Jane Austen's profits from *Emma* were barely £40. In 1821 the last unsold copies were remaindered by Murray, at the bargain price of 2 shillings a set.

Today, a first edition of *Emma* would (if one could be found) cost upwards of £15,000; the worldwide earnings from this peerless novel are incalculable. That she died with not the faintest inkling of the 'praise' and 'pewter' that *Emma* would one day command, as one of the greatest masterpieces in English litera-ture, is perhaps the only one of life's ironies that would have given Jane Austen no amusement.

Principal Characters

Emma Woodhouse, the protagonist of the story, is a pretty, high-spirited, intellectual, and slightly spoiled woman of 21. Though vowing she will never marry, she delights in making matches for others.

Mr Henry Woodhouse is Emma's valetudinarian father. Frequently, his punctilious kindness is at war with invalid caution, and he has a dislike of all kinds of novelty and change.

Mr George Knightley, Emma's brother-in-law, aged about 37, is among the very few people to find any fault with Emma. Knightley is highly respected and considered very much a gentleman, and there is a no-nonsense air about him. He is the standard against which all the men in Emma's life are measured. He is constantly disputing with Mrs Weston about Emma's spoiled upbringing because of his long and deep-seated affection for her.

Mr Frank Churchill is an amiable man who manages to be liked by everyone except for Mr Knightley, who considers him quite immature. Frank thoroughly enjoys dancing and music and likes to live life to the fullest. Frank may be viewed as a less villainous version of characters from other Austen novels, such as Mr Wickham from *Pride and Prejudice* or Willoughby from *Sense and Sensibility*.

Jane Fairfax is an orphan whose only family consists of an aunt, Miss Bates, and a grandmother, Mrs Bates. She is regarded as a very elegant woman with the best of manners and is also very well educated and exceptionally talented in singing and playing the piano; in fact, she is the sole person that Emma envies.

Harriet Smith, a young friend of Emma's, is a very pretty girl who is too easily led by others, especially Emma. The illegitimate daughter of initially unknown parents, Harriet has been educated at a nearby school. Emma takes her under her wing early in the novel, and she becomes the subject of some of Emma's misguided matchmaking attempts. Harriet rebuffs a marriage proposal from farmer

Robert Martin because of Emma's belief that he is beneath her, despite Harriet's own humble origins.

Philip Elton is the good-looking and ambitious young vicar. Emma wants him to marry Harriet; he wants to marry Emma. Mr Elton displays his mercenary nature by quickly marrying another woman of means after Emma's rejection.

Mrs Weston, formerly Miss Taylor, was Emma's governess for sixteen years and remains her closest friend and confidante after she marries Mr Weston in the opening chapter. Mrs Weston acts as a surrogate mother to Emma and, occasionally, as a voice of moderation and reason.

Augusta Elton is Mr Elton's monied but abrasive wife. She is portrayed to be a very pretentious woman who always likes to be the centre of attention and is generally disliked by Emma and her circle. She patronizes Jane, which earns Jane the sympathy of others.

Mr Weston, formerly a captain of the militia and widower of Miss Churchill, came from a great Yorkshire family. He is a man 'of unexceptional character, easy fortune, suitable age and pleasant manners'

who marries Anna Taylor, Emma's companion and friend. Father of Frank Churchill.

Robert Martin is a sensible young man of 24, though somewhat abrupt in manner. He loves Harriet Smith and is refused by her because of Emma's intervention. He is a tenant farmer and is highly regarded by his landlord, Mr Knightley.

Mrs Goddard is the mistress of 'a real, honest, old-fashioned boarding-school ... She was a plain, motherly kind of woman who had worked hard in her youth, and now thought herself entitled to the occasional holiday of a tea-visit' at one of which she introduces Harriet Smith to Emma.

Miss Bates is an old maid whose mother is a friend of Mr Woodhouse's. She is slighted by Emma for being ridiculous. Emma is later confronted by Mr Knightley about it and tries to make amends

A Jane Austen Timeline

1775	1795	1796	1798

Jane Austen

Lady Susan, Marianne and Elinor (early version of *Sense and Sensibility*)

Susan (an early version of *Northanger Abbey*)

Jane Austen born, seventh child of the Rector of Steventon

First Impressions (an early version of *Pride and Prejudice*)

UK and Ireland

Edward Jenner administers first smallpox inoculation

John Keats born

Irish Rebellion

J.M.W. Turner, painter, born

Europe

French Revolution (1789–1799)

French defeat Dutch, Napoleon takes Josephine as mistress

Eugene Delacroix, painter, born

Premiere of Mozart's *La Finta Giardinera*

Napoleon marries Josephine

Rest of the World

Treaty of Madrid establishes boundaries between Spanish and US possessions

Horatio Nelson achieves a decisive victory at the Battle of the Nile

American Revolution (1775–1783)

Tennessee becomes 16th state of the USA

1775	1795	1796	1798

1801   **1803**   **1805**   **1809**

Austen family
moves to Bath

Susan accepted
by Crosbie & Co.
of Bath but
unpublished

Jane Austen's
father dies.
She moves
to Southampton
with her family

Jane Austen moves
to her brother
Edmund's home
at Chawton

British defeat French at
the Battle of Corunna
Charles Darwin born

War with France
resumes after Peace
of Amiens (1802–3)

Act of Union
between Britain
and Ireland

Battle of Trafalgar

Treaty of Luneville ends war
between France and Austria

Napoleon divorces
Josephine

The French withdraw
from Egypt

Battle of Austerlitz

Louisiana Purchase
from France

Abraham Lincoln born

Thomas Jefferson becomes
President of the USA

Lewis and Clarke reach
the Pacific

1801   **1803**   **1805**   **1809**

1811 1813 1814

Jane Austen

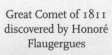

Mansfield Park
published

Sense and Sensibility
published

Pride and Prejudice
published

UK and Ireland

David Livingstone,
missionary and
explorer, born

Sheridan Le Fanu born

Prince of Wales becomes
Regent due to mental
illness of George III

Napoleon defeated at the
Battle of Leipzig

Europe

Great Comet of 1811
discovered by Honoré
Flaugergues

Napoleon abdicates,
Louis XVIII becomes
King of France

Richard Wagner
born

British occupy and burn
large parts of Washington
including the White House

Rest of the World

Harriet Beecher
Stowe born

Simón Bolìvar given
title of 'El Libertador'

1811 1813 1814

1816   **1817**   **1818**   **1871**

Jane Austen dies
at Winchester
leaving *Sanditon*   *Northanger Abbey*   A *Memoir of Jane
Austen* by J.E.
unfinished   and *Persuasion*   Austen-Leigh
Emma published   published   published

Brother Henry makes
public Jane Austen's
identity as author

Charlotte Brontë
born   Mary Shelley's   George Eliot's
Joseph Hooker   *Frankenstein*   *Middlemarch*
Richard Brinsley   born   published   published
Sheridan dies

Elgin Marbles displayed
at the British Museum

'ear Without a Summer' due to
Iount Tambora eruption (1815)

Premiere of Rossini's
Barber of Seville

End of Franco-
First performance   Prussian War
of *Silent Night*

H.M. Stanley meets David
Livingstone on the shore of
Henry David   Lake Tanganyika
Thoreau born

Harper & Row,
publishers, founded

Argentina gains   USA adopts the Stars and
independence from Spain   Stripes as national flag

1816   **1817**   **1818**   **1871**

Jane Austen's England

Bath   The Austens lived in Bath from 1801 until the Reverend Austen's death in 1805. Home of The Jane Austen Centre.

Chawton   In 1809 Mrs Austen, Jane and Cassandra moved to Chawton, into a house provided by Jane's brother Edward. The Jane Austen House Museum is in Chawton.

Godmersham Park   Owned by Edward Austen and frequently visited by Jane and Cassandra.

Lyme   In 1804 the Austens took a short holiday in Lyme, which featured twelve years later in *Persuasion*.

Southampton   Home to the Austens from 1806 to 1809.

Steventon   The Steventon rectory (now demolished) was Jane Austen's home from her birth in 1775 until 1801.

Regency Fashion

Between 1795 and 1820 fashions were based on the Empire silhouette – dresses were closely fitted to the torso just under the breasts and fell loosely below. In different contexts, such styles are commonly called *Directoire* (referring to the Directory which held executive power in France), *Empire* (referring to Napoleon's 1804–1814/15 empire, or *Regency* (referring to the 1811–1820 period of George IV's formal regency, but often loosely used to refer to various periods between the eighteenth century and the Victorian).

Inspired by neoclassical tastes, the short-waisted gowns sported soft, flowing skirts. They were often made of white, almost transparent muslin, which was easily washed and draped loosely like the garments on Greek and Roman statues. Thus, during the 1795–1820 period, it was often possible for middle- and upper-class women to wear clothes that were neither confining nor cumbersome, and still be considered decently and fashionably dressed.

Among middle- and upper-class women there was a somewhat basic distinction between 'morning dress' (worn at home in the afternoons as well as mornings) and evening attire; generally, both men and women changed clothes in preparation for the evening meal and possible entertainments to follow. There were also further gradations, such as afternoon dress, walking dress, riding habits, travelling dress, dinner dress, etc.

Fashionable women of the Regency era wore several layers of undergarments. The first was the chemise, or shift, a thin garment with tight, short sleeves (and a low neckline if worn under evening wear). Chemises and shifts also prevented the transparent muslin or silk gowns from being too revealing.

High-waisted classical fashions required no corset for the slight of figure. The top layer was the petticoat, which had a scooped neckline and was sleeveless, and was fitted at the back with hooks and eyelets. These petticoats were often worn between the underwear and the outer dress. The lower edge of the petticoat was intended to be seen, since women would often lift their outer dresses to spare the relatively delicate material of the outer dress from mud or damp (so exposing only the coarser and cheaper fabric of the petticoat to risk). Often exposed to view, petticoats were decorated at the hem with rows of tucks or lace, or ruffles.

'Drawers' (underpants with short legs) were only beginning to be worn by a few women during this period. They were tied separately around the waist.

Hairstyles

During this period, the classical influence extended to hairstyles. Often masses of curls were worn over the forehead and ears, with the longer back hair drawn up into loose buns or *Psyche knots* influenced by Greek and Roman styles. By the later 1810s, the front hair was parted in the center and worn in tight ringlets over the ears.

Emma

Chapter 1

Emma Woodhouse, handsome, clever, and rich, with a comfortable home and happy disposition, seemed to unite some of the best blessings of existence; and had lived nearly twenty-one years in the world with very little to distress or vex her.

She was the youngest of the two daughters of a most affectionate, indulgent father; and had, in consequence of her sister's marriage, been mistress of his house from a very early period. Her mother had died too long ago for her to have more than an indistinct remembrance of her caresses; and her place had been supplied by an excellent woman as governess, who had fallen little short of a mother in affection.

Sixteen years had Miss Taylor been in Mr Woodhouse's family, less as a governess than a friend, very fond of both daughters, but particularly of Emma. Between *them* it was more the intimacy of sisters. Even before Miss Taylor had ceased to hold the nominal office of governess, the mildness of her temper had hardly allowed her to impose any restraint; and the shadow of authority being now long passed away, they had been living together as friend and friend very mutually attached, and Emma doing just what she liked: highly esteeming Miss Taylor's judgement, but directed chiefly by her own.

The real evils, indeed, of Emma's situation were the power of having rather too much her own way, and a disposition to think a little too well of herself: these were the disadvantages which threatened alloy to her many enjoyments. The danger, however, was at present so unperceived that they did not by any means rank as misfortunes with her.

Sorrow came – a gentle sorrow – but not at all in the shape of any disagreeable consciousness. Miss Taylor married. It was Miss

Taylor's loss which first brought grief. It was on the wedding day of this beloved friend that Emma first sat in mournful thought of any continuance. The wedding over, and the bride people gone, her father and herself were left to dine together, with no prospect of a third to cheer a long evening. Her father composed himself to sleep after dinner, as usual, and she had then only to sit and think of what she had lost.

The event had every promise of happiness for her friend. Mr Weston was a man of unexceptionable character, easy fortune, suitable age, and pleasant manners; and there was some satisfaction in considering with what self-denying, generous friendship she had always wished and promoted the match; but it was a black morning's work for her. The want of Miss Taylor would be felt every hour of every day. She recalled her past kindness – the kindness, the affection of sixteen years – how she had taught and how she had played with her from five years old – how she had devoted all her powers to attach and amuse her in health – and how nursed her through the various illnesses of childhood. A large debt of gratitude was owing here; but the intercourse of the last seven years, the equal footing and perfect unreserve which had soon followed Isabella's marriage, on their being left to each other, was yet a dearer, tenderer recollection. It had been a friend and companion such as few possessed: intelligent, well-informed, useful, gentle, knowing all the ways of the family, interested in all its concerns, and peculiarly interested in herself, in every pleasure, every scheme of hers – one to whom she could speak every thought as it arose, and who had such an affection for her as could never find fault.

How was she to bear the change? It was true that her friend was going only half a mile from them; but Emma was aware that great must be the difference between a Mrs Weston, only half a mile from them, and a Miss Taylor in the house; and with all her advantages, natural and domestic, she was now in great danger of suffering from intellectual solitude. She dearly loved her father, but he was no companion for her. He could not meet her in conversation, rational or playful.

The evil of the actual disparity in their ages (and Mr Woodhouse had not married early) was much increased by his constitution and habits; for having been a valetudinarian all his life, without activity of mind or body, he was a much older man in ways than in years; and though everywhere beloved for the friendliness of his heart and his amiable temper, his talents could not have recommended him at any time.

Her sister, though comparatively but little removed by matrimony, being settled in London, only sixteen miles off, was much beyond her daily reach; and many a long October and November evening must be struggled through at Hartfield, before Christmas brought the next visit from Isabella and her husband, and their little children, to fill the house, and give her pleasant society again.

Highbury, the large and populous village almost amounting to a town, to which Hartfield, in spite of its separate lawn, and shrubberies, and name, did really belong, afforded her no equals. The Woodhouses were first in consequence there. All looked up to them. She had many acquaintances in the place, for her father was universally civil, but not one among them who could be accepted in lieu of Miss Taylor for even half a day. It was a melancholy change; and Emma could not but sigh over it, and wish for impossible things, till her father awoke, and made it necessary to be cheerful. His spirits required support. He was a nervous man, easily depressed; fond of everybody that he was used to, and hating to part with them; hating change of every kind. Matrimony, as the origin of change, was always disagreeable; and he was by no means yet reconciled to his own daughter's marrying, nor could ever speak of her but with compassion, though it had been entirely a match of affection, when he was now obliged to part with Miss Taylor too; and from his habits of gentle selfishness, and of being never able to suppose that other people could feel differently from himself, he was very much disposed to think

Miss Taylor had done as sad a thing for herself as for them, and would have been a great deal happier if she had spent all the rest of her life at Hartfield. Emma smiled and chatted as cheerfully as she could, to keep him from such thoughts; but when tea came, it was impossible for him not to say exactly as he had said at dinner.

'Poor Miss Taylor! I wish she were here again. What a pity it is that Mr Weston ever thought of her!'

'I cannot agree with you, papa; you know I cannot. Mr Weston is such a good-humoured, pleasant, excellent man, that he thoroughly deserves a good wife; and you would not have had Miss Taylor live with us for ever, and bear all my odd humours, when she might have a house of her own?'

'A house of her own! but where is the advantage of a house of her own? This is three times as large; and you have never any odd humours, my dear.'

'How often we shall be going to see them, and they coming to see us! We shall be always meeting! We must begin; we must go and pay our wedding-visit very soon.'

'My dear, how am I to get so far? Randalls is such a distance. I could not walk half so far.'

'No, papa; nobody thought of your walking. We must go in the carriage, to be sure.'

'The carriage! But James will not like to put the horses to for such a little way; and where are the poor horses to be while we are paying our visit?'

'They are to be put into Mr Weston's stable, papa. You know we have settled all that already. We talked it all over with Mr Weston last night. And as for James, you may be very sure he will always like going to Randalls, because of his daughter's being housemaid there. I only doubt whether he will ever take us anywhere else. That was your doing, papa. You got Hannah that good place. Nobody thought of Hannah till you mentioned her – James is so obliged to you!'

'I am very glad I did think of her. It was very lucky, for I would not have had poor James think himself slighted upon any account; and I am sure she will make a very good servant; she is a civil, pretty-spoken girl; I have a great opinion of her. Whenever I see her, she always curtseys and asks me how I do, in a very pretty manner; and when you have had her here to do needlework, I observe she always turns the lock of the door the right way, and never bangs it. I am sure she will be an excellent servant; and it will be a great comfort to poor Miss Taylor to have somebody about that she is used to see. Whenever James goes over to see his daughter, you know, she will be hearing of us. He will be able to tell her how we all are.'

Emma spared no exertions to maintain this happier flow of ideas, and hoped, by the help of backgammon, to get her father tolerably through the evening, and be attacked by no regrets but her own. The backgammon-table was placed; but a visitor imme-diately afterwards walked in and made it unnecessary.

Mr Knightley, a sensible man about seven- or eight-and-thirty, was not only a very old and intimate friend of the family, but particularly connected with it, as the elder brother of Isabella's husband. He lived about a mile from Highbury, was a frequent visitor, and always welcome, and at this time more welcome than usual, as coming directly from their mutual connections in London. He had returned to a late dinner after some days' absence, and now walked up to Hartfield to say that all were well in Brunswick Square. It was a happy circumstance, and animated Mr Woodhouse for some time. Mr Knightley had a cheerful manner, which always did him good; and his many enquiries after 'poor Isabella' and her children were answered most satis-factorily. When this was over, Mr Woodhouse gratefully observed: 'It is very kind of you, Mr Knightley, to come out at this late hour to call upon us. I am afraid you must have had a shocking walk.'

'Not at all, sir. It is a beautiful moonlight night; and so mild that I must draw back from your great fire.'

'But you must have found it very damp and dirty. I wish you may not catch cold.'

'Dirty, sir! Look at my shoes. Not a speck on them.'

'Well, that is quite surprising, for we have had a vast deal of rain here. It rained dreadfully hard for half an hour while we were at breakfast. I wanted them to put off the wedding.'

'By the by, I have not wished you joy. Being pretty well aware of what sort of joy you must both be feeling, I have been in no hurry with my congratulations; but I hope it all went off tolerably well. How did you all behave? Who cried most?'

'Ah! poor Miss Taylor! 'tis a sad business.'

'Poor Mr and Miss Woodhouse, if you please; but I cannot possibly say "poor Miss Taylor". I have a great regard for you and Emma; but when it comes to the question of dependence or independence! at any rate, it must be better to have only one to please than two.'

'Especially when *one* of those two is such a fanciful, troublesome creature!' said Emma playfully. 'That is what you have in your head, I know – and what you would certainly say if my father were not by.'

'I believe it is very true, my dear, indeed,' said Mr Woodhouse, with a sigh. 'I am afraid I am sometimes very fanciful and troublesome.'

'My dearest papa! You do not think I could mean you, or suppose Mr Knightley to mean *you*. What a horrible idea! Oh, no! I meant only myself. Mr Knightley loves to find fault with me, you know – in a joke – it is all a joke. We always say what we like to one another.'

Mr Knightley, in fact, was one of the few people who could see faults in Emma Woodhouse, and the only one who ever told her of them; and though this was not particularly agreeable to Emma herself, she knew it would be so much less so to her father, that she would not have him really suspect such a circumstance as her not being thought perfect by everybody.

'Emma knows I never flatter her,' said Mr Knightley, 'but I meant no reflection on anybody. Miss Taylor has been used to have two persons to please; she will now have but one. The chances are that she must be a gainer.'

'Well,' said Emma, willing to let it pass, 'you want to hear about the wedding; and I shall be happy to tell you, for we all behaved charmingly. Everybody was punctual, everybody in their best looks: not a tear, and hardly a long face to be seen. Oh, no; we all felt that we were going to be only half a mile apart, and were sure of meeting every day.'

'Dear Emma bears everything so well,' said her father. 'But, Mr Knightley, she is really very sorry to lose poor Miss Taylor, and I am sure she *will* miss her more than she thinks for.'

Emma turned away her head, divided between tears and smiles.

'It is impossible that Emma should not miss such a companion,' said Mr Knightley. 'We should not like her so well as we do, sir, if we could suppose it: but she knows how much the marriage is to Miss Taylor's advantage; she knows how very acceptable it must be, at Miss Taylor's time of life, to be settled in a home of her own, and how important to her to be secure of a comfortable provision, and therefore cannot allow herself to feel so much pain as pleasure. Every friend of Miss Taylor must be glad to have her so happily married.'

'And you have forgotten one matter of joy to me,' said Emma, 'and a very considerable one – that I made the match myself. I made the match, you know, four years ago; and to have it take place, and be proved in the right, when so many people said Mr Weston would never marry again, may comfort me for anything.'

Mr Knightley shook his head at her. Her father fondly replied, 'Ah! my dear, I wish you would not make matches and foretell things, for whatever you say always comes to pass. Pray do not make any more matches.'

'I promise you to make none for myself, papa; but I must, indeed, for other people. It is the greatest amusement in the world! And after such success, you know! Everybody said that Mr Weston would never marry again. Oh dear, no! Mr Weston who had been a widower so long, and who seemed so perfectly comfortable without a wife, so constantly occupied either in his business in town or among his friends here, always acceptable wherever he went, always cheerful – Mr Weston need not spend a single evening in the year alone if he did not like it. Oh no! Mr Weston certainly would never marry again. Some people even talked of a promise to his wife on her deathbed, and others of the son and the uncle not letting him. All manner of solemn nonsense was talked on the subject, but I believed none of it. Ever since the day (about four years ago) that Miss Taylor and I met with him in Broadway Lane, when, because it began to mizzle, he darted away with so much gallantry, and borrowed two umbrellas for us from Farmer Mitchell's, I made up my mind on the subject. I planned the match from that hour; and when such success has blessed me in this instance, dear papa, you cannot think that I shall leave off match-making.'

'I do not understand what you mean by "success",' said Mr Knightley. 'Success supposes endeavour. Your time has been properly and delicately spent, if you have been endeavouring for the last four years to bring about this marriage. A worthy employment for a young lady's mind! but if, which I rather imagine, your making the match, as you call it, means only your planning it, your saying to yourself one idle day, "I think it would be a very good thing for Miss Taylor if Mr Weston were to marry her," and saying it again to yourself every now and then afterwards – why do you talk of success? where is your merit? What are you proud of? You made a lucky guess; and *that* is all that can be said.'

'And have you never known the pleasure and triumph of a lucky guess? I pity you. I thought you cleverer; for, depend upon it, a lucky guess is never merely luck. There is always some talent in it. And as to my poor word "success", which you quarrel with, I do not know that I am so entirely without any claim to it. You have drawn two pretty pictures; but I think there may be a third – a something between the do-nothing and the do-all. If I had not promoted Mr Weston's visits here, and given many little encouragements, and smoothed many little matters, it might not have come to anything after all. I think you must know Hartfield enough to comprehend that.'

'A straightforward, open-hearted man like Weston, and a rational, unaffected woman like Miss Taylor, may be safely left to manage their own concerns. You are more likely to have done harm to yourself, than good to them, by interference.'

'Emma never thinks of herself, if she can do good to others,' rejoined Mr Woodhouse, understanding but in part. 'But, my dear, pray do not make any more matches; they are silly things, and break up one's family circle grievously.'

'Only one more, papa; only for Mr Elton. Poor Mr Elton! You like Mr Elton, papa; I must look about for a wife for him. There is nobody in Highbury who deserves him – and he has been here a whole year, and has fitted up his house so comfortably, that it would be a shame to have him single any longer; and I thought when he was joining their hands today, he looked so very much as if he would like to have the same kind office done for him! I think very well of Mr Elton, and this is the only way I have of doing him a service.'

'Mr Elton is a very pretty young man, to be sure, and a very good young man, and I have great regard for him. But if you want to show him any attention, my dear, ask him to come and dine with us some day. That will be a much better thing. I dare say Mr Knightley will be so kind as to meet him.'

'With a great deal of pleasure, sir, at any time,' said Mr Knightley, laughing: 'and I agree with you entirely that it will be a much better thing. Invite him to dinner, Emma, and help him to the best of the fish and the chicken, but leave him to choose his own wife. Depend upon it, a man of six- or seven-and-twenty can take care of himself.'

Chapter 2

Mr Weston was a native of Highbury, and born of a respectable family, which for the last two or three generations had been rising into gentility and property. He had received a good education, but, on succeeding early in life to a small independence, had become indisposed for any of the more homely pursuits in which his brothers were engaged; and had satisfied an active, cheerful mind and social temper by entering into the militia of his county, then embodied.

Captain Weston was a general favourite; and when the chances of his military life had introduced him to Miss Churchill, of a great Yorkshire family, and Miss Churchill fell in love with him, nobody was surprised, except her brother and his wife, who had never seen him, and who were full of pride and importance, which the connection would offend.

Miss Churchill, however, being of age, and with the full command of her fortune – though her fortune bore no proportion to the family estate – was not to be dissuaded from the marriage, and it took place, to the infinite mortification of Mr and Mrs Churchill, who threw her off with due decorum. It was an unsuitable connection, and did not produce much happiness. Mrs Weston ought to have found more in it, for she had a husband whose warm heart and sweet temper made him think everything due to her in return for the great goodness of being in love with him; but though she had one sort of spirit, she had not the best. She had resolution enough to pursue her own will in spite of her brother, but not enough to refrain from unreasonable regrets at that brother's unreasonable anger, nor from missing the luxuries of her former home. They lived beyond their income, but still it was nothing in comparison of Enscombe: she did not cease to love her husband; but she wanted at once to be the wife of Captain Weston, and Miss Churchill of Enscombe.

Captain Weston, who had been considered, especially by the Churchills, as making such an amazing match, was proved to have much the worst of the bargain; for when his wife died, after a three years' marriage, he was rather a poorer man than at first, and with a child to maintain. From the expense of the child, however, he was soon relieved. The boy had, with the additional softening claim of a lingering illness of his mother's, been the means of a sort of reconciliation; and Mr and Mrs Churchill, having no children of their own, nor any other young creature of equal kindred to care for, offered to take the whole charge of the little Frank soon after her decease. Some scruples and some reluctance the widower-father may be supposed to have felt; but as they were overcome by other considerations, the child was given up to the care and the wealth of the Churchills, and he had only his own comfort to seek, and his own situation to improve as he could.

A complete change of life became desirable. He quitted the militia and engaged in trade, having brothers already established in a good way in London, which afforded him a favourable opening. It was a concern which brought just employment enough. He had still a small house in Highbury, where most of his leisure days were spent; and between useful occupation and the pleasures of society, the next eighteen or twenty years of his life passed cheerfully away. He had, by that time, realised an easy competence – enough to secure the purchase of a little estate adjoining Highbury, which he had always longed for – enough to marry a woman as portionless even as Miss Taylor, and to live according to the wishes of his own friendly and social disposition.

It was now some time since Miss Taylor had begun to influence his schemes. but as it was not the tyrannic influence of youth on youth, it had not shaken his determination of never settling till he could purchase Randalls, and the sale of Randalls was long looked forward to; but he had gone steadily on, with these objects in view, till they were accomplished. He had made his fortune, bought his house, and obtained his wife; and was beginning a new period of existence, with every probability of greater happiness than in any yet passed through. He had never been an unhappy man; his own temper had secured him from that, even in his first marriage; but his second must show him how delightful a well-judging and truly amiable woman could be, and must give him the pleasantest proof of its being a great deal better to choose than to be chosen, to excite gratitude than to feel it.

He had only himself to please in his choice; his fortune was his own; for as to Frank, it was more than being tacitly brought up as his uncle's heir, it had become so avowed an adoption as to have him assume the name of Churchill on coming of age. It was most unlikely, therefore, that he should ever want his father's assistance. His father had no apprehension of it. The aunt was a capricious woman, and governed her husband entirely; but it was not in Mr Weston's nature to imagine that any caprice could be strong enough to affect one so dear, and, as he believed, so deservedly dear. He saw his son every year in London, and was proud of him; and his fond report of him as a very fine young man had made Highbury feel a sort of pride in him too. He was looked on as sufficiently belonging to the place to make his merits and prospects a kind of common concern.

Mr Frank Churchill was one of the boasts of Highbury, and a lively curiosity to see him prevailed, though the compliment was so little returned that he had never been there in his life. His coming to visit his father had been often talked of but never achieved.

Now, upon his father's marriage, it was very generally proposed, as a most proper attention, that the visit should take place. There was not a dissentient voice on the subject, either when Mrs Perry drank tea with Mrs and Miss Bates, or when Mrs and Miss Bates returned the visit. Now was the time for Mr Frank Churchill to come among them; and the hope strengthened when it was understood that he had written to his new mother on the occasion. For a few days, every morning visit in Highbury included some mention of the handsome letter Mrs Weston had received. 'I suppose you have heard of the handsome letter Mr Frank Churchill has written to Mrs Weston? I understand it was a very handsome letter, indeed. Mr Woodhouse told me of it. Mr Woodhouse saw the letter, and he says he never saw a handsomer letter in his life.'

It was, indeed, a highly-prized letter. Mrs Weston had, of course, formed a very favourable idea of the young man; and such a pleasing attention was an irresistible proof of his great good sense, and a most welcome addition to every source and every expression of congratulation which her marriage had already secured. She felt herself a most fortunate woman; and she had lived long enough to know how fortunate she might well be thought, where the only regret was for a partial separation from friends whose friendship for her had never cooled, and who could ill bear to part with her.

She knew that at times she must be missed; and could not think, without pain, of Emma's losing a single pleasure, or suffering an hour's ennui from the want of her companionableness: but dear Emma was of no feeble character; she was more equal to her situation than most girls would have been, and had sense and energy, and spirits that might be hoped would bear her well and happily through its little difficulties and privations. And then there was such comfort in the very easy distance of Randalls from Hartfield, so convenient for even solitary female walking, and in Mr Weston's disposition and circumstances, which would make the approaching season no hindrance to their spending half the evenings in the week together.

Her situation was altogether the subject of hours of gratitude to Mrs Weston, and of moments only of regret; and her satisfaction – her more than satisfaction – her cheerful enjoyment, was so just and so apparent, that Emma, well as she knew her father, was sometimes taken by surprise at his being still able to pity 'poor Miss Taylor,' when they left her at Randalls in the centre of every domestic comfort, or saw her go away in the evening attended by her pleasant husband to a carriage of her own. But never did she go without Mr Woodhouse's giving a gentle sigh, and saying: 'Ah, poor Miss Taylor! She would be very glad to stay.'

There was no recovering Miss Taylor – nor much likelihood of ceasing to pity her; but a few weeks brought some alleviation to Mr Woodhouse. The compliments of his neighbours were over; he was no longer teased by being wished joy of so sorrowful an event; and the wedding-cake, which had been a great distress to him, was all eaten up. His own stomach could bear nothing rich, and he could never believe other people to be different from himself. What was unwholesome to him he regarded as unfit for anybody; and he had, therefore, earnestly tried to dissuade them from having any wedding-cake at all, and when that proved vain, as earnestly tried to prevent anybody's eating it. He had been at the pains of consulting Mr Perry, the apothecary, on the subject. Mr Perry was an intelligent, gentlemanlike man, whose frequent visits were one of the comforts of Mr Woodhouse's life; and, upon being applied to, he could not but acknowledge (though it seemed rather against the bias of inclination) that wedding-cake might certainly disagree with many – perhaps with most people, unless taken moderately. With such an opinion, in confirmation of his own, Mr Woodhouse hoped to influence every visitor of the newly-married pair; but still the cake was eaten; and there was no rest for his benevolent nerves till it was all gone.

There was a strange rumour in Highbury of all the little Perrys being seen with a slice of Mrs Weston's wedding-cake in their hands; but Mr Woodhouse would never believe it.

Chapter 3

Mr Woodhouse was fond of society in his own way. He liked very much to have his friends come and see him; and from various united causes, from his long residence at Hartfield, and his good nature, from his fortune, his house, and his daughter, he could command the visits of his own little circle, in a great measure, as he liked. He had not much intercourse with any families beyond that circle; his horror of late hours, and large dinner-parties, made him unfit for any acquaintance but such as would visit him on his own terms. Fortunately for him, Highbury, including Randalls in the same parish, and Donwell Abbey in the parish adjoining, the seat of Mr Knightley, comprehended many such. Not unfrequently, through Emma's persuasion, he had some of the chosen and the best to dine with him: but evening parties were what he preferred; and, unless he fancied himself at any time unequal to company, there was scarcely an evening in the week in which Emma could not make up a card-table for him.

Real, long-standing regard brought the Westons and Mr Knightley; and by Mr Elton, a young man living alone without liking it, the privilege of exchanging any vacant evening of his own blank solitude for the elegancies and society of Mr Woodhouse's drawing-room, and the smiles of his lovely daughter, was in no danger of being thrown away.

After these came a second set: among the most come-at-able of whom were Mrs and Miss Bates, and Mrs Goddard, three ladies almost always at the service of an invitation from Hartfield, and who were fetched and carried home so often, that Mr Woodhouse thought it no hardship for either James or the horses. Had it taken place only once a year, it would have been a grievance.

Mrs Bates, the widow of a former vicar of Highbury, was a very old lady, almost past everything but tea and quadrille. She lived with her single daughter in a very small way, and was considered with all the regard and respect which a harmless old lady, under such untoward circumstances, can excite. Her daughter enjoyed a most uncommon degree of popularity for a woman neither young, handsome, rich, nor married. Miss Bates stood in the very worst predicament in the world for having much of the public favour; and she had no intellectual superiority to make atonement to herself, or frighten those who might hate her into outward respect. She had never boasted either beauty or cleverness. Her youth had passed without distinction, and her middle of life was devoted to the care of a failing mother, and the endeavour to make a small income go as far as possible. And yet she was a happy woman, and a woman whom no one named without goodwill. It was her own universal goodwill and contented temper which worked such wonders. She loved everybody, was interested in everybody's happiness, quicksighted to everybody's merits; thought herself a most fortunate creature, and surrounded with blessings in such an excellent mother, and so many good neighbours and friends, and a home that wanted for nothing. The simplicity and cheerfulness of her nature, her contented and grateful spirit, were a recommendation to everybody, and a mine of felicity to herself. She was a great talker upon little matters, which exactly suited Mr Woodhouse, full of trivial communications and harmless gossip.

Mrs Goddard was the mistress of a school – not of a seminary, or an establishment, or anything which professed, in long sentences of refined nonsense, to combine liberal acquirements with elegant morality, upon new principles and new systems – and where young ladies for enormous pay might be screwed out of health and into vanity – but a real, honest, old-fashioned boarding-school, where a reasonable quantity of accomplishments were sold at a reasonable price, and where girls might be sent to be out of the way, and scramble themselves into a little education, without any danger of coming back prodigies. Mrs Goddard's school was in high repute, and very deservedly, for Highbury was reckoned a particularly healthy spot: she had an ample house and garden, gave the children plenty of wholesome food, let them run about a great deal in the summer, and in winter dressed their chilblains with her own hands. It was no wonder that a train of twenty young couples now walked after her to church. She was a plain, motherly kind of woman, who had worked hard in her youth, and now thought herself entitled to the occasional holiday of a tea-visit; and having formerly owed much to Mr Woodhouse's kindness, felt his particular claim on her to leave her neat parlour, hung round with fancy work, whenever she could, and win or lose a few sixpences by his fireside.

These were the ladies whom Emma found herself very frequently able to collect; and happy was she, for her father's sake, in the power; though, as far as she was herself concerned, it was no remedy for the absence of Mrs Weston. She was delighted to see her father look comfortable, and very much pleased with herself for contriving things so well; but the quiet prosings of three such women made her feel that every evening so spent was indeed one of the long evenings she had fearfully anticipated.

As she sat one morning, looking forward to exactly such a dose of the present day, a note was brought from Mrs Goddard requesting, in most respectful terms, to be allowed to bring Miss Smith with her: a most welcome request; for Miss Smith was a girl of seventeen, whom Emma knew very well by sight, and had long felt an interest in, on account of her beauty. A very gracious invitation was returned, and the evening no longer dreaded by the fair mistress of the mansion.

Harriet Smith was the natural daughter of somebody. Somebody had placed her, several years back, at Mrs Goddard's school, and somebody had lately raised her from the condition of scholar to that of parlour boarder. This was all that was generally known of her history. She had *no* visible friends, but what had been acquired at Highbury, and was *now* just returned from a long visit in the country to some young ladies who had been at school there with her.

She was a very pretty girl, and her beauty happened to be of a sort which Emma particularly admired. She was short, plump, and fair, with a fine bloom, blue eyes, light hair, regular features, and a look of great sweetness; and, before the end of the evening, Emma was as much pleased with her manners as her person, and quite determined to continue the acquaintance.

She was not struck by anything remarkably clever in Miss Smith's conversation, but she found her altogether very engaging – not inconveniently shy, not unwilling to talk – and yet so far from pushing, showing so proper and becoming a deference, seeming so pleasantly grateful for being admitted to Hartfield, and so artlessly impressed by the appearance of everything in so superior a style to what she had been used to, that she must have good sense, and deserve encouragement. Encouragement should be given. Those soft blue eyes, and all those natural graces, should not be wasted on the inferior society of Highbury and its connections. The acquaintance she had already formed were unworthy of her. The friends from whom she had just parted, though very good sort of people, must be doing her harm. They were a family of the name of Martin, whom Emma well knew by character, as renting a large farm of Mr Knightley, and residing in the parish of Donwell – very creditably, she believed; she knew Mr Knightley thought highly of them; but they must be coarse and unpolished, and very unfit to be the intimates of a girl who wanted only a little more knowledge and elegance to be quite perfect. *She* would notice her; she would improve her; she would detach her from her bad acquaintance, and introduce her into good society; she would form her opinions and her manners. It would be an interesting, and certainly a very kind undertaking; highly becoming her own situation in life, her leisure, and powers.

She was so busy in admiring those soft blue eyes, in talking and listening, and forming all these schemes in the in-betweens, that the evening flew away at a very unusual rate; and the supper-table, which always closed such parties, and for which she had been used to sit and watch the due time, was all set out and ready, and moved forwards to the fire, before she was aware. With an alacrity beyond the common impulse of a spirit which yet was never indifferent to the credit of doing everything well and attentively, with the real good-will of a mind delighted with its own ideas, did she then do all the honours of the meal, and help and recommend the minced chicken and scalloped oysters, with an urgency which she knew would be acceptable to the early hours and civil scruples of their guests.

Upon such occasions poor Mr Woodhouse's feelings were in sad warfare. He loved to have the cloth laid, because it had been the fashion of his youth, but his conviction of suppers being very unwholesome made him rather sorry to see anything put on it; and while his hospitality would have welcomed his visitors to everything, his care for their health made him grieve that they would eat.

Such another small basin of thin gruel as his own was all that he could, with thorough self-approbation, recommend; though he might constrain himself, while the ladies were comfortably clearing the nicer things, to say: 'Mrs Bates, let me propose your venturing on one of these eggs. An egg boiled very soft is not unwholesome. Serle understands boiling an egg better than anybody. I would not recommend an egg boiled by anybody else – but you need not be afraid, they are very small, you see – one of our small eggs will not hurt you. Miss Bates, let Emma help you to a *little* bit of tart – a *very* little bit. Ours are all apple-tarts. You need not be afraid of unwholesome preserves here. I do not advise the custard. Mrs Goddard, what say you to *half* a glass of wine? A *small* half-glass, put into a tumbler of water? I do not think it could disagree with you.'

Emma allowed her father to talk – but supplied her visitors in a much more satisfactory style; and on the present evening had particular pleasure in sending them away happy. The happiness of Miss Smith was quite equal to her intentions. Miss Woodhouse was so great a personage in Highbury, that the prospect of the introduction had given as much panic as pleasure; but the humble, grateful little girl went off with highly gratified feelings, delighted with the affability with which Miss Woodhouse had treated her all the evening, and actually shaken hands with her at last!

Chapter 4

Harriet Smith's intimacy at Hartfield was soon a settled thing. Quick and decided in her ways, Emma lost no time in inviting, encouraging, and telling her to come very often; and as their acquaintance increased, so did their satisfaction in each other. As a walking companion, Emma had very early foreseen how useful she might find her. In that respect Mrs Weston's loss had been important. Her father never went beyond the shrubbery, where two divisions of the ground sufficed him for his long walk, or his short, as the year varied; and since Mrs Weston's marriage her exercise had been too much confined. She had ventured once alone to Randalls, but it was not pleasant; and a Harriet Smith, therefore, one whom she could summon at any time to a walk, would be a valuable addition to her privileges. But in every respect, as she saw more of her, she approved her, and was confirmed in all her kind designs.

Harriet certainly was not clever, but she had a sweet, docile, grateful disposition, was totally free from conceit, and only desiring to be guided by anyone she looked up to. Her early attach-ment to herself was very amiable; and her inclination for good company, and power of appreciating what was elegant and clever, showed that there was no want of taste, though strength of understanding must not be expected. Altogether she was quite convinced of Harriet Smith's being exactly the young friend she wanted – exactly the something which her home required. Such a friend as Mrs Weston was out of the question. Two such could never be granted. Two such she did not want. It was quite a different sort of thing, a sentiment distinct and independent. Mrs Weston was the object of a regard which had its basis in gratitude and esteem. Harriet would be loved as one to whom she could be useful. For Mrs Weston there was nothing to be done; for Harriet everything.

Her first attempts at usefulness were in an endeavour to find out who were the parents; but Harriet could not tell. She was ready to tell everything in her power, but on this subject questions were vain. Emma was obliged to fancy what she liked; but she could never believe that in the same situation *she* should not have discovered the truth. Harriet had no penetration. She had been satisfied to hear and believe just what Mrs Goddard chose to tell her; and looked no farther.

Mrs Goddard and the teachers, and the girls, and the affairs of the school in general, formed naturally a great part of the conversation – and but for her acquaintance with the Martins of Abbey Mill Farm, it must have been the whole. But the Martins occupied her thoughts a good deal; she had spent two very happy months with them, and now loved to talk of the pleasures of her visit, and describe the many comforts and wonders of the place. Emma encouraged her talkativeness, amused by such a picture of another set of beings, and enjoying the youthful simplicity which could speak with so much exultation of Mrs Martin's having 'two parlours, two very good parlours, indeed; one of them quite as large as Mrs Goddard's drawing-room; and of her having an upper maid who had lived five-and-twenty years with her; and of their having eight cows, two of them Alderneys, and one a little Welsh cow, a very pretty little Welsh cow, indeed; and of Mrs Martin's saying, as she was so fond of it, it should be called *her* cow; and of their having a very handsome summer-house in their garden, where some day next year they were all to drink tea; a very handsome summer-house, large enough to hold a dozen people.'

For some time she was amused, without thinking beyond the immediate cause; but as she came to understand the family better, other feelings arose. She had taken up a wrong idea, fancying it was a mother and daughter, a son and son's wife, who all lived together; but when it appeared that the Mr Martin, who bore a part in the narrative, and was always mentioned with approbation for his great good-nature in doing something or other, was a single man – that there was no young Mrs Martin, no wife in the case – she did suspect danger to her poor little friend from all this hospitality and kindness, and that, if she were not taken care of, she might be required to sink herself for ever.

With this inspiriting notion, her questions increased in number and meaning; and she particularly led Harriet to talk more of Mr Martin, and there was evidently no dislike to it. Harriet was very ready to speak of the share he had had in their moonlight walks and merry evening games; and dwelt a good deal upon his being so very good-humoured and obliging. 'He had gone three miles round one day in order to bring her some walnuts, because she had said how fond she was of them, and in everything else he was so very obliging. He had his shepherd's son into the parlour one night on purpose to sing to her. She was very fond of singing. He could sing a little himself. She believed he was very clever, and understood everything. He had a very fine flock, and, while she was with them, he had been bid more for his wool than anybody in the country. She believed everybody spoke well of him. His mother and sisters were very fond of him. Mrs Martin had told her one day (and there was a blush as she said it) that it was impossible for anybody to be a better son, and therefore she was sure, whenever he married, he would make a good husband. Not that she *wanted* him to marry. She was in no hurry at all.'

'Well done, Mrs Martin!' thought Emma. 'You know what you are about.'

'And when she had come away, Mrs Martin was so very kind as to send Mrs Goddard a beautiful goose – the finest goose Mrs Goddard had ever seen. Mrs Goddard had dressed it on a Sunday, and asked all the three teachers, Miss Nash, and Miss Prince, and Miss Richardson, to sup with her.'

'Mr Martin, I suppose, is not a man of information beyond the line of his own business? He does not read?'

'Oh, yes! – that is, no – I do not know – but I believe he has read a good deal – but not what you would think anything of. He reads the Agricultural Reports, and some other books that lay in one of the window seats – but he reads all *them* to himself. But sometimes of an evening, before we went to cards, he would read something aloud out of the *Elegant Extracts*, very entertaining. And I know he has read the *Vicar of Wakefield*. He never read the *Romance of the Forest*, nor the *Children of the Abbey*. He had never heard of such books before I mentioned them, but he is determined to get them now as soon as ever he can.'

The next question was: 'What sort of looking man is Mr Martin?'

'Oh! not handsome – not at all handsome. I thought him very plain at first, but I do not think him so plain now. One does not, you know, after a time. But did you never see him? He is in Highbury every now and then, and he is sure to ride through every week in his way to Kingston. He has passed you very often.'

'That may be, and I may have seen him fifty times, but without having any idea of his name. A young farmer, whether on horseback or on foot, is the very last sort of person to raise my curiosity. The yeomanry are precisely the order of people with whom I feel I can have nothing to do. A degree or two lower, and a creditable appearance might interest me; I might hope to be useful to their families in some way or other. But a farmer can need none of my help, and is, therefore, in one sense, as much above my notice, as in every other he is below it.'

'To be sure. Oh, yes! it is not likely you should ever have observed him; but he knows you very well indeed – I mean by sight.'

'I have no doubt of his being a very respectable young man. I know, indeed, that he is so, and, as such, wish him well. What do you imagine his age to be?'

'He was four-and-twenty the 8th of last June, and my birthday is the 23rd – just a fortnight and a day's difference – which is very odd.'

'Only four-and-twenty. That is too young to settle. His mother is perfectly right not to be in a hurry. They seem very comfortable as they are, and if she were to take any pains to marry him, she would probably repent it. Six years hence, if he could meet with a good sort of young woman in the same rank as his own, with a little money, it might be very desirable.'

'Six years hence! dear Miss Woodhouse, he would be thirty years old!'

'Well, and that is as early as most men can afford to marry, who are not born to an independence. Mr Martin, I imagine, has his fortune entirely to make – cannot be at all beforehand with the world. Whatever money he might come into when his father died, whatever his share of the family property, it is, I dare say, all afloat, all employed in his stock, and so forth; and though, with diligence and good luck, he may be rich in time, it is next to impossible that he should have realised anything yet.'

'To be sure, so it is. But they live very comfortably. They have no indoors man, else they do not want for anything; and Mrs Martin talks of taking a boy another year.'

'I wish you may not get into a scrape, Harriet, whenever he does marry – I mean, as to being acquainted with his wife; for though his sisters, from a superior education, are not to be alto-gether objected to, it does not follow that he might marry anybody at all fit for you to notice. The misfortune of your birth ought to make you particularly careful as to your associates. There can be no doubt of your being a gentleman's daughter, and you must support your claim to that station by everything within your own power, or there will be plenty of people who would take pleasure in degrading you.'

'Yes, to be sure, I suppose there are. But while I visit at Hartfield, and you are so kind to me, Miss Woodhouse, I am not afraid of what anybody can do.'

'You understand the force of influence pretty well, Harriet; but I would have you so firmly established in good society, as to be independent even of Hartfield and Miss Woodhouse. I want to see you permanently well connected, and to that end it will be advisable to have as few odd acquaintance as may be; and, therefore, I say, that if you should still be in this country when Mr Martin marries, I wish you may not be drawn in by your intimacy with the sisters, to be acquainted with the wife, who will probably be some mere farmer's daughter, without education.'

'To be sure. Yes. Not that I think Mr Martin would ever marry anybody but what had had some education, and been very well brought up. However, I do not mean to set up my opinion against yours – and I am sure I shall not wish for the acquaintance of his wife. I shall always have a great regard for the Miss Martins, especially Elizabeth, and should be very sorry to give them up, for they are quite as well educated as me. But if he marries a very ignorant vulgar woman, certainly I had better not visit her, if I can help it.'

Emma watched her through the fluctuations of this speech, and saw no alarming symptoms of love. The young man had been the first admirer, but she trusted there was no other hold, and that there would be no serious difficulty, on Harriet's side, to oppose any friendly arrangement of her own.

They met Mr Martin the very next day, as they were walking on the Donwell road. He was on foot, and after looking very respectfully at her, looked with most unfeigned satisfaction at her companion. Emma was not sorry to have such an opportunity of survey; and walking a few yards forward, while they talked together, soon made her quick eye sufficiently acquainted with Mr Robert Martin. His appearance was very neat, and he looked like a sensible young man, but his person had no other advantage: and when he came to be contrasted with gentlemen, she thought he must lose all the ground he had gained in Harriet's inclination. Harriet was not insensible of manner; she had voluntarily noticed her father's gentleness with admiration as well as wonder. Mr Martin looked as if he did not know what manner was.

They remained but a few minutes together, as Miss Woodhouse must not be kept waiting; and Harriet then came running to her with a smiling face, and in a flutter of spirits, which Miss Woodhouse hoped very soon to compose.

'Only think of our happening to meet him! How very odd. It was quite a chance, he said, that he had not gone round by Randalls. He did not think we ever walked this road. He thought we walked towards Randalls most days. He has not been able to get the *Romance of the Forest* yet. He was so busy the last time he was at Kingston that he quite forgot it, but he goes again tomorrow. So very odd we should happen to meet! Well, Miss Woodhouse, is he like what you expected? What do you think of him? Do you think him so very plain?'

'He is very plain, undoubtedly; remarkably plain; but that is nothing compared with his entire want of gentility. I had no right to expect much, and I did not expect much; but I had no idea that he could be so very clownish, so totally without air. I had imagined him, I confess, a degree or two nearer gentility.'

'To be sure,' said Harriet, in a mortified voice, 'he is not so genteel as real gentlemen.'

'I think, Harriet, since your acquaintance with us, you have been repeatedly in the company of some such very real gentlemen, that you must yourself be struck with the difference in Mr Martin. At Hartfield, you have had very good specimens of well-educated, well-bred men. I should be surprised if, after seeing them, you could be in company with Mr Martin again without perceiving him to be a very inferior creature – and rather wondering at yourself for having ever thought him at all agreeable before. Do not you begin to feel that now? Were not you struck? I am sure you must have been struck by his awkward look and abrupt manner, and the uncouthness of a voice which I heard to be wholly unmodulated as I stood here.'

'Certainly, he is not like Mr Knightley. He has not such a fine air and way of walking as Mr Knightley. I see the difference plain enough. But Mr Knightley is so very fine a man!'

'Mr Knightley's air is so remarkably good that it is not fair to compare Mr Martin with *him*. You might not see one in a hundred with *gentleman* so plainly written as in Mr Knightley. But he is not the only gentleman you have been lately used to. What say you to Mr Weston and Mr Elton? Compare Mr Martin with either of *them*. Compare their manner of carrying themselves, of walking, of speaking, of being silent. You must see the difference.'

'Oh, yes, there is a great difference. But Mr Weston is almost an old man. Mr Weston must be between forty and fifty.'

'Which makes his good manners the more valuable. The older a person grows, Harriet, the more important it is that their manners should not be bad; the more glaring and disgusting any loudness, or coarseness, or awkwardness becomes. What is passable in youth is detestable in later age. Mr Martin is now awkward and abrupt; what will he be at Mr Weston's time of life?'

'There is no saying, indeed,' replied Harriet, rather solemnly.

'But there may be pretty good guessing. He will be a completely gross, vulgar farmer, totally inattentive to appearances, and thinking of nothing but profit and loss.'

'Will he, indeed? that will be very bad.'

'How much his business engrosses him already, is very plain from the circumstance of his forgetting to enquire for the book you recommended. He was a great deal too full of the market to think of anything else – which is just as it should be for a thriving man. What has he to do with books? And I have no doubt that he will thrive, and be a very rich man in time; and his being illiterate and coarse need not disturb *us*.'

'I wonder he did not remember the book,' was all Harriet's answer, and spoken with a degree of grave displeasure which Emma thought might be safely left to itself. She, therefore, said no more for some time. Her next beginning was: 'In one respect, perhaps, Mr Elton's manners are superior to Mr Knightley's or Mr Weston's. They have more gentleness. They might be more safely held up as a pattern. There is an openness, a quickness, almost a bluntness in Mr Weston, which everybody likes in *him,* because there is so much good humour with it – but that would not do to be copied. Neither would Mr Knightley's downright, decided, commanding sort of manner, though it suits *him* very well: his figure, and look, and situation in life seem to allow it; but if any young man were to set about copying him, he would not be sufferable. On the contrary, I think a young man might be very safely recommended to take Mr Elton as a model. Mr Elton is good-humoured, cheerful, obliging, and gentle. He seems to me to be grown particularly gentle of late. I do not know whether he has any design of ingratiating himself with either of us, Harriet, by additional softness, but it strikes me that his manners are softer than they used to be. If he means anything, it must be to please you. Did not I tell you what he said of you the other day?'

She then repeated some warm personal praise which she had drawn from Mr Elton, and now did full justice to; and Harriet blushed and smiled, and said she had always thought Mr Elton very agreeable.

Mr Elton was the very person fixed on by Emma for driving the young farmer out of Harriet's head. She thought it would be an excellent match; and only too palpably desirable, natural, and probable, for her to have much merit in planning it. She feared it was what everybody else must think of and predict. It was not likely, however, that anybody should have equalled her in the date of the plan, as it had entered her brain during the very first evening of Harriet's coming to Hartfield. The longer she considered it, the greater was her sense of its expediency. Mr Elton's situation was most suitable, quite the gentleman himself, and without low connections; at the same time, not of any family that could fairly object to the doubtful birth of Harriet. He had a comfortable home for her, and Emma imagined a very sufficient income; for though the vicarage of Highbury was not large, he was known to have some independent property; and she thought very highly of him as a good-humoured, well-meaning, respectable young man, without any deficiency of useful understanding or knowledge of the world.

She had already satisfied herself that he thought Harriet a beautiful girl, which she trusted, with such frequent meetings at Hartfield, was foundation enough on his side; and on Harriet's there could be little doubt that the idea of being preferred by him would have all the usual weight and efficacy. And he was really a very pleasing young man, a young man whom any woman not fastidious might like. He was reckoned very handsome; his person much admired in general, though not by her, there being a want of elegance of feature which she could not dispense with: but the girl who could be gratified by a Robert Martin's riding about the country to get walnuts for her might very well be conquered by Mr Elton's admiration.

Chapter 5

'I do not know what your opinion may be, Mrs Weston,' said Mr Knightley, 'of this great intimacy between Emma and Harriet Smith, but I think it a bad thing.'

'A bad thing! Do you really think it a bad thing? why so?'

'I think they will neither of them do the other any good.'

'You surprise me! Emma must do Harriet good; and by supplying her with a new object of interest, Harriet may be said to do Emma good. I have been seeing their intimacy with the greatest pleasure. How very differently we feel! Not think they will do each other any good! This will certainly be the beginning of one of our quarrels about Emma, Mr Knightley.'

'Perhaps you think I am come on purpose to quarrel with you, knowing Weston to be out, and that you must still fight your own battle.'

'Mr Weston would undoubtedly support me, if he were here, for he thinks exactly as I do on the subject. We were speaking of it only yesterday, and agreeing how fortunate it was for Emma that there should be such a girl in Highbury for her to associate with. Mr Knightley, I shall not allow you to be a fair judge in this case. You are so much used to live alone, that you do not know the value of a companion; and, perhaps, no man can be a good judge of the comfort a woman feels in the society of one of her own sex, after being wed to it all her life. I can imagine your objection to Harriet Smith. She is not the superior young woman which Emma's friends ought to be. But, on the other hand, as Emma wants to see her better informed, it will be an inducement to her to read more herself. They will read together. She means it, I know.'

'Emma has been meaning to read more ever since she was twelve years old. I have seen a great many lists of her drawing-up, at various times, of books that she meant to read regularly through – and very good lists they were, very well chosen, and very neatly arranged – sometimes alphabetically, and sometimes by some other rule. The list she drew up when only fourteen – I remember thinking it did her judgement so much credit, that I preserved it some time, and I dare say she may have made out a very good list now. But I have done with expecting any course of steady reading from Emma. She will never submit to anything requiring industry and patience, and a subjection of the fancy to the understanding. Where Miss Taylor failed to stimulate, I may safely affirm that Harriet Smith will do nothing. You never could persuade her to read half so much as you wished. You know you could not.'

'I dare say,' replied Mrs Weston smiling, 'that I thought so then; but since we have parted, I can never remember Emma omitting to do anything I wished.'

'There is hardly any desiring to refresh such a memory as *that*,' said Mr Knightley feelingly; and for a moment or two he had done. 'But I,' he soon added, 'who have had no such charm thrown over my sense, must still see, hear, and remember. Emma is spoiled by being the cleverest of her family. At ten years old she had the misfortune of being able to answer questions which puzzled her sister at seventeen. She was always quick and assured; Isabella slow and diffident. And ever since she was twelve, Emma has been mistress of the house and of you all. In her mother she lost the only person able to cope with her. She inherits her mother's talents, and must have been under subjection to her.'

'I should have been sorry, Mr Knightley, to be dependent on *your* recommendation, had I quitted Mr Woodhouse's family and wanted another situation; I do not think you would have spoken a good word for me to anybody. I am sure you always thought me unfit for the office I held.'

'Yes,' said he, smiling. 'You are better placed *here* – very fit for a wife, but not at all for a governess. But you were preparing yourself to be an excellent wife all the time you were at Hartfield. You might not give Emma such a complete education as your powers would seem to promise; but you were receiving a very good education from *her*, on the very material matrimonial point of submitting your own will, and doing as you were bid; and if Weston had asked me to recommend him a wife, I should certainly have named Miss Taylor.'

'Thank you. There will be very little merit in making a good wife to such a man as Mr Weston.'

'Why, to own the truth, I am afraid you are rather thrown away, and that with every disposition to bear, there will be nothing to be borne. We will not despair, however. Weston may grow cross from the wantonness of comfort, or his son may plague him.'

'I hope not *that*. It is not likely. No, Mr Knightley, do not foretell vexation from that quarter.'

'Not I, indeed. I only name possibilities. I do not pretend to Emma's genius for foretelling and guessing. I hope, with all my heart, the young man may be a Weston in merit, and a Churchill in fortune. But Harriet Smith – I have not half done about Harriet Smith. I think her the very worst sort of companion that Emma could possibly have. She knows nothing herself, and looks upon Emma as knowing everything. She is a flatterer in all her ways; and so much the worse, because undesigned. Her ignorance is hourly flattery. How can Emma imagine she has anything to learn herself while Harriet is presenting such a delightful inferiority? And as for Harriet, I will venture to say that *she* cannot gain by the acquaintance. Hartfield will only put her out of conceit with all the other places she belongs to. She will grow just refined enough to be uncomfortable with those among whom birth and circumstances have placed her home. I am much mistaken if Emma's doctrines give any strength of mind, or tend at all to make a girl adapt herself rationally to the varieties of her situation in life. They only give a little polish.'

'I either depend more upon Emma's good sense than you do, or am more anxious for her present comfort; for I cannot lament the acquaintance. How well she looked last night!'

'Oh, you would rather talk of her person than her mind, would you? Very well; I shall not attempt to deny Emma's being pretty.'

'Pretty! say beautiful rather. Can you imagine anything nearer perfect beauty than Emma altogether – face and figure?'

'I don't know what I could imagine, but I confess that I have seldom seen a face or figure more pleasing to me than hers. But I am a partial old friend.'

'Such an eye! – the true hazel eye – and so brilliant! regular features, open countenance, with a complexion – oh, what a bloom of full health, and such a pretty height and size! such a firm and upright figure! There is health not merely in her bloom, but in her air, her head, her glance. One hears sometimes of a child being "the picture of health;" now, Emma always gives me the idea of being the complete picture of grown-up health. She is loveliness itself. Mr Knightley, is not she?'

'I have not a fault to find with her person,' he replied. 'I think her all you describe. I love to look at her; and I will add this praise, that I do not think her personally vain. Considering how very handsome she is, she appears to be little occupied with it; her vanity lies another way. Mrs Weston, I am not to be talked out of my dislike of her intimacy with Harriet Smith, or my dread of its doing them both harm.'

'And I, Mr Knightley, am equally stout in my confidence of its not doing them any harm. With all dear Emma's little faults, she is an excellent creature. Where shall we see a better daughter, or a kinder sister, or a truer friend? No, no; she has qualities which may be trusted; she will never lead anyone really wrong; she will make no lasting blunder; where Emma errs once, she is in the right a hundred times.'

'Very well; I will not plague you any more. Emma shall be an angel, and I will keep my spleen to myself till Christmas brings John and Isabella. John loves Emma with a reasonable, and therefore not a blind affection, and Isabella always thinks as he does, except when he is not quite frightened enough about the children. I am sure of having their opinions with me.'

'I know that you all love her really too well to be unjust or unkind; but excuse me, Mr Knightley, if I take the liberty (I consider myself, you know, as having somewhat of the privilege of speech that Emma's mother might have had) the liberty of hinting that I do not think any possible good can arise from Harriet Smith's intimacy being made a matter of much discussion among you. Pray excuse me; our supposing any little inconvenience may be apprehended from the intimacy, it cannot be expected that Emma, accountable to nobody but her father, who perfectly approves the acquaintance, should put an end to it, so long as it is a source of pleasure to herself. It has been so many years my province to give advice, that you cannot be surprised, Mr Knightley, at this little remains of office.'

'Not at all,' cried he; 'I am much obliged to you for it. It is very good advice, and it shall have a better fate than your advice has often found; for it shall be attended to.'

'Mrs John Knightley is easily alarmed, and might be made unhappy about her sister.'

'Be satisfied,' said he, 'I will not raise any outcry. I will keep my ill humour to myself. I have a very sincere interest in Emma. Isabella does not seem more my sister; has never excited a greater interest; perhaps, hardly so great. There is an anxiety, a curiosity in what one feels for Emma. I wonder what will become of her.'

'So do I,' said Mrs Weston gently, 'very much.'

'She always declares she will never marry, which, of course, means just nothing at all. But I have no idea that she has yet ever seen a man she cared for. It would not be a bad thing for her to be very much in love with a proper object. I should like to see Emma in love, and in some doubt of a return; it would do her good. But there is nobody hereabouts to attach her; and she goes so seldom from home.'

'There does, indeed, seem as little to tempt her to break her resolution at present,' said Mrs Weston, 'as can well be; and while she is so happy at Hartfield, I cannot wish her to be forming any attachment which would be creating such difficulties on poor Mr Woodhouse's account. I do not recommend matrimony at present to Emma, though I mean no slight to the estate, I assure you.'

Part of her meaning was to conceal some favourite thoughts of her own and Mr Weston's on the subject as much as possible. There were wishes at Randalls respecting Emma's destiny, but it was not desirable to have them suspected; and the quiet transition which Mr Knightley soon afterwards made to 'What does Weston think of the weather? – shall we have rain?' – convinced her that he had nothing more to say or surmise about Hartfield.

Chapter 6

Emma could not feel a doubt of having given Harriet's fancy a proper direction, and raised the gratitude of her young vanity to a very good purpose; for she found her decidedly more sensible than before of Mr Elton's being a remarkably handsome man, with most agreeable manners; and as she had no hesitation in following up the assurance of his admiration by agreeable hints, she was soon pretty confident of creating as much liking on Harriet's side as there could be any occasion for. She was quite convinced of Mr Elton's being in the fairest way of falling in love, if not in love already. She had no scruple with regard to him. He talked of Harriet; and praised her so warmly that she could not suppose anything wanting which a little time would not add. His perception of the striking improvement of Harriet's manner, since her introduction at Hartfield, was not one of the least agreeable proofs of his growing attachment.

'You have given Miss Smith all that she required,' said he; 'you have made her graceful and easy. She was a beautiful creature when she came to you; but, in my opinion, the attractions you have added are infinitely superior to what she received from nature.'

'I am glad you think I have been useful to her; but Harriet only wanted drawing out, and receiving a few, very few hints. She had all the natural grace of sweetness of temper and artlessness in herself. I have done very little.'

'If it were admissible to contradict a lady – ' said the gallant Mr Elton.

'I have, perhaps, given her a little more decision of character – have taught her to think on points which had not fallen in her way before.'

'Exactly so; that is what principally strikes me. So much superadded decision of character! Skilful has been the hand!'

'Great has been the pleasure, I am sure. I never met with a disposition more truly amiable.'

'I have no doubt of it.' And it was spoken with a sort of sighing animation which had a vast deal of the lover. She was not less pleased, another day, with the manner in which he seconded a sudden wish of hers – to have Harriet's picture.

'Did you ever have your likeness taken, Harriet?' said she; 'did you ever sit for your picture?'

Harriet was on the point of leaving the room, and only stopped to say, with a very interesting naiveté, 'Oh dear, no – never.'

No sooner was she out of sight than Emma exclaimed: 'What an exquisite possession a good picture of her would be! I would give any money for it. I almost long to attempt her likeness myself. You do not know it, I dare say, but two or three years ago I had a great passion for taking likenesses, and attempted several of my friends, and was thought to have a tolerable eye in general; but, from one cause or another, I gave it up in disgust. But really, I could almost venture if Harriet would sit to me. It would be such a delight to have her picture!'

'Let me entreat you,' cried Mr Elton; 'it would indeed be a delight; let me entreat you, Miss Woodhouse, to exercise so charming a talent in favour of your friend. I know what your drawings are. How could you suppose me ignorant? Is not this room rich in specimens of your landscapes and flowers! and has not Mrs Weston some inimitable figure pieces in her drawing-room at Randalls?'

Yes, good man! thought Emma, but what has all that to do with taking likenesses? You know nothing of drawing. Don't pretend to be in raptures about mine. Keep your raptures for Harriet's face. 'Well, if you give me such kind encouragement, Mr Elton, I believe I shall try what I can do. Harriet's features are very delicate, which makes a likeness difficult; and yet, there is a peculiarity in the shape of the eye, and the lines about the mouth, which one ought to catch.'

'Exactly so – the shape of the eye and the lines about the mouth – I have not a doubt of your success. Pray, pray attempt it. As you will do it, it will indeed, to use your own words, be an exquisite possession.'

'But I am afraid, Mr Elton, Harriet will not like to sit; she thinks so little of her own beauty. Did not you observe her manner of answering me? How completely it meant "Why should my picture be drawn." '

'Oh, yes, I observed it, I assure you. It was not lost on me. But still I cannot imagine she would not be persuaded.'

Harriet was soon back again, and the proposal almost immediately made; and she had no scruples which could stand many minutes against the earnest pressing of both the others. Emma wished to go to work directly, and therefore produced the portfolio containing her various attempts at portraits, for not one of them had ever been finished, that they might decide together on the best size for Harriet. Her many beginnings were displayed. Miniatures, half-lengths, whole-lengths, pencil, crayon, and watercolours had been all tried in turn. She had always wanted to do everything, and had made more progress, both in drawing and music, than many might have done with so little labour as she would ever submit to. She played and sang, and drew in almost every style; but steadiness had always been wanting; and in nothing had she approached the degree of excellence which she would have been glad to command, and ought not to have failed of. She was not much deceived as to her own skill, either as an artist or a musician; but she was not unwilling to have others deceived, or sorry to know her reputation for accomplishment often higher than it deserved.

There was merit in every drawing – in the least finished, perhaps the most. Her style was spirited; but had there been much less, or had there been ten times more, the delight and admiration of her two companions would have been the same.

They were both in ecstasies. A likeness pleases everybody; and Miss Woodhouse's performances must be capital.

'No great variety of faces for you,' said Emma. 'I had only my own family to study from. There is my father – another of my father – but the idea of sitting for his picture made him so nervous, that I could only take him by stealth, neither of them very like, therefore. Mrs Weson again, and again, and again, you see. Dear Mrs Weston – always my kindest friend on every occasion. She would sit whenever I asked her. There is my sister; and really quite her own little elegant figure – and the face not unlike. I should have made a good likeness of her, if she would have sat longer; but she was in such a hurry to have me draw her four children that she would not be quiet. Then, here comes all my attempts at three of those four children – there they are, Henry, and John, and Bella, from one end of the sheet to the other, and any one of them might do for any one of the rest. She was so eager to have them drawn that I could not refuse; but there is no making children of three or four years old stand still, you know; nor can it be very easy to take any likeness of them, beyond the hair and complexion, unless they are coarser featured than any mamma's children ever were. Here is my sketch of the fourth, who was a baby. I took him as he was sleeping on the sofa, and it is as strong a likeness of his cockade as you would wish to see. He had nestled down his head most conveniently: that's very like. I am rather proud of little George. The corner of the sofa is very good. Then here is my last' – unclosing a pretty sketch of a gentleman in small size, whole length – 'my last and my best – my brother, Mr John Knightley. This did not want much of being finished, when I put it away in a pet, and vowed I would never take another likeness. I could not help being provoked; for, after all my pains, and when I had really made a very good likeness of it – (Mrs Weston and I were quite agreed in thinking it very like) – only too handsome – too flattering – but that was a fault on the right side – after all this, came poor dear Isabella's cold approbation of "Yes, it was a little like; but, to be sure, it did not do him justice." We had had a great deal of trouble in persuading him to sit at all. It was made a great favour of; and altogether it was more than I could bear; and so I never would finish it, to have it apologised over as an unfavourable likeness to every morning visitor in Brunswick Square; and, as I said, I did then forswear ever drawing anybody again. But, for Harriet's sake, or rather for my own, and as there are no husbands and wives in the case at present, I will break my resolution now.'

Mr Elton seemed very properly struck and delighted by the idea, and was repeating, 'No husbands and wives in the case *at present* indeed, as you observe. Exactly so. No husbands and wives,' with so interesting a consciousness, that Emma began to consider whether she had not better leave them together at once. But as she wanted to be drawing, the declaration must wait a little longer.

She had soon fixed on the size and sort of portrait. It was to be a whole-length in watercolours, like Mr John Knightley's, and was destined, if she could please herself, to hold a very honourable station over the mantelpiece.

The sitting began; and Harriet, smiling and blushing, and afraid of not keeping her attitude and countenance, presented a very sweet mixture of youthful expression to the steady eyes of the artist. But there was no doing anything, with Mr Elton fidgeting behind her, and watching every touch. She gave him credit for stationing himself where he might gaze and gaze again without offence; but was really obliged to put an end to it, and request him to place himself elsewhere. It then occurred to her to employ him in reading.

'If he would be so good as to read to them, it would be a kindness indeed! It would amuse away the difficulties of her part, and lessen the irksomeness of Miss Smith's.'

Mr Elton was only too happy. Harriet listened, and Emma drew in peace. She must allow him to be still frequently coming to look; anything less would certainly have been too little in a lover; and he was ready at the smallest intermission of the pencil to jump up and see the progress, and be charmed. There was no being displeased with such an encourager, for his admiration made him discern a likeness almost before it was possible. She could not respect his eyes, but his love and his complaisance were unexceptionable.

The sitting was altogether very satisfactory: she was quite enough pleased with the first day's sketch to wish to go on. There was no want of likeness; she had been fortunate in the attitude; and as she meant to throw in a little improvement to the figure, to give a little more height, and considerably more elegance, she had great confidence of its being in every way a pretty drawing at last, and of its filling its destined place with credit to them both, a standing memorial of the beauty of one, the skill of the other, and the friendship of both; with as many other agreeable associations as Mr Elton's very promising attachment was likely to add.

Harriet was to sit again the next day; and Mr Elton, just as he ought, entreated for the permission of attending and reading to them again.

'By all means. We shall be most happy to consider you as one of the party.'

The same civilities and courtesies, the same success and satisfaction, took place on the morrow, and accompanied the whole progress of the picture, which was rapid and happy. Everybody who saw it was pleased, but Mr Elton was in continual raptures, and defended it through every criticism.

'Miss Woodhouse has given her friend the only beauty she wanted,' observed Mrs Weston to him, not in the least suspecting that she was addressing a lover.

'The expression of the eye is most correct, but Miss Smith has not those eyebrows and eyelashes. It is the fault of her face that she has them not.'

'Do you think so?' replied he. 'I cannot agree with you. It appears to me a most perfect resemblance in every feature. I never saw such a likeness in my life. We must allow for the effect of shade you know.'

'You have made her too tall, Emma,' said Mr Knightley.

Emma knew that she had, but would not own it; and Mr Elton warmly added: 'Oh no – certainly not too tall – not in the least too tall. Consider, she is sitting down, which naturally presents a different – which in short gives exactly the idea – and the proportions must be preserved, you know. Proportions, fore-shortening – oh no! it gives one exactly the idea of such a height as Miss Smith's – exactly so, indeed.'

'It is very pretty,' said Mr Woodhouse. 'So prettily done! Just as your drawings always are, my dear. I do not know anybody who draws so well as you do. The only thing I do not thoroughly like is that she seems to be sitting out-of-doors, with only a little shawl over her shoulders; and it makes one think she must catch cold.'

'But, my dear papa, it is supposed to be summer; a warm day in summer. Look at the tree.'

'But it is never safe to sit out-of-doors, my dear.'

'You, sir, may say anything,' cried Mr Elton, 'but I must confess that I regard it as a most happy thought the placing of Miss Smith out of doors; and the tree is touched with such inimitable spirit! Any other situation would have been much less in character. The *naïveté* of Miss Smith's manners – and altogether – oh, it is most admirable! I cannot keep my eyes from it. I never saw such a likeness.'

The next thing wanted was to get the picture framed; and here were a few difficulties. It must be done directly; it must be done in London; the order must go through the hands of some intelligent person whose taste could be depended on; and Isabella, the usual doer of all commissions, must not be applied to, because it was December, and Mr Woodhouse could not bear the idea of her stirring out of her house in the fogs of December. But no sooner was the distress known to Mr Elton than it was removed. His gallantry was always on the alert. 'Might he be trusted with the commission, what infinite pleasure should he have in executing it! he could ride to London at any time. It was impossible to say how much he should be gratified by being employed on such an errand.'

'He was too good! – she could not endure the thought! – she would not give him such a troublesome office for the world' – brought on the desired repetition of entreaties and assurances – and a very few minutes settled the business.

Mr Elton was to take the drawing to London, choose the frame, and give the directions; and Emma thought she could so pack it as to ensure its safety without much incommoding him, while he seemed mostly fearful of not being incommoded enough.

'What a precious deposit!' said he, with a tender sigh, as he received it.

'This man is almost too gallant to be in love,' thought Emma. 'I should say so, but that I suppose there may be a hundred different ways of being in love. He is an excellent young man, and will suit Harriet exactly; it will be an "exactly so", as he says himself; but he does sigh and languish, and study for compliments rather more than I could endure as a principal. I come in for a pretty good share as a second. But it is his gratitude on Harriet's account.'

Chapter 7

The very day of Mr Elton's going to London produced a fresh occasion for Emma's services towards her friend. Harriet had been at Hartfield, as usual, soon after breakfast; and, after a time, had gone home to return again to dinner; she returned, and sooner than had been talked of, and with an agitated, hurried look, announcing something extraordinary to have happened which she was longing to tell. Half a minute brought it all out. She had heard, as soon as she got back to Mrs Goddard's, that Mr Martin had been there an hour before, and finding she was not at home, nor particularly expected, had left a little parcel for her from one of his sisters, and gone away; and, on opening this parcel, she had actually found, besides the two songs which she had lent Elizabeth to copy, a letter to herself; and this letter was from him – from Mr Martin – and contained a direct proposal of marriage. 'Who could have thought it? She was so surprised she did not know what to do. Yes, quite a proposal of marriage; and a very good letter, at least she thought so. And he wrote as if he really loved her very much – but she did not know – and so, she was come as fast as she could to ask Miss Woodhouse what she should do.' Emma was half ashamed of her friend for seeming so pleased and so doubtful.

'Upon my word,' she cried, 'the young man is determined not to lose anything for want of asking. He will connect himself well if he can.'

'Will you read the letter?' cried Harriet. 'Pray do, I'd rather you would.'

Emma was not sorry to be pressed. She read, and was surprised. The style of the letter was much above her expectation. There were not merely no grammatical errors, but as a composition it would not have disgraced a gentleman; the language, though plain, was strong and unaffected, and the sentiments it conveyed very much to the credit of the writer. It was short, but expressed good sense, warm attachment, liberality, propriety, even delicacy of feeling. She paused over it, while Harriet stood anxiously watching for her opinion, with a 'Well, well,' and was at last forced to add, 'Is it a good letter? or is it too short?'

'Yes, indeed, a very good letter,' replied Emma, rather slowly; 'so good a letter, Harriet, that, everything considered, I think one of his sisters must have helped him. I can hardly imagine the young man whom I saw talking with you the other day could express himself so well, if left quite to his own powers, and yet it is not the style of a woman; no, certainly, it is too strong and concise; not diffuse enough for a woman. No doubt he is a sensible man, and I suppose may have a natural talent for – thinks strongly and clearly – and when he takes a pen in hand, his thoughts naturally find proper words. It is so with some men. Yes, I understand the sort of mind. Vigorous, decided, with sentiments to a certain point not coarse. A better written letter, Harriet' (returning it), 'than I had expected.'

'Well,' said the still waiting Harriet; 'well – and – and what shall I do?'

'What shall you do! in what respect? Do you mean with regard to this letter?'

'Yes.'

'But what are you in doubt of? You must answer it of course, and speedily.'

'Yes. But what shall I say? Dear Miss Woodhouse, do advise me.'

'Oh, no, no; the letter had much better be all your own. You will express yourself very properly, I am sure. There is no danger of your not being intelligible, which is the first thing. Your meaning must be unequivocal; no doubts or demurs; and such expressions of gratitude and concern for the pain you are inflicting as propriety requires, will present themselves unbidden to your mind, I am persuaded. *You* need not be prompted to write with the appearance of sorrow for his disappointment.'

'You think I ought to refuse him then?' said Harriet, looking down.

'Ought to refuse him! My dear Harriet, what do you mean? Are you in any doubt as to that? I thought – but I beg your pardon, perhaps I have been under a mistake. I certainly have been misunderstanding you, if you feel in doubt as to the *purport* of your answer. I had imagined you were consulting me only as to the wording of it.'

Harriet was silent. With a little reserve of manner, Emma continued: 'You mean to return a favourable answer, I collect.'

'No, I do not; that is, I do not mean – what shall I do? What would you advise me to do? Pray, dear Miss Woodhouse, tell me what I ought to do.'

'I shall not give you any advice, Harriet. I will have nothing to do with it. This is a point which you must settle with your own feelings.'

'I had no notion that he liked me so very much,' said Harriet, contemplating the letter. For a little while Emma persevered in her silence; but, beginning to apprehend the bewitching flattery of that letter might be too powerful, she thought it best to say: 'I lay it down as a general rule, Harriet, that if a woman *doubts* as to whether she would accept a man or not, she certainly ought to refuse him. If she can hesitate as to "Yes", she ought to say "No", directly. It is not a state to be safely entered into with doubtful feelings, with half a heart. I thought it my duty as a friend, and older than yourself, to say thus much to you. But do not imagine that I want to influence you.'

'Oh, no, I am sure you are a great deal too kind to – but if you would just advise me what I had best do – no, no, I do not mean that – as you say, one's mind ought to be quite made up – one should not be hesitating – it is a very serious thing. It will be safer to say "No", perhaps. Do you think I had better say "No"?'

'Not for the world,' said Emma, smiling graciously, 'would I advise you either way. You must be the best judge of your own happiness. If you prefer Mr Martin to every other person, if you think him the most agreeable man you have ever been in company with, why should you hesitate? You blush, Harriet. Does anybody else occur to you at this moment under such a definition? Harriet, Harriet, do not deceive yourself; do not be run away with by gratitude and compassion. At this moment whom are you thinking of?'

The symptoms were favourable. Instead of answering, Harriet turned away confused, and stood thoughtfully by the fire; and though the letter was still in her hand, it was now mechanically twisted about without regard. Emma waited the result with impatience, but not without strong hopes. At last, with some hesitation, Harriet said: 'Miss Woodhouse, as you will not give me your opinion, I must do as well as I can by myself; and I have now quite determined, and really almost made up my mind to refuse Mr Martin. Do you think I am right?'

'Perfectly, perfectly right, my dearest Harriet; you are doing just what you ought. While you were at all in suspense, I kept my feelings to myself, but now that you are so completely decided, I have no hesitation in approving. Dear Harriet, I give myself joy of this. It would have grieved me to lose your acquaintance, which must have been the consequence of your marrying Mr Martin. While you were in the smallest degree wavering, I said nothing about it, because I would not influence; but it would have been the loss of a friend to me. I could not have visited Mrs Robert Martin, of Abbey Hill Farm. Now I am secure of you for ever.'

Harriet had not surmised her own danger, but the idea of it struck her forcibly.

'You could not have visited me!' she cried, looking aghast. 'No, to be sure you could not; but I never thought of that before. That would have been too dreadful! What an escape! Dear Miss Woodhouse, I would not give up the pleasure and honour of being intimate with you for anything in the world.'

'Indeed, Harriet, it would have been a severe pang to lose you; but it must have been. You would have thrown yourself out of all good society. I must have given you up.'

'Dear me! How should I ever have borne it? It would have killed me never to come to Hartfield any more.'

'Dear, affectionate creature! You banished to Abbey Mill Farm! *You* confined to the society of the illiterate and vulgar all your life! I wonder how the young man could have the assurance to ask it. He must have a pretty good opinion of himself.'

'I do not think he is conceited, either, in general,' said Harriet, her conscience opposing such censure; 'at least, he is very good-natured, and I shall always feel much obliged to him, and have a great regard for – but that is quite a different thing from – and you know, though he may like me, it does not follow that I should – and, certainly, I must confess that since my visiting here, I have seen people – and if one comes to compare them, person and manners, there is no comparison at all, one is so very handsome and agreeable. However, I do really think Mr Martin a very amiable young man, and have a great opinion of him; and his being so much attached to me, and his writing such a letter; but as to leaving you, it is what I would not do upon any consideration.'

'Thank you, thank you, my own sweet little friend. We will not be parted. A woman is not to marry a man merely because she is asked, or because he is attached to her, and can write a tolerable letter.'

'Oh, no; and it is but a short letter too.'

Emma felt the bad taste of her friend, but let it pass with a 'Very true: and it would be a small consolation to her, for the clownish manner which might be offending her every hour of the day, to know that her husband could write a good letter.'

'Oh yes, very. Nobody cares for a letter; the thing is, to be always happy with pleasant companions. I am quite determined to refuse him. But how shall I do? What shall I say?'

Emma assured her there would be no difficulty in the answer, and advised its being written directly, which was agreed to, in the hope of her assistance; and though Emma continued to protest against any assistance being wanted, it was, in fact, given in the formation of every sentence. The looking over his letter again, in replying to it, had such a softening tendency, that it was particularly necessary to brace her up with a few decisive expressions; and she was so very much concerned at the idea of making him unhappy, and thought so much of what his mother and sisters would think and say, and was so anxious that they should not fancy her ungrateful, that Emma believed, if the young man had come in her way at that moment, he would have been accepted after all.

This letter, however, was written, and sealed, and sent. The business was finished, and Harriet safe. She was rather low all the evening; but Emma could allow for her amiable regrets, and sometimes relieved them by speaking of her own affection, sometimes by bringing forward the idea of Mr Elton.

'I shall never be invited to Abbey Mill again,' was said in rather a sorrowful tone.

'Nor, if you were, could I ever bear to part with you, my Harriet. You are a great deal too necessary at Hartfield to be spared to Abbey Mill.'

'And I am sure I should never want to go there; for I am never happy but at Hartfield.'

Some time afterwards it was, 'I think Mrs Goddard would be very much surprised if she knew what had happened. I am sure Miss Nash would; for Miss Nash thinks her own sister very well married, and it is only a linen-draper.'

'One should be sorry to see greater pride or refinement in the teacher of a school, Harriet. I dare say Miss Nash would envy you such an opportunity as this of being married. Even this conquest would appear valuable in her eyes. As to anything superior for you, I suppose she is quite in the dark. The attentions of a certain person can hardly be among the tittle-tattle of Highbury yet. Hitherto I fancy you and I are the only people to whom his looks and manners have explained themselves.'

Harriet blushed and smiled, and said something about wondering that people should like her so much. The idea of Mr Elton was certainly cheering; but still, after a time, she was tenderhearted again towards the rejected Mr Martin.

'Now he has got my letter,' said she softly. 'I wonder what they are all doing – whether his sisters know – if he is unhappy, they will be unhappy too. I hope he will not mind it so very much.'

'Let us think of those among our absent friends who are more cheerfully employed,' cried Emma. 'At this moment, perhaps, Mr Elton is showing your picture to his mother and sisters, telling how much more beautiful is the original, and after being asked for it five or six times, allowing them to hear your name – your own dear name.'

'My picture! But he has left my picture in Bond Street.'

'Has he so! Then I know nothing of Mr Elton. No, my dear little modest Harriet, depend upon it, the picture will not be in Bond Street till just before he mounts his horse tomorrow. It is his companion all this evening, his solace, his delight. It opens his designs to his family, it introduces you among them, it diffuses through the party those pleasantest feelings of our nature – eager curiosity and warm prepossession. How cheerful, how animated, how auspicious, how busy their imaginations all are!'

Harriet smiled again, and her smiles grew stronger.

Chapter 8

Harriet slept at Hartfield that night. For some weeks past she had been spending more than half her time there, and gradually getting to have a bedroom appropriated to herself; and Emma judged it best in every respect, safest and kindest, to keep her with them as much as possible just at present. She was obliged to go the next morning for an hour or two to Mrs Goddard's, but it was then to be settled that she should return to Hartfield, to make a regular visit of some days.

While she was gone, Mr Knightley called, and sat some time with Mr Woodhouse and Emma, till Mr Woodhouse, who had previously made up his mind to walk out, was persuaded by his daughter not to defer it, and was induced by the entreaties of both, though against the scruples of his own civilities, to leave Mr Knightley for that purpose. Mr Knightley, who had nothing of ceremony about him, was offering, by his short, decided answers, an amusing contrast to the protracted apologies and civil hesitations of the other.

'Well, I believe, if you will excuse me, Mr Knightley, if you will not consider me as doing a very rude thing, I shall take Emma's advice and go out for a quarter of an hour. As the sun is out, I believe I had better take my three turns while I can. I treat you without ceremony, Mr Knightley. We invalids think we are privileged people.'

'My dear sir, do not make a stranger of me.'

'I leave an excellent substitute in my daughter. Emma will be happy to entertain you. And therefore I think I will beg your excuse, and take my three turns – my winter walk.'

'You cannot do better, sir.'

'I would ask for the pleasure of your company, Mr Knightley, but I am a very slow walker, and my pace would be tedious to you; and, besides, you have another long walk before you, to Donwell Abbey.'

'Thank you, sir, thank you; I am going this moment myself; and I think the sooner *you* go the better. I will fetch your great coat and open the garden door for you.'

Mr Woodhouse at last was off; but Mr Knightley, instead of being immediately off likewise, sat down again, seemingly inclined for more chat. He began speaking of Harriet, and speaking of her with more voluntary praise than Emma had ever heard before.

'I cannot rate her beauty as you do,' said he; 'but she is a pretty little creature, and I am inclined to think very well of her disposition. Her character depends upon those she is with; but in good hands she will turn out a valuable woman.'

'I am glad you think so; and the good hands, I hope, may not be wanting.'

'Come,' said he, 'you are anxious for a compliment, so I will tell you that you have improved her. You have cured her of her schoolgirl's giggle; she really does you credit.'

'Thank you. I should be mortified, indeed, if I did not believe I had been of some use; but it is not everybody who will bestow praise where they may. *You* do not often overpower me with it.'

'You are expecting her again, you say, this morning?'

'Almost every moment. She has been gone longer already than she intended.'

'Something has happened to delay her; some visitors, perhaps.'

'Highbury gossips! Tiresome wretches!'

'Harriet may not consider everybody tiresome that you would.'

Emma knew this was too true for contradiction, and, therefore, said nothing. He presently added, with a smile: 'I do not pretend to fix on times or places, but I must tell you that I have good reason to believe your little friend will soon hear of something to her advantage.'

'Indeed! how so? of what sort?'

'A very serious sort, I assure you,' still smiling.

'Very serious! I can think of but one thing – who is in love with her? Who makes you their confidant?'

Emma was more than half in hopes of Mr Elton's having dropped a hint. Mr Knightley was a sort of general friend and adviser, and she knew Mr Elton looked up to him.

'I have reason to think,' he replied, 'that Harriet Smith will soon have an offer of marriage, and from a most unexceptionable quarter – Robert Martin is the man. Her visit to Abbey Mill, this summer, seems to have done his business. He is desperately in love, and means to marry her.'

'He is very obliging,' said Emma; 'but is he sure that Harriet means to marry him?'

'Well, well, means to make her an offer, then. Will that do? He came to the Abbey two evenings ago, on purpose to consult me about it. He knows I have a thorough regard for him and all his family, and, I believe, considers me as one of his best friends. He came to ask me whether I thought it would be imprudent in him to settle so early; whether I thought her too young – in short, whether I approved his choice altogether; having some apprehension, perhaps, of her being considered (especially since *your* making so much of her) as in a line of society above him. I was very much pleased with all that he said. I never hear better sense from anyone than Robert Martin. He always speaks to the purpose; open, straightforward, and very well judging. He told me everything; his circumstances and plans, and what they all proposed doing in the event of his marriage. He is an excellent young man, both as son and brother. I had no hesitation in advising him to marry. He proved to me that he could afford it, and that being the case, I was convinced he could not do better. I praised the fair lady too, and altogether sent him away very happy. If he had never esteemed my opinion before, he would have thought highly of me then; and I dare say, left the house thinking me the best friend and counsellor man ever had. This happened the night before last. Now, as we may fairly suppose, he would not allow much time to pass before he spoke to the lady, and as he does not appear to have spoken yesterday, it is not unlikely that he should be at Mrs Goddard's today; and she may be detained by a visitor, without thinking him at all a tiresome wretch.'

'Pray, Mr Knightley,' said Emma, who had been smiling to herself through a great part of this speech, 'how do you know that Mr Martin did not speak yesterday?'

'Certainly,' replied he, surprised, 'I do not absolutely know it, but it may be inferred. Was not she the whole day with you?'

'Come,' said she, 'I will tell you something in return for what you have told me. He did speak yesterday – that is, he wrote, and was refused.'

This was obliged to be repeated before it could be believed; and Mr Knightley actually looked red with surprise and displeasure, as he stood up, in tall indignation, and said: 'Then she is a greater simpleton than I ever believed her. What is the foolish girl about?'

'Oh, to be sure,' cried Emma, 'it is always incomprehensible to a man, that a woman should ever refuse an offer of marriage. A man always imagines a woman to be ready for anybody who asks her.'

'Nonsense! a man does not imagine any such thing. But what is the meaning of this? Harriet Smith refuse Robert Martin! Madness, if it is so; but I hope you are mistaken.'

'I saw her answer! – nothing could be clearer.'

'You saw her answer! – you wrote her answer too. Emma, this is your doing. You persuaded her to refuse him.'

'And if I did (which, however, I am far from allowing), I should not feel that I had done wrong. Mr Martin is a very respectable young man, but I cannot admit him to be Harriet's equal; and am rather surprised, indeed, that he should have ventured to address her. By your account he does seem to have had some scruples. It is a pity that they were ever got over.'

'Not Harriet's equal!' exclaimed Mr Knightley, loudly and warmly; and with calmer asperity added, a few moments afterwards, 'No, he is not her equal, indeed, for he is as much her superior in sense as in situation. Emma, your infatuation about that girl blinds you. What are Harriet Smith's claims, either of birth, nature, or education, to any connection higher than Robert Martin? She is the natural daughter of nobody knows whom, with probably no settled provision at all, and certainly no respectable relations. She is known only as parlour boarder at a common school. She is not a sensible girl, nor a girl of any information. She has been taught nothing useful, and is too young and too simple to have acquired anything herself. At her age she can have no experience; and, with her little wit, is not very likely ever to have any that can avail her. She is pretty, and she is good tempered, and that is all. My only scruple in advising the match was on his account, as being beneath his deserts, and a bad connection for him. I felt that, as to fortune, in all probability he might do much better, and that, as to a rational companion or a useful helpmate, he could not do worse. But I could not reason so to a man in love, and was willing to trust to there being no harm in her; to her having that sort of disposition, which, in good hands like his, might be easily led aright, and turn out very well. The advantage of the match I felt to be all on her side; and had not the smallest doubt (nor have I now) that there would be a general cry out upon her extreme good luck. Even *your* satisfaction I made sure of. It crossed my mind immediately that you would not regret your friend leaving Highbury, for the sake of her being settled so well. I remember saying to myself, "Even Emma, with all her partiality for Harriet, will think this a good match." '

'I cannot help wondering at your knowing so little of Emma as to say any such thing. What! think a farmer (and with all his sense and all his merit Mr Martin is nothing more) a good match for my intimate friend! Not regret her leaving Highbury, for the sake of marrying a man whom I could never admit as an acquaintance of my own! I wonder you should think it possible for me to have such feelings. I assure you mine are very different. I must think your statement by no means fair. You are not just to Harriet's claims. They would be estimated very differently by others as well as myself; Mr Martin may be the richest of the two, but he is undoubtedly her inferior as to rank in society. The sphere in which she moves is much above his. It would be a degradation.'

'A degradation to illegitimacy and ignorance to be married to a respectable, intelligent, gentleman-farmer!'

'As to the circumstances of her birth, though in a legal sense she may be called Nobody, it will not hold in common sense. She is not to pay for the offence of others, by being held below the level of those with whom she is brought up. There can scarcely be a doubt that her father is a gentleman – and a gentleman of fortune. Her allowance is very liberal; nothing has ever been grudged for her improvement or comfort. That she is a gentleman's daughter is indubitable to me; that she associates with gentlemen's daughters, no one, I apprehend, will deny. She is superior to Mr Robert Martin.'

'Whoever might be her parents,' said Mr Knightley, 'whoever may have had the charge of her, it does not appear to have been any part of their plan to introduce her into what you would call good society. After receiving a very indifferent education, she is left in Mrs Goddard's hands to shift as she can – to move, in short, in Mrs Goddard's line, to have Mrs Goddard's acquaintance. Her friends evidently thought this good enough for her; and it *was* good enough. She desired nothing better herself. Till you chose to turn her into a friend, her mind had no distaste for her own sex, nor any ambition beyond it. She was as happy as possible with the Martins in the summer. She had no sense of superiority then. If she has it now, you have given it. You have been no friend to Harriet Smith, Emma. Robert Martin would never have proceeded so far, if he had not felt persuaded of her not being disinclined to him. I know him well. He has too much real feeling to address any woman on the haphazard of selfish passion. And as to conceit, he is the furthest from it of any man I know. Depend upon it, he had encouragement.'

It was most convenient to Emma not to make a direct reply to this assertion; she chose rather to take up her own line of the subject again.

'You are a very warm friend to Mr Martin; but, as I said before, are unjust to Harriet. Harriet's claims to marry well are not so contemptible as you represent them. She is not a clever girl, but she has better sense than you are aware of, and does not deserve to have her understanding spoken of so slightingly. Waiving that point, however, and supposing her to be, as you describe her, only pretty and good-natured, let me tell you, that in the degree she possesses them, they are not trivial recommendations to the world in general, for she is, in fact, a beautiful girl, and must be thought so by ninety-nine people out of a hundred; and till it appears that men are much more philosophic on the subject of beauty than they are generally supposed, till they do fall in love with well-informed minds instead of handsome faces, a girl, with such loveliness as Harriet, had a certainty of being admired and sought after, of having the power of choosing from among many, consequently a claim to be nice. Her good nature, too, is not so very slight a claim, comprehending, as it does, real, thorough sweetness of temper and manner, a very humble opinion of herself, and a great readiness to be pleased with other people. I am very much mistaken if your sex in general would not think such beauty, and such temper, the highest claim a woman could possess.'

'Upon my word, Emma, to hear you abusing the reason you have, is almost enough to make me think so too. Better be without sense than misapply it as you do.'

'To be sure,' cried she playfully. 'I know *that* is the feeling of you all. I know that such a girl as Harriet is exactly what every man delights in – what at once bewitches his senses and satisfies his judgement. Oh, Harriet may pick and choose. Were you, yourself, ever to marry, she is the very woman for you. And is she, at seventeen, just entering into life, just beginning to be known, to be wondered at because she does not accept the first offer she receives? No – pray, let her have time to look about her.'

'I have always thought it a very foolish intimacy,' said Mr Knightley presently, 'though I have kept my thoughts to myself; but I now perceive that it will be a very unfortunate one for Harriet. You will puff her up with such ideas of her own beauty, and of what she has a claim to, that, in a little while, nobody within her reach will be good enough for her. Vanity working on a weak head produces every sort of mischief. Nothing so easy as for a young lady to raise her expectations too high. Miss Harriet Smith may not find offers of marriage flow in so fast, though she is a very pretty girl. Men of sense, whatever you may choose to say, do not want silly wives. Men of family would not be very fond of connecting themselves with a girl of such obscurity – and most prudent men would be afraid of the inconvenience and disgrace they might be involved in, when the mystery of her parentage came to be revealed. Let her marry Robert Martin, and she is safe, respectable, and happy for ever; but if you encourage her to expect to marry greatly, and teach her to be satisfied with nothing less than a man of consequence and large fortune, she may be a parlour boarder at Mrs Goddard's all the rest of her life – or, at least (for Harriet Smith is a girl who will marry somebody or other) till she grow desperate, and is glad to catch at the old writing-master's son.'

'We think so very differently on this point, Mr Knightley, that there can be no use in canvassing it. We shall only be making each other more angry. But as to my *letting* her marry Robert Martin, it is impossible; she has refused him, and so decidedly, I think, as must prevent any second application. She must abide by the evil of having refused him, whatever it may be; and as to the refusal itself, I will not pretend to say that I might not influence her a little; but I assure you there was very little for me or for anybody to do. His appearance is so much against him, and his manner so bad, that if she ever were disposed to favour him, she is not now. I can imagine, that, before she had seen anybody superior, she might tolerate him. He was the brother of her friends, and he took pains to please her; and altogether, having seen nobody better (that must have been his great assistant), she might not, while she was at Abbey Mill, find him disagreeable. But the case is altered now. She knows now what gentlemen are; and nothing but a gentleman in education and manner has any chance with Harriet.'

'Nonsense, arrant nonsense, as ever was talked!' cried Mr Knightley. 'Robert Martin's manners have sense, sincerity, and good humour to recommend them; and his mind has more true gentility than Harriet Smith could understand.'

Emma made no answer, and tried to look cheerfully unconcerned, but was really feeling uncomfortable, and wanting him very much to be gone. She did not repent what she had done; she still thought herself a better judge of such a point of female right and refinement than he could be; but yet she had a sort of habitual respect for his judgement in general, which made her dislike having it so loudly against her; and to have him sitting just opposite to her in angry state was very disagreeable. Some minutes passed in this unpleasant silence, with only one attempt on Emma's side to talk of the weather, but he made no answer. He was thinking. The result of his thoughts appeared at last in these words: 'Robert Martin has no great loss – if he can but think so; and I hope it will not be long before he does. Your views for

Harriet are best known to yourself; but as you make no secret of your love of match-making, it is fair to suppose that views, and plans, and projects you have; and as a friend I shall just hint to you, that if Elton is the man, I think it will be all labour in vain.'

Emma laughed and disclaimed. He continued: 'Depend upon it, Elton will not do. Elton is a very good sort of man, and a very respectable vicar of Highbury, but not at all likely to make an imprudent match. He knows the value of a good income as well as anybody. Elton may talk sentimentally, but he will act rationally. He is as well acquainted with his own claims as you can be with Harriet's. He knows that he is a very handsome young man, and a great favourite wherever he goes; and from his general way of talking in unreserved moments, when there are only men present, I am convinced that he does not mean to throw himself away. I have heard him speak with great animation of a large family of young ladies that his sisters are intimate with, who have all twenty thousand pounds apiece.'

'I am very much obliged to you,' said Emma, laughing again. 'If I had set my heart on Mr Elton's marrying Harriet, it would have been very kind to open my eyes; but at present I only want to keep Harriet to myself. I have done with match-making, indeed. I could never hope to equal my own doings at Randalls. I shall leave off while I am well.'

'Good morning to you,' said he, rising, and walking off abruptly. He was very much vexed. He felt the disappointment of the young man, and was mortified to have been the means of promoting it, by the sanction he had given; and the part which, he was persuaded, Emma had taken in the affair was provoking him exceedingly.

Emma remained in a state of vexation too; but there was more indistinctness in the causes of hers than in his. She did not always feel so absolutely satisfied with herself, so entirely convinced that her opinions were right and her adversary's wrong, as Mr Knightley. He walked off in more complete self-approbation than he left for her. She was not so materially cast down, however, but that a little time and the return of Harriet were very adequate restoratives. Harriet's staying away so long was beginning to make her uneasy. The possibility of the young man's coming to Mrs Goddard's that morning, and meeting with Harriet and pleading his own cause, gave alarming ideas. The dread of such a failure, after all, became the prominent uneasiness; and when Harriet appeared, and in very good spirits, and without having any such reason to give for her long absence, she felt a satisfaction which settled her with her own mind, and convinced her that, let Mr Knightley think or say what he would, she had done nothing which woman's friendship and woman's feelings would not justify.

He had frightened her a little about Mr Elton; but when she considered that Mr Knightley could not have observed him as she had done, neither with the interest nor (she must be allowed to tell herself, in spite of Mr Knightley's pretensions) with the skill of such an observer on such a question as herself, that he had spoken it hastily and in anger, she was able to believe, that he had rather said what he wished resentfully to be true, than what he knew anything about. He certainly might have heard Mr Elton speak with more unreserve than she had ever done, and Mr Elton might not be of an imprudent, inconsiderate disposition, as to money matters; he might naturally be rather attentive than other-wise to them; but then, Mr Knightley did not make due allowance for the influence of a strong passion, at war with all interested motives. Mr Knightley saw no such passion, and of course thought nothing of its effects; but she saw too much of it to feel a doubt of its overcoming any hesitations that a reasonable prudence might originally suggest; and more than a reasonable, becoming degree of prudence, she was very sure did not belong to Mr Elton.

Harriet's cheerful look and manner established hers; she came back, not to think of Mr Martin, but to talk of Mr Elton. Miss Nash had been telling her something, which she repeated immediately with great delight. Mr Perry had been to Mrs Goddard's to attend a sick child, and Miss Nash had seen him; and he had told Miss Nash that as he was coming back yesterday from Clayton Park he had met Mr Elton, and found, to his great surprise, that Mr Elton was actually on his road to London, and not meaning to return till the morrow, though it was the whist club night, which he had been never known to miss before; and Mr Perry had remonstrated with him about it, and told him how shabby it was in him, their best player, to absent himself, and tried very much to persuade him to put off his journey only one day; but it would not do; Mr Elton had been determined to go on, and had said in a very *particular* way indeed, that he was going on business which he would not put off for any inducement in the world; and something about a very enviable commission, and being the bearer of something exceedingly precious. Mr Perry could not quite understand him, but he was very sure there must be a *lady* in the case, and he told him so; and Mr Elton only looked very conscious and smiling, and rode off in great spirits. Miss Nash had told her all this, and had talked a great deal more about Mr Elton; and said, looking so very significantly at her, 'that she did not pretend to understand what his business might be, but she only knew that any woman whom Mr Elton could prefer, she should think the luckiest woman in the world; for, beyond a doubt, Mr Elton had not his equal for beauty or agreeableness.'

Chapter 9

Mr Knightley might quarrel with her, but Emma could not quarrel with herself. He was so much displeased, that it was longer than usual before he came to Hartfield again; and when they did meet, his grave looks showed that she was not forgiven. She was sorry but could not repent. On the contrary, her plans and proceedings were more and more justified, and endeared to her by the general appearances of the next few days.

The picture, elegantly framed, came safely to hand soon after Mr Elton's return, and being hung over the mantelpiece of the common sitting-room, he got up to look at it, and sighed out his half sentences of admiration, just as he ought; and as for Harriet's feelings, they were vividly forming themselves into as strong and steady an attachment as her youth and sort of mind admitted. Emma was soon perfectly satisfied of Mr Martin's being no otherwise remembered, than as he furnished a contrast with Mr Elton, of the utmost advantage to the latter.

Her views of improving her little friend's mind, by a great deal of useful reading and conversation, had never yet led to more than a few first chapters, and the intention of going on tomorrow. It was much easier to chat than to study; much pleasanter to let her imagination range and work at Harriet's fortune, than to be labouring to enlarge her comprehension, or exercise it on sober facts; and the only literary pursuit which engaged Harriet at present, the only mental provision she was making for the evening of life, was the collection and transcribing all the riddles of every sort that she could meet with, into a thin quarto of hot-pressed paper, made up by her friend, and ornamented with cyphers and trophies.

In this age of literature, such collections on a very grand scale are not uncommon. Miss Nash, head-teacher at Mrs Goddard's, had written out at least three hundred; and Harriet, who had taken the first hint of it from her, hoped, with Miss Woodhouse's help, to get a great many more. Emma assisted with her invention, memory, and taste; and as Harriet wrote a very pretty hand, it was likely to be an arrangement of the first order, in form as well as quantity.

Mr Woodhouse was almost as much interested in the business as the girls, and tried very often to recollect something worth their putting in. 'So many clever riddles as there used to be when he was young – he wondered he could not remember them; but he hoped he should in time.' And it always ended in 'Kitty, a fair but frozen maid.'

His good friend Perry, too, whom he had spoken to on the subject, did not at present recollect anything of the riddle kind; but he had desired Perry to be upon the watch, and as he went about so much, something, he thought, might come from that quarter.

It was by no means his daughter's wish that the intellects of Highbury in general should be put under requisition. Mr Elton was the only one whose assistance she asked. He was invited to contribute any really good enigmas, charades or conundrums, that he might recollect; and she had the pleasure of seeing him most intently at work with his recollections; and at the same time, as she could perceive, most earnestly careful that nothing ungallant, nothing that did not breathe a compliment to the sex, should pass his lips. They owed to him their two or three politest puzzles; and the joy and exultation with which at last he recalled, and rather sentimentally recited, that well known charade:

My first doth affliction denote,
Which my second is destin'd to feel;
And my whole is the best antidote
That affliction to soften and heal,

made her quite sorry to acknowledge that they had transcribed it some pages ago already.

'Why will not you write one yourself for us, Mr Elton?' said she; 'that is the only security for its freshness; and nothing could be easier to you.'

'Oh, no, he had never written, hardly ever, anything of the kind in his life. The stupidest fellow! He was afraid not even Miss Woodhouse' – he stopped a moment – 'or Miss Smith could inspire him.'

The very next day, however, produced some proof of inspiration. He called for a few moments, just to leave a piece of paper on the table containing, as he said, a charade which a friend of his had addressed to a young lady, the object of his admiration; but which, from his manner, Emma was immediately convinced must be his own.

'I do not offer it for Miss Smith's collection,' said he. 'Being my friend's, I have no right to expose it in any degree to the public eye, but perhaps you may not dislike looking at it.'

The speech was more to Emma than to Harriet, which Emma could understand. There was deep consciousness about him, and he found it easier to meet her eyes than her friend's. He was gone the next moment; after another moment's pause: 'Take it,' said Emma, smiling, and pushing the paper towards Harriet – 'it is for you. Take your own.'

But Harriet was in a tremor, and could not touch it; and Emma, never loath to be first, was obliged to examine it herself.

To Miss—

CHARADE

My first displays the wealth and pomp of kings,
    Lords of the earth! their luxury and ease.
Another view of man, my second brings,
    Behold him there, the monarch of the seas!

But ah! united, what reverse we have!
    Man's boasted power and freedom, all are flown:
Lord of the earth and sea, he bends a slave,
    And woman, lovely woman, reigns alone.

    Thy ready wit the word will soon supply,
    May its approval beam in that soft eye!

She cast her eye over it, pondered, caught the meaning, read it through again to be quite certain, and quite mistress of the lines, and then passing it to Harriet, sat happily smiling, and saying to herself, while Harriet was puzzling over the paper in all the confusion of hope and dullness, 'Very well, Mr Elton, very well, indeed. I have read worse charades. *Courtship* – a very good hint. I give you credit for it. This is feeling your way. This is saying very plainly – "Pray, Miss Smith, give me leave to pay my addresses to you. Approve my charade and my attentions in the same glance."

May its approval beam in that soft eye!

Harriet exactly. Soft is the very word for her eye – of all epithets, the justest that could be given.

Thy ready wit the word will soon supply.

Humph – Harriet's ready wit. All the better. A man must be very much in love indeed, to describe her so. Ah! Mr Knightley, I wish you had the benefit of this; I think this would convince you. For once in your life you would be obliged to own yourself mistaken. An excellent charade, indeed, and very much to the purpose. Things must come to a crisis soon now.'

She was obliged to break off from these very pleasant observations, which were otherwise of a sort to run into great length, by the eagerness of Harriet's wondering questions.

'What can it be, Miss Woodhouse? – what can it be? I have not an idea – I cannot guess it in the least. What can it possibly be? Do try to find it out, Miss Woodhouse. Do help me. I never saw anything so hard. Is it kingdom? I wonder who the friend was – and who could be the young lady. Do you think it is a good one? Can it be woman?

And woman, lovely woman, reigns alone.

Can it be Neptune?

Behold him there, the monarch of the seas!

Or a trident? or a mermaid? or a shark? Oh, no; shark is only one syllable. It must be very clever, or he would not have brought it. Oh, Miss Woodhouse, do you think we shall ever find it out?'

'Mermaids and sharks! Nonsense! My dear Harriet, what are you thinking of? Where would be the use of his bringing us a charade made by a friend upon a mermaid or a shark? Give me the paper and listen.

'For "Miss —", read Miss Smith,

My first displays the wealth and pomp of kings,
    Lords of the earth! their luxury and ease.

That is *court*.

Another view of man, my second brings,
    Behold him there, the monarch of the seas!

That is *ship* – plain as it can be. Now for the cream.

But ah! united (*courtship*, you know), what reverse we have!
Man's boasted power and freedom, all are flown:
Lord of the earth and sea, he bends a slave,
And woman, lovely woman, reigns alone.

A very proper compliment! and then follows the application which I think, my dear Harriet, you cannot find much difficulty in comprehending. Read it in comfort to yourself. There can be no doubt of its being written for you and to you.'

Harriet could not long resist so delightful a persuasion. She read the concluding lines, and was all flutter and happiness. She could not speak. But she was not wanted to speak. It was enough for her to feel. Emma spoke for her.

'There is so pointed and so particular a meaning in this compliment,' said she, 'that I cannot have a doubt as to Mr Elton's intentions. You are his object – and you will soon receive the completest proof of it. I thought it must be so. I thought I could not be so deceived; but now it is clear; the state of his mind is as clear and decided as my wishes on the subject have been ever since I knew you. Yes, Harriet, just so long have I been wanting the very circumstance to happen which has happened. I could never tell whether an attachment between you and Mr Elton were most desirable or most natural. Its probability and its eligibility have really so equalled each other! I am very happy. I congratulate you, my dear Harriet, with all my heart. This is an attachment which a woman may well feel proud in creating. This is a connection which offers nothing but good. It will give you everything that you want – consideration, independence, a proper home – it will fix you in the centre of all your real friends, close to Hartfield and to me, and confirm our intimacy for ever. This, Harriet, is an alliance which can never raise a blush in either of us.'

'Dear Miss Woodhouse!' and 'Dear Miss Woodhouse!' was all that Harriet, with many tender embraces, could articulate at first; but when they did arrive at something more like conversation, it was sufficiently clear to her friend that she saw, felt, anticipated, and remembered just as she ought. Mr Elton's superiority had very ample acknowledgement.

'Whatever you say is always right,' cried Harriet, 'and therefore I suppose, and believe, and hope it must be so; but otherwise I could not have imagined it. It is so much beyond anything I deserve. Mr Elton, who might marry anybody! There cannot be two opinions about *him*. He is so very superior. Only think of those sweet verses – "To Miss —". Dear me, how clever! Could it really be meant for me?'

'I cannot make a question, or listen to a question about that. It is a certainty. Receive it on my judgement. It is a sort of prologue to the play, a motto to the chapter; and will be soon followed by matter-of-fact prose.'

'It is a sort of thing which nobody could have expected. I am sure, a month ago, I had no more idea myself. The strangest things do take place!'

'When Miss Smiths and Mr Eltons get acquainted – they do indeed – and really it is strange; it is out of the common course that what is so evidently, so palpably desirable – what courts the pre-arrangement of other people – should so immediately shape itself into the proper form. You and Mr Elton are by situation called together; you belong to one another by every circumstance of your respective homes. Your marrying will be equal to the match at Randalls. There does seem to be something in the air of Hartfield which gives love exactly the right direction, and sends it into the very channel where it ought to flow.

The course of true love never did run smooth –

A Hartfield edition of Shakespeare would have a long note on that passage.'

'That Mr Elton should really be in love with me – me, of all people, who did not know him, to speak to him at Michaelmas. And he, the very handsomest man that ever was, and a man that everybody looks up to, quite like Mr Knightley. His company so sought after, that everybody says he need not eat a single meal by himself if he does not choose it; that he has more invitations than there are days in the week. And so excellent in the Church! Miss Nash has put down all the texts he has ever preached from since he came to Highbury. Dear me! When I look back to the first time I saw him! How little did I think! The two Abbots and I ran into the front room, and peeped through the blind when we heard he was going by, and Miss Nash came and scolded us away, and stayed to look through herself; however, she called me back presently, and let me look too, which was very good-natured. And how beautiful we thought he looked! He was arm in arm with Mr Cole.'

'This is an alliance which, whoever – whatever your friends may be, must be agreeable to them, provided, at least, they have common sense; and we are not to be addressing our conduct to fools. If they are anxious to see you *happily* married, here is a man whose amiable character gives every assurance of it; if they wish to have you settled in the same country and circle which they have chosen to place you in, here it will be accomplished; and if their only object is that you should, in the common phrase, be *well*

married, here is the comfortable fortune, the respectable establishment, the rise in the world which must satisfy them.'

'Yes, very true. How nicely you talk! I love to hear you. You
understand everything. You and Mr Elton are one as clever as the
other. This charade! If I had studied a twelvemonth, I could never
have made anything like it.'

'I thought he meant to try his skill, by his manner of declining
it yesterday.'

'I do think it is, without exception, the best charade I ever
read.'

'I never read one more to the purpose, certainly.'

'It is as long again as almost all we have had before.'

'I do not consider its length as particularly in its favour. Such
things in general cannot be too short.'

Harriet was too intent on the lines to hear. The most satisfactory comparisons were rising in her mind.

'It is one thing,' said she presently, her cheeks in a glow, 'to
have very good sense in a common way, like everybody else, and if
there is anything to say, to sit down and write a letter, and say just
what you must, in a short way; and another to write verses and
charades like this.'

Emma could not have desired a more spirited rejection of Mr
Martin's prose.

'Such sweet lines!' continued Harriet, 'these two last! But how
shall I ever be able to return the paper, or say I have found it out?
Oh, Miss Woodhouse, what can we do about that?'

'Leave it to me. You do nothing. He will be here this evening, I
dare say, and then I will give it him back, and some nonsense or
other will pass between us, and you shall not be committed. Your
soft eyes shall choose their own time for beaming. Trust to me.'

'Oh, Miss Woodhouse, what a pity that I must not write this
beautiful charade into my book; I am sure I have not got one half
so good.'

'Leave out the two last lines, and there is no reason why you
should not write it into your book.'

'Oh, but those two lines are – '

'The best of all. Granted – for private enjoyment; and for private enjoyment keep them. They are not at all the less written, you know, because you divide them. The couplet does not cease to be, nor does its meaning change. But take it away, and all *appropriation* ceases, and a very pretty gallant charade remains, fit for any collection. Depend upon it, he would not like to have his charade slighted much better than his passion. A poet in love must be encouraged in both capacities, or neither. Give me the book. I will write it down, and then there can be no possible reflection on you.'

Harriet submitted, though her mind could hardly separate the parts, so as to feel quite sure that her friend were not writing down a declaration of love. It seemed too precious an offering for any degree of publicity.

'I shall never let that book go out of my own hands,' said she.

'Very well,' replied Emma, 'a most natural feeling, and the longer it lasts, the better I shall be pleased. But here is my father coming; you will not object to my reading the charade to him. It will be giving him so much pleasure. He loves anything of the sort, and especially anything that pays woman a compliment. He has the tenderest spirit of gallantry towards us all. You must let me read it to him.'

Harriet looked grave.

'My dear Harriet, you must not refine too much upon this charade. You will betray your feelings improperly, if you are too conscious and too quick, and appear to *affix* more meaning or even quite all the meaning which may be affixed to it. Do not be overpowered by such a little tribute of admiration. If he had been anxious for secrecy, he would not have left the paper while I was by, but he rather pushed it towards me than towards you. Do not let us be too solemn on the business. He has encouragement enough to proceed, without our sighing out our souls over this charade.'

'Oh, no; I hope I shall not be ridiculous about it. Do as you please.'

Mr Woodhouse came in, and very soon led to the subject again, by the recurrence of his very frequent enquiry of 'Well, my dears, how does your book go on? Have you got anything fresh?'

'Yes, papa; we have something to read you, something quite fresh. A piece of paper was found on the table this morning (dropped, we suppose, by a fairy) containing a very pretty charade, and we have just copied it in.'

She read it to him, just as he liked to have anything read, slowly and distinctly, and two or three times over, with explanations of every part as she proceeded; and he was very much pleased, and, as she had foreseen, especially struck with the complimentary conclusion.

'Aye, that's very just, indeed; that's very properly said. Very true. "Woman, lovely woman." It is such a pretty charade, my dear, that I can easily guess what fairy brought it. Nobody could have written so prettily but you, Emma.'

Emma only nodded and smiled. After a little thinking, and a very tender sigh, he added: 'Ah, it is no difficulty to see who you take after. Your dear mother was so clever at all those things. If I had but her memory. But I can remember nothing; not even that particular riddle which you have heard me mention; I can only recollect the first stanza; and there are several:

> Kitty, a fair but frozen maid,
>   Kindled a flame I yet deplore;
> The hoodwink'd boy I called to aid,
> Though of his near approach afraid,
>   So fatal to my suit before.

And that is all that I can recollect of it; but it is very clever all the way through. But I think, my dear, you said you had got it.'

'Yes, papa, it is written out in our second page. We copied it from the *Elegant Extracts*. It was Garrick's, you know.'

'Aye, very true – I wish I could recollect more of it:

Kitty, a fair but frozen maid.

The name makes me think of poor Isabella; for she was very near being christened Catherine, after her grandmamma. I hope we shall have her here next week. Have you thought, my dear, where you shall put her, and what room there will be for the children?'

'Oh, yes; she will have her own room of course; the room she always has; and there is the nursery for the children – just as usual, you know. Why should there be any change?'

'I do not know, my dear; but it is so long since she was here – not since last Easter, and then only for a few days. Mr John Knightley's being a lawyer is very inconvenient. Poor Isabella! she is sadly taken away from us all; and how sorry she will be, when she comes, not to see Miss Taylor here.'

'She will not be surprised, papa, at least.'

'I do not know, my dear. I am sure I was very much surprised when I first heard she was going to be married.'

'We must ask Mr and Mrs Weston to dine with us, while Isabella is here.'

'Yes, my dear, if there is time. But' (in a very depressed tone) 'she is coming for only one week. There will not be time for anything.'

'It is unfortunate that they cannot stay longer, but it seems a case of necessity. Mr John Knightley must be in town again on the 28th; and we ought to be thankful, papa, that we are to have the whole of the time they can give to the country, that two or three days are not to be taken out for the Abbey. Mr Knightley promises to give up his claim this Christmas, though you know it is longer since they were with him than with us.'

'It would be very hard, indeed, my dear, if poor Isabella were to be anywhere but at Hartfield.'

Mr Woodhouse could never allow for Mr Knightley's claims on his brother, or anybody's claims on Isabella, except his own. He sat musing a little while, and then said: 'But I do not see why poor Isabella should be obliged to go back so soon, though he does. I think, Emma, I shall try and persuade her to stay longer with us. She and the children might stay very well.'

'Ah, papa, that is what you never have been able to accomplish, and I do not think you ever will. Isabella cannot bear to stay behind her husband.'

This was too true for contradiction. Unwelcome as it was, Mr Woodhouse could only give a submissive sigh; and as Emma saw his spirits affected by the idea of his daughter's attachment to her husband, she immediately led to such a branch of the subject as must raise them.

'Harriet must give us as much of her company as she can while my brother and sister are here. I am sure she will be pleased with the children. We are very proud of the children, are not we, papa? I wonder which she will think the handsomest, Henry or John?'

'Aye, I wonder which she will. Poor little dears, how glad they will be to come. They are very fond of being at Hartfield, Harriet.'

'I dare say they are, sir. I am sure I do not know who is not.'

'Henry is a fine boy, but John is very like his mamma. Henry is the eldest; he was named after me, not after his father. John, the second, is named after his father. Some people are surprised, I believe, that the eldest was not, but Isabella would have him called Henry, which I thought very pretty of her. And he is a very clever boy, indeed. They are all remarkably clever; and they have so many pretty ways. They will come and stand by my chair and say, "Grandpapa, can you give me a bit of string?" and once Henry asked me for a knife, but I told him knives were only made for grandpapas. I think their father is too rough with them very often.'

'He appears rough to you,' said Emma, 'because you are so very gentle yourself; but if you could compare him with other papas, you would not think him rough. He wishes his boys to be active and hardy; and if they misbehave, can give them a sharp word now and then; but he is an affectionate father – certainly Mr

John Knightley is an affectionate father. The children are all fond of him.'

'And then their uncle comes in and tosses them up to the ceiling in a very frightful way.'

'But they like it, papa; there is nothing they like so much. It is such enjoyment to them, that if their uncle did not lay down the rule of their taking turns, whichever began would never give way to the other.'

'Well, I cannot understand it.'

'That is the case with us all, papa. One half of the world cannot understand the pleasures of the other.'

Later in the morning, and just as the girls were going to separate, in preparation for the regular four o'clock dinner, the hero of this inimitable charade walked in again. Harriet turned away; but Emma could receive him with the usual smile, and her quick eye soon discerned in his the consciousness of having made a push, of having thrown a die; and she imagined he was come to see how it might turn up. His ostensible reason, however, was to ask whether Mr Woodhouse's party could be made up in the evening without him, or whether he should be in the smallest degree necessary at Hartfield. If he were, everything else must give way; but otherwise his friend Cole had been saying so much about his dining with him – had made such a point of it – that he had promised him conditionally to come.

Emma thanked him, but could not allow of his disappointing his friend on their account; her father was sure of his rubber. He re-urged – she re-declined; and he seemed then about to make his bow, when, taking the paper from the table, she returned it.

'Oh, here is the charade you were so obliging as to leave with us; thank you for the sight of it. We admired it so much that I have ventured to write it into Miss Smith's collection. Your friend will not take it amiss, I hope. Of course, I have not transcribed beyond the first eight lines.'

Mr Elton certainly did not very well know what to say. He looked rather doubtingly – rather confused; said something about 'honour' – glanced at Emma and at Harriet, and then, seeing the book open on the table, took it up, and examined it very attentively. With the view of passing off an awkward moment, Emma smilingly said: 'You must make my apologies to your friend; but so good a charade must not be confined to one or two. He may be sure of every woman's approbation while he writes with such gallantry.'

'I have no hesitation in saying,' replied Mr Elton, though hesitating a good deal while he spoke – 'I have no hesitation in saying – at least if my friend feels at all as *I* do – I have not the smallest doubt that, could he see his little effusion honoured as *I* see it (looking at the book again and replacing it on the table), he would consider it as the proudest moment of his life.'

After this speech he was gone as soon as possible. Emma could not think it too soon; for with all his good and agreeable qualities there was a sort of parade in his speeches which was very apt to incline her to laugh. She ran away to indulge the inclination, leaving the tender and the sublime of pleasure to Harriet's share.

Chapter 10

Though now the middle of December, there had yet been no weather to prevent the young ladies from tolerably regular exercise; and on the morrow, Emma had a charitable visit to pay to a poor sick family who lived a little way out of Highbury.

Their road to this detached cottage was down Vicarage Lane, a lane leading at right angles from the broad, though irregular, main street of the place; and, as may be inferred, containing the blessed abode of Mr Elton. A few inferior dwellings were first to be passed, and then, about a quarter of a mile down the lane, rose the vicarage, an old and not very good house, almost as close to the road as it could be. It had no advantage of situation; but had been very much smartened up by the present proprietor; and, such as it was, there could be no possibility of the two friends passing it without a slackened pace and observing eyes. Emma's remark was: 'There it is. There go you and your riddle book one of these days.' Harriet's was: 'Oh, what a sweet house! How very beautiful! There are the yellow curtains that Miss Nash admires so much.'

'I do not often walk this way *now*,' said Emma, as they proceeded, 'but *then* there will be an inducement, and I shall gradually get intimately acquainted with all the hedges, gates, pools, and pollards, of this part of Highbury.'

Harriet, she found, had never in her life been within sight the vicarage; and her curiosity to see it was so extreme, that, considering exteriors and probabilities, Emma could only class it as a proof of love, with Mr Elton's seeing ready wit in her.

'I wish we could contrive it,' said she; 'but I cannot think of any tolerable pretence for going in; no servant that I want to enquire about of his housekeeper – no message from my father.'

She pondered, but could think of nothing. After a mutual silence of some minutes, Harriet thus began again: 'I do so wonder, Miss Woodhouse, that you should not be married, or going to be married – so charming as you are.'

Emma laughed, and replied: 'My being charming, Harriet, is not quite enough to induce me to marry; I must find other people charming – one other person at least. And I am not only not going to be married at present, but have very little intention of ever marrying at all.'

'Ah, so you say, but I cannot believe it.'

'I must see somebody very superior to anyone I have seen yet, to be tempted; Mr Elton, you know' (recollecting herself) 'is out of the question; and I do not wish to see any such person. I would rather not be tempted. I cannot really change for the better. If I were to marry, I must expect to repent it.'

'Dear me! – it is so odd to hear a woman talk so!'

'I have none of the usual inducements of women to marry. Were I to fall in love, indeed, it would be a different thing; but I never have been in love; it is not my way, or my nature; and I do not think I ever shall. And, without love, I am sure I should be a fool to change such a situation as mine. Fortune I do not want; employment I do not want; consequence I do not want; I believe few married women are half as much mistress of their husband's house as I am of Hartfield; and never, never could I expect to be so truly beloved and important; so always first and always right in any man's eyes as I am in my father's.'

'But then, to be an old maid at last, like Miss Bates!'

'That is as formidable an image as you could present, Harriet; and if I thought I should ever be like Miss Bates – so silly, so satisfied, so smiling, so prosing, so undistinguishing, and unfastidious, and so apt to tell everything relative to everybody about me, I would marry tomorrow. But between us, I am convinced there never can be any likeness, except in being unmarried.'

'But still, you will be an old maid – and that's so dreadful!'

'Never mind, Harriet, I shall not be a poor old maid; and it is poverty only which makes celibacy contemptible to a generous public! A single woman with a very narrow income must be a ridiculous, disagreeable old maid! the proper sport of boys and girls; but a single woman of good fortune is always respectable, and may be as sensible and pleasant as anybody else! And the distinction is not quite so much against the candour and common sense of the world as appears at first; for a very narrow income has a tendency to contract the mind, and sour the temper. Those who can barely live, and who live perforce in a very small, and generally very inferior, society, may well be illiberal and cross. This does not apply, however, to Miss Bates; she is only too good-natured and too silly to suit me; but, in general, she is very much to the taste of everybody, though single, and though poor. Poverty certainly has not contracted her mind; I really believe, if she had only a shilling in the world, she would be very likely to give away sixpence of it; and nobody is afraid of her – that is a great charm.'

'Dear me! but what shall you do? How shall you employ yourself when you grow old?'

'If I know myself, Harriet, mine is an active, busy mind, with a great many independent resources; and I do not perceive why I should be more in want of employment at forty or fifty than one-and-twenty. Woman's usual occupations of eye, and hand, and mind, will be as open to me then as they are now, or with no important variation. If I draw less, I shall read more; if I give up music, I shall take to carpet-work. And as for objects of interest, objects for the affections, which is, in truth, the great point of inferiority, the want of which is really the great evil to be avoided in *not* marrying, I shall be very well off, with all the children of a sister I love so much to care about. There will be enough of them in all probability, to supply every sort of sensation that declining life can need. There will be enough for every hope and every fear; and though my attachment to none can equal that of a parent, it suits my ideas of comfort better than what is warmer and blinder. My nephews and nieces: I shall often have a niece with me.'

'Do you know Miss Bates's niece? That is, I know you must have seen her a hundred times – but are you acquainted?'

'Oh, yes; we are always forced to be acquainted whenever she comes to Highbury. By the by, *that* is almost enough to put one out of conceit with a niece. Heaven forbid at least, that I should ever bore people half so much about all the Knightleys together as she does about Jane Fairfax. One is sick of the very name of Jane Fairfax. Every letter from her is read forty times over; her compliments to all friends go round and round again; and if she does but send her aunt the pattern of a stomacher, or knit a pair of garters for her grandmother, one hears of nothing else for a month. I wish Jane Fairfax very well, but she tires me to death.'

They were now approaching the cottage, and all idle topics were superseded. Emma was very compassionate; and the distresses of the poor were as sure of relief from her personal attention and kindness, her counsel and her patience, as from her purse. She understood their ways, could allow for their ignorance and their temptations, had no romantic expectations of extraordinary virtue from those for whom education had done so little, entered into their troubles with ready sympathy, and always gave her assistance with as much intelligence as goodwill. In the present instance it was sickness and poverty together which she came to visit; and after remaining there as long as she could give comfort or advice, she quitted the cottage with such an impression of the scene as made her say to Harriet, as they walked away: 'These are the sights, Harriet, to do one good. How trifling they make everything else appear! I feel now as if I could think of nothing but these poor creatures all the rest of the day; and yet who can say how soon it may all vanish from my mind?'

'Very true,' said Harriet. 'Poor creatures! one can think of nothing else.'

'And really, I do not think the impression will soon be over,' said Emma, as she crossed the low hedge, and tottering footstep which ended the narrow slippery path through the cottage garden, and brought them into the lane again. 'I do not think it will,' stopping to look once more at all the outward wretchedness of the place, and recall the still greater within.

'Oh, dear no,' said her companion.

They walked on. The lane made a slight bend; and when that bend was passed, Mr Elton was immediately in sight and so near as to give Emma time only to say further: 'Ah, Harriet, here come a very sudden trial of our stability in good thoughts. Well' (smiling), 'I hope it may be allowed that if compassion has produced exertion and relief to the sufferers, it has done all that is truly important. If we feel for the wretched enough to do all we can for them, the rest is empty sympathy, only distressing to ourselves.'

Harriet could just answer, 'Oh, dear, yes,' before the gentleman joined them. The wants and sufferings of the poor family, however, were the first subject on meeting. He had been going to call on them. His visit he would now defer; but they had a very interesting parley about what could be done and should be done. Mr Elton then turned back to accompany them.

'To fall in with each other on such an errand as this,' thought Emma; 'to meet in a charitable scheme; this will bring a great increase of love on each side. I should not wonder if it were to bring on the declaration. It must, if I were not here. I wish I were anywhere else.'

Anxious to separate herself from them as far as she could, she soon afterwards took possession of a narrow footpath, a little raised on oneside of the lane, leaving them together in the main road. But she had not been there two minutes when she found that Harriet's habits of dependence and imitation were bringing her up too, and that, in short, they would both be soon after her. This would not do; she immediately stopped, under pretence of having some alteration to make in the lacing of her half-boot, and stooping down in complete occupation of the footpath, begged them to have the goodness to walk on, and she would follow in half a minute. They did as they were desired; and by the time she judged it reasonable to have done with her boot, she had the comfort of further delay in her power, being overtaken by a child from the cottage, setting out, according to orders, with her pitcher, to fetch broth from Hartfield. To walk by the side of this child, and talk to and question her, was the most natural thing in the world, or would have been the most natural, had she been acting just then without design; and by this means the others were still able to keep ahead, without any obligation of waiting for her. She gained on them, however, involuntarily; the child's pace was quick, and theirs rather slow; and she was the more concerned at it, from their being evidently in a conversation which interested them. Mr Elton was speaking with animation, Harriet listening with a very pleased attention; and Emma having sent the child on, was beginning to think how she might draw back a little more, when they both looked around, and she was obliged to join them.

Mr Elton was still talking, still engaged in some interesting detail; and Emma experienced some disappointment when she found that he was only giving his fair companion an account of the yesterday's party at his friend Cole's, and that she was come in herself for the Stilton cheese, the North Wiltshire, the butter, the celery, the beetroot, and all the dessert.

'This would soon have led to something better, of course,' was her consoling reflection; 'anything interests between those who love; and anything will serve as introduction to what is near the heart. If I could but have kept longer away.'

They now walked on together quietly till within view of the vicarage pales, when a sudden resolution of at least getting Harriet into the house, made her again find something very much amiss about her boot, and fall behind to arrange it once more. She then broke the lace off short, and dexterously throwing it into a ditch, was presently obliged to entreat them to stop, and acknowledge her inability to put herself to rights so as to be able to walk home in tolerable comfort.

'Part of my lace is gone,' said she, 'and I do not know how I am to contrive. I really am a most troublesome companion to you both, but I hope I am not often so ill-equipped. Mr Elton, I must beg leave to stop at your house, and ask your housekeeper for a bit of ribband or string, or anything just to keep my boot on.'

Mr Elton looked all happiness at this proposition; and nothing could exceed his alertness and attention in conducting them into his house, and endeavouring to make everything appear to advantage. The room they were taken into was the one he chiefly occupied, and looking forwards; behind it was another with which it immediately communicated; the door between them was open, and Emma passed into it with the housekeeper, to receive her assistance in the most comfortable manner. She was obliged to leave the door ajar as she found it; but she fully intended that Mr Elton should close it. It was not closed,however, it still remained ajar; but by engaging the housekeeper in incessant conversation, she hoped to make it practicable for him to choose his own subject in the adjoining room. For ten minutes she could hear nothing but herself. It could be protracted no longer. She was then obliged to be finished, and make her appearance.

The lovers were standing together at one of the windows. It had a most favourable aspect; and, for half a minute, Emma felt the glory of having schemed successfully. But it would not do; he had not come to the point. He had been most agreeable, most delightful; he had told Harriet that he had seen them go by, and had purposely followed them; other little gallantries and allusions had been dropped, but nothing serious.

'Cautious, very cautious,' thought Emma; 'he advances inch by inch, and will hazard nothing till be believes himself secure.'

Still, however, though everything had not been accomplished by her ingenious device, she could not but flatter herself that it had been the occasion of much present enjoyment to both, and must be leading them forward to the great event.

Chapter 11

Mr Elton must now be left to himself. It was no longer in Emma's power to superintend his happiness, or quicken his measures. The coming of her sister's family was so very near at hand, that first in anticipation, and then in reality, it became henceforth her prime object of interest; and during the ten days of their stay at Hartfield it was not to be expected – she did not herself expect – that anything beyond occasional, fortuitous assistance could be afforded by her to the lovers. They might advance rapidly if they would, however; they must advance somehow or other, whether they would or no. She hardly wished to have more leisure for them. There are people, who, the more you do for them, the less they will do for themselves.

Mr and Mrs John Knightley, from having been longer than usual absent from Surrey, were exciting, of course, rather more than the usual interest. Till this year, every long vacation since their marriage had been divided between Hartfield and Donwell Abbey; but all the holidays of this autumn had been given to sea-bathing for the children; and it was therefore many months since they had been seen in a regular way by their Surrey connections, or seen at all by Mr Woodhouse, who could not be induced to get so far as London, even for poor Isabella's sake; and who, conse-quently, was now most nervously and apprehensively happy in forestalling this too short visit.

He thought much of the evils of the journey for her, and not a little of the fatigues of his own horses and coachman, who were to bring some of the party the last half of the way; but his alarms were needless, the sixteen miles being happily accomplished, and Mr and Mrs John Knightley, their five children, and a competent number of nursery-maids, all reaching Hartfield in safety. The bustle and joy of such an arrival, the many to be talked to, welcomed, encouraged, and variously dispersed and disposed of, produced a noise and confusion which his nerves could not have borne under any other cause, nor have endured much longer even for this; but the ways of Hartfield and the feelings of her father were so respected by Mrs John Knightley, that in spite of maternal solicitude for the immediate enjoyment of her little ones, and for their having instantly all the liberty and attendance, all the eating and drinking, and sleeping and playing, which they could possibly wish for, without the smallest delay, the children were never allowed to be long a disturbance to him, either in themselves or in any restless attendance on them.

Mrs John Knightley was a pretty, elegant little woman, of gentle, quiet manners, and a disposition remarkably amiable and affectionate, wrapped up in her family, a devoted wife, a doting mother, and so tenderly attached to her father and sister that, but for these higher ties, a warmer love might have seemed impossible. She could never see a fault in any of them. She was not a woman of strong understanding, or any quickness; and with this resemblance of her father, she inherited also much of his constitution; was delicate in her own health, over careful of that of her children, had many fears, and many nerves, and was as fond of her own Mr Wingfield in town as her father could be of Mr Perry. They were alike, too, in a general benevolence of temper, and a strong habit of regard for every old acquaintance. Mr John Knightley was a tall, gentlemanlike, and very clever man, rising in his profession; domestic and respectable in his private character; but with reserved manners which prevented him being generally pleasing; and capable of being sometimes out of humour. He was not an ill-tempered man, not so often unreasonably cross as to deserve such a reproach; but his temper was not his great perfection; and, indeed, with such a worshipping wife, it was hardly possible that any natural defects in it should not be increased. The extreme sweetness of her temper must hurt his. He had all the clearness and quickness of mind which she wanted; and he could sometimes act an ungracious, or say a severe thing. He was not a great favourite with his fair sister-in-law. Nothing wrong in him escaped her. She was quick in feeling the little injuries to Isabella, which Isabella never felt herself. Perhaps she might have passed over more had his manners been flattering to Isabella's sister, but they were only those of a calmly kind brother and friend, without praise and without blindness; but hardly any degree of personal compliment could have made her regardless of that greatest fault of all in her eyes which he sometimes fell into, the want of respectful forbearance towards her father. There he had not always the patience that could have been wished. Mr Woodhouse's peculiarities and fidgetiness were sometimes provoking him to a rational remonstrance or sharp retort equally illbestowed. It did not often happen; for Mr John Knightley had really a great regard for his father-in-law, and generally a strong sense of what was due to him: but it was too often for Emma's charity, especially as there was all the pain of apprehension frequently to be endured, though the offence came not. The beginning, however, of every visit displayed none but the properest feelings, and this being of necessity so short might be hoped to pass away in unsullied cordiality. They had not been long seated and composed when Mr Woodhouse, with a melancholy shake of the head and a sigh, called his daughter's attention to the sad change at Hartfield since she had been there last.

'Ah, my dear,' said he, 'poor Miss Taylor! It is a grievous business.'

'Oh, yes, sir,' cried she, with ready sympathy, 'how you must miss her! And dear Emma too. What a dreadful loss to you both! I have been so grieved for you. I could not imagine how you could possibly do without her. It is a sad change, indeed; but I hope she is pretty well, sir.'

'Pretty well, my dear – I hope – pretty well. I do not know but that the place agrees with her tolerably.'

Mr John Knightley here asked Emma, quietly, whether there were any doubts of the air of Randalls.

'Oh, no, none in the least. I never saw Mrs Weston better in my life – never looking so well. Papa is only speaking his own regret.'

'Very much to the honour of both,' was the handsome reply.

'And do you see her, sir, tolerably often?' asked Isabella, in the plaintive tone which just suited her father.

Mr Woodhouse hesitated. 'Not near so often, my dear, as I could wish.'

'Oh, papa, we have missed seeing them but one entire day since they married. Either in the morning or evening of every day, excepting one, have we seen either Mr Weston or Mrs Weston, and generally both, either at Randalls or here; and, as you may suppose, Isabella, most frequently here. They are very, very kind in their visits. Mr Weston is really as kind as herself. Papa, if you speak in that melancholy way, you will be giving Isabella a false idea of us all. Everybody must be aware that Miss Taylor must be missed; but everybody ought also to be assured that Mr and Mrs Weston do really prevent our missing her by any means to the extent we ourselves anticipated – which is the exact truth.'

'Just as it should be,' said Mr John Knightley, 'and just as I hoped it was from your letters. Her wish of showing you attention could not be doubted, and his being a disengaged and social man makes it all easy. I have been always telling you, my love, that I had no idea of the change being so very material to Hartfield as you apprehended; and now you have Emma's account, I hope you will be satisfied.'

'Why, to be sure,' said Mr Woodhouse – 'yes, certainly. I cannot deny that Mrs Weston – poor Mrs Weston – does come and see us pretty often; but then, she is always obliged to go away again.'

'It would be very hard upon Mr Weston if she did not, papa. You quite forget poor Mr Weston.'

'I think, indeed,' said John Knightley, pleasantly, 'that Mr Weston has some little claim. You and I, Emma, will venture to take the part of the poor husband. I being a husband, and you not being a wife, the claims of the man may very likely strike us with equal force. As for Isabella, she has been married long enough to see the convenience of putting all the Mr Westons aside as much as she can.'

'Me, my love?' cried his wife, hearing and understanding only in part. 'Are you talking about me? I am sure nobody ought to be, or can be, a greater advocate for matrimony than I am; and if it had not been for the misery of her leaving Hartfield, I should never have thought of Miss Taylor but as the most fortunate woman in the world; and as to slighting Mr Weston – that excellent Mr Weston – I think there is nothing he does not deserve. I believe he is one of the very best-tempered men that ever existed. Excepting yourself and your brother, I do not know his equal for temper. I shall never forget his flying Henry's kite for him that very windy day last Easter; and ever since his particular kindness last September twelvemonth in writing that note, at twelve o'clock at night, on purpose to assure me that there was no scarlet fever at Cobham, I have been convinced there could not be a more feeling heart nor a better man in existence. If anybody can deserve him, it must be Miss Taylor.'

'Where is the young man?' said John Knightley. 'Has he been here on this occasion, or has he not?'

'He has not been here yet,' replied Emma. 'There was a strong expectation of his coming soon after the marriage, but it ended in nothing; and I have not heard him mentioned lately.'

'But you should tell them of the letter, my dear,' said her father. 'He wrote a letter to poor Mrs Weston, to congratulate her, and a very proper, handsome letter it was. She showed it to me. I thought it very well done of him, indeed. Whether it was his own idea, you know, one cannot tell. He is but young, and his uncle, perhaps – '

'My dear papa, he is three-and-twenty. You forget how time passes.'

'Three-and-twenty! is he indeed? Well, I could not have thought it; and he was but two years old when he lost his poor mother. Well, time does fly, indeed! and my memory is very bad. However, it was an exceeding good, pretty letter, and gave Mr and Mrs Weston a great deal of pleasure. I remember it was written from Weymouth, and dated Sept. 28th, and began "My dear Madam", but I forget how it went on; and it was signed "F. C. Weston Churchill". I remember that perfectly.'

'How very pleasing and proper of him!' cried the good-hearted Mrs John Knightley. 'I have no doubt of his being a most amiable young man. But how sad it is that he should not live at home with his father! There is something so shocking in a child's being taken away from his parents and natural home. I never could comprehend how Mr Weston could part with him. To give up one's child. I really never could think well of anybody who proposed such a thing to anybody else.'

'Nobody ever did think well of the Churchills, I fancy,' observed Mr John Knightley coolly. 'But you need not imagine Mr Weston to have felt what you would feel in giving up Henry or John. Mr Weston is rather an easy cheerful-tempered man, than a man of strong feelings; he takes things as he finds them, and makes enjoyment of them somehow or other, depending, I suspect, much more upon what is called *society* for his comforts, that is, upon the power of eating and drinking and playing whist with his neighbours five times a week, than upon family affection, or anything that home affords.'

Emma could not like what bordered on a reflection on Mr Weston, and had half a mind to take it up; but she struggled, and let it pass. She would keep the peace if possible; and there was something honourable and valuable in the strong domestic habits, the all-sufficiency of home to himself, whence resulted her brother's disposition to look down on the common rate of social intercourse, and those to whom it was important. It had a high claim to forbearance.

Chapter 12

Mr Knightley was to dine with them, rather against the inclination of Mr Woodhouse, who did not like that anyone should share with him in Isabella's first day. Emma's sense of right, however, had decided it; and, besides the consideration of what was due to each brother, she had particular pleasure, from the circumstance of the late disagreement between Mr Knightley and herself, in procuring him the proper invitation.

She hoped they might now become friends again. She thought it was time to make up. Making up, indeed, would not do. *She* certainly had not been in the wrong, and *he* would never own that he had. Concession must be out of the question; but it was time to appear to forget that they had ever quarrelled; and she hoped it might rather assist the restoration of friendship, that when he came into the room she had one of the children with her – the youngest, a nice little girl about eight months old, who was now making her first visit to Hartfield, and very happy to be danced about in her aunt's arms. It did assist; for though he began with grave looks and short questions, he was soon led on to talk of them all in the usual way, and to take the child out of her arms with all the unceremoniousness of perfect amity. Emma felt they were friends again; and the conviction giving her at first great satisfaction, and then a little sauciness, she could not help saying, as he was admiring the baby: 'What a comfort it is that we think alike about our nephews and nieces! As to men and women, our opinions are sometimes very different; but with regard to these children I observe we never disagree.'

'If you were as much guided by nature in your estimate of men and women, and as little under the power of fancy and whim in your dealings with them, as you are where these children are concerned, we might always think alike.'

'To be sure – our discordances must always arise from my being in the wrong.'

'Yes,' said he, smiling, 'and reason good. I was sixteen years old when you were born.'

'A material difference, then,' she replied; 'and no doubt you were much my superior in judgement at that period of our lives; but does not the lapse of one-and-twenty years bring our understandings a good deal nearer?'

'Yes, a good deal *nearer.*'

'But still, not near enough to give me a chance of being right, if we think differently.'

'I have still the advantage of you by sixteen years' experience, and by not being a pretty young woman and a spoiled child. Come, my dear Emma, let us be friends, and say no more about it. Tell your aunt, little Emma, that she ought to set you a better example than to be renewing old grievances, and that if she were not wrong before, she is now.'

'That's true,' she cried, 'very true. Little Emma, grow up a better woman than your aunt. Be infinitely cleverer, and not half so conceited. Now, Mr Knightley, a word or two more, and I have done. As far as good intentions went, we were *both* right, and I must say that no effects on my side of the argument have yet proved wrong. I only want to know that Mr Martin is not very, very bitterly disappointed.'

'A man cannot be more so,' was his short, full answer.

'Ah! Indeed I am very sorry. Come, shake hands with me.'

This had just taken place, and with great cordiality, when John Knightley made his appearance; and, 'How d'ye do, George?' and 'John, how are you!' succeeded in the true English style, burying under a calmness that seemed all but indifference the real attachment which would have led either of them if requisite, to do everything for the good of the other.

The evening was quiet and conversable, as Mr Woodhouse declined cards entirely, for the sake of comfortable talk with his dear Isabella, and the little party made two natural divisions; on one side he and his daughter; on the other the two Mr Knightleys; their subjects totally distinct, or very rarely mixing, and Emma only occasionally joining in one or the other.

The brothers talked of their own concerns and pursuits, but principally of those of the elder, whose temper was by much the most communicative, and who was always the greater talker. As a magistrate, he had generally some point of law to consult John about, or, at least, some curious anecdote to give; and as a farmer, as keeping in hand the home farm at Donwell, he had to tell what every field was to bear next year, and to give all such local information as could not fail of being interesting to a brother whose home it had equally been the longest part of his life, and whose attachments were strong. The plan of a drain, the change of a fence, the felling of a tree, and the destination of every acre of wheat, turnips, or spring corn, was entered into with as much equality of interest by John as his cooler manners rendered possible; and if his willing brother ever left him anything to enquire about, his enquiries even approached a tone of eagerness.

While they were thus comfortably occupied, Mr Woodhouse was enjoying a full flow of happy regrets and fearful affection with his daughter.

'My poor dear Isabella,' said he, fondly taking her hand, and interrupting, for a few moments, her busy labours for some one of her five children, 'how long it is, how terribly long since you were here! And how tired you must be after your journey! You must go to bed early, my dear – and I recommend a little gruel to you before you go. You and I will have a nice basin of gruel together. My dear Emma, suppose we all have a little gruel.'

Emma could not suppose any such thing, knowing as she did, that both the Mr Knightleys were as unpersuadable on that article as herself – and two basins only were ordered. After a little more discourse in praise of gruel, with some wondering at its not being taken every evening by everybody, he proceeded to say, with an air of grave reflection: 'It was an awkward business, my dear, your spending the autumn at Southend instead of coming here. I never had much opinion of the sea air.'

'Mr Wingfield most strenuously recommended it, sir, or we should not have gone. He recommended it for all the children, but particularly for the weakness in little Bella's throat – both sea air and bathing.'

'Ah, my dear, but Perry had many doubts about the sea doing her any good; and as to myself, I have been long perfectly convinced, though perhaps I never told you so before, that the sea is very rarely of use to anybody. I am sure it almost killed me once.'

'Come, come,' cried Emma, feeling this to be an unsafe subject, 'I must beg you not to talk of the sea. It makes me envious and miserable; I who have never seen it! Southend is prohibited, if you please. My dear Isabella, I have not heard you make one enquiry about Mr Perry yet; and he never forgets you.'

'Oh, good Mr Perry, how is he, sir?'

'Why, pretty well; but not quite well. Poor Perry is bilious, and he has no time to take care of himself; he tells me he has not time to take care of himself – which is very sad – but he is always wanted all round the country. I suppose there is not a man in such practice anywhere. But then there is not so clever a man anywhere.'

'And Mrs Perry and the children, how are they? Do the children grow? I have a great regard for Mr Perry. I hope he will be calling soon. He will be so pleased to see my little ones.'

'I hope he will be here tomorrow, for I have a question or two to ask him about myself of some consequence. And, my dear, whenever he comes, you had better let him look at little Bella's throat.'

'Oh, my dear sir, her throat is so much better that I have hardly any uneasiness about it. Either bathing has been of the greatest service to her, or else it is to be attributed to an excellent embrocation of Mr Wingfield's, which we have been applying at times ever since August.'

'It is not very likely, my dear, that bathing should have been of use to her; and if I had known you were wanting an embrocation, I would have spoken to – '

'You seem to me to have forgotten Mrs and Miss Bates,' said Emma; 'I have not heard one enquiry after them.'

'Oh! the good Bateses. I am quite ashamed of myself, but you mention them in most of your letters. I hope they are quite well. Good old Mrs Bates! I will call upon her tomorrow, and take my children. They are always so pleased to see my children. And that excellent Miss Bates! – such thorough worthy people! How are they, sir?'

'Why, pretty well, my dear, upon the whole. But poor Mrs Bates had a bad cold about a month ago.'

'How sorry I am! but colds were never so prevalent as they have been this autumn. Mr Wingfield told me that he has never known them more general or heavy, except when it has been quite an influenza.'

'That has been a good deal the case, my dear, but not to the degree you mention. Perry says that colds have been very general, but not so heavy as he has very often known them in November. Perry does not call it altogether a sickly season.'

'No, I do not know that Mr Wingfield considers it *very* sickly, except – '

'Ah, my poor dear child, the truth is, that in London it is always a sickly season. Nobody is healthy in London. Nobody can be. It is a dreadful thing to have you forced to live there – so far off! – and the air so bad.'

'No, indeed, *we* are not at all in a bad air. Our part of London is very superior to most others. You must not confound us with London in general, my dear sir. The neighbourhood of Brunswick Square is very different from almost all the rest. We are so very airy! I should be unwilling, I own, to live in any other part of the town; there is hardly any other that I could be satisfied to have my children in; but we are so remarkably airy! Mr Wingfield thinks the vicinity of Brunswick Square decidedly the most favourable as to air.'

'Ah, my dear, it is not like Hartfield. You make the best of it – but after you have been a week at Hartfield, you are all of you different creatures; you do not look like the same. Now I cannot say that I think you are any of you looking well at present.'

'I am sorry to hear you say so, sir; but I assure you, excepting those little nervous headaches and palpitations which I am never entirely free from anywhere, I am quite well myself; and if the children were rather pale before they went to bed, it was only because they were a little more tired than usual, from their journey and the happiness of coming. I hope you will think better of their looks tomorrow; for I assure you Mr Wingfield told me, that he did not believe he had ever sent us off altogether, in such good case. I trust, at least, that you do not think Mr Knightley looking ill,' turning her eyes with affectionate anxiety towards her husband.

'Middling, my dear; I cannot compliment you. I think Mr John Knightley very far from looking well.'

'What is the matter, sir? Did you speak to me!' cried Mr John Knightley, hearing his own name.

'I am sorry to find, my love, that my father does not think you looking well; but I hope it is only from being a little fatigued. I could have wished, however, as you know, that you had seen Mr Wingfield before you left home.'

'My dear Isabella,' exclaimed he hastily, 'pray do not concern yourself about my looks. Be satisfied with doctoring and coddling yourself and the children, and let me look as I choose.'

'I did not thoroughly understand what you were telling your brother,' cried Emma, 'about your friend Mr Graham's intending to have a bailiff from Scotland to look after his new estate. But will it answer? Will not the old prejudice be too strong?'

And she talked in this way so long and successfully that, when forced to give her attention again to her father and sister, she had nothing worse to hear than Isabella's kind enquiry after Jane Fairfax; and Jane Fairfax, though no great favourite with her in general, she was, at that moment, very happy to assist in praising.

'That sweet, amiable Jane Fairfax!' said Mrs John Knightley. 'It is so long since I have seen her, except now and then for a moment accidentally in town. What happiness it must be to her good old grandmother and excellent aunt, when she comes to visit them! I always regret excessively, on dear Emma's account, that she cannot be more at Highbury; but now their daughter is married, I suppose Colonel and Mrs Campbell will not be able to part with her at all. She would be such a delightful companion for Emma.'

Mr Woodhouse agreed to it all, but added: 'Our little friend Harriet Smith, however, is just such another pretty kind of young person. You will like Harriet. Emma could not have a better companion than Harriet.'

'I am most happy to hear it; but only Jane Fairfax one knows to be so very accomplished and superior, and exactly Emma's age.'

This topic was discussed very happily, and others succeeded of similar moment, and passed away with similar harmony; but the evening did not close without a little return of agitation. The gruel came, and supplied a great deal to be said – much praise and many comments – undoubting decision of its wholesomeness for every constitution, and pretty severe philippics upon the many houses where it was never met with tolerable; but, unfortunately, among the failures which the daughter had to instance, the most recent, and therefore most prominent, was in her own cook at Southend, a young woman hired for the time, who never had been able to understand what she meant by a basin of nice smooth gruel, thin, but not too thin. Often as she had wished for and ordered it, she had never been able to get anything tolerable. Here was a dangerous opening.

'Ah,' said Mr Woodhouse, shaking his head, and fixing his eye on her with tender concern. The ejaculation in Emma's ear expressed, 'Ah, there is no end of the sad consequences of your going to Southend. It does not bear talking of.' And for a little while she hoped he would not talk of it, and that a silent rumination might suffice to restore him to the relish of his own smooth gruel. After an interval of some minutes, however, he began with: 'I shall always be very sorry that you went to the sea this autumn, instead of coming here.'

'But why should you be sorry, sir? I assure you it did the children a great deal of good.'

'And, moreover, if you must go to the sea, it had better not have been to Southend. Southend is an unhealthy place. Perry was surprised to hear you had fixed upon Southend.'

'I know there is such an idea with many people, but indeed it is quite a mistake, sir. We all had our health perfectly well there, never found the least inconvenience from the mud, and Mr Wingfield says it is entirely a mistake to suppose the place unhealthy; and I am sure he may be depended on, for he thoroughly understands the nature of the air, and his own brother and family have been there repeatedly.'

'You should have gone to Cromer, my dear, if you went anywhere. Perry was a week at Cromer once, and he holds it to be the best of all the sea bathing places. A fine open sea, he says, and very pure air. And, by what I understand, you might have had lodgings there quite away from the sea – a quarter of a mile off – very comfortable. You should have consulted Perry.'

'But, my dear sir, the difference of the journey; only consider how great it would have been. A hundred miles, perhaps, instead of forty.'

'Ah, my dear, as Perry says, where health is at stake nothing else should be considered; and if one is to travel, there is not much to choose between forty miles and a hundred. Better not move at all, better stay in London altogether, than travel forty miles to get into a worse air. This is just what Perry said. It seemed to him a very ill-judged measure.'

Emma's attempts to stop her father had been vain; and when he had reached such a point as this, she could not wonder at her brother-in-law's breaking out.

'Mr Perry,' said he, in a voice of very strong displeasure, 'would do as well to keep his opinion till it is asked for. Why does he make it any business of his to wonder at what I do? – at my taking my family to one part of the coast or another? I may be allowed, I hope, the use of my judgement as well as Mr Perry. I want his directions no more than his drugs.' He paused, and growing cooler in a moment, added, with only sarcastic dryness, 'If Mr Perry can tell me how to convey a wife and five children a distance of a hundred and thirty miles with no greater expense or inconvenience than a distance of forty, I should be as willing to prefer Cromer to Southend as he could himself.'

'True, true,' cried Mr Knightley, with most ready interposition – 'very true. That's a consideration, indeed. But, John, as to what I was telling you of my idea of moving the path to Langham, of turning it more to the right that it may not cut through the home meadows, I cannot conceive any difficulty. I should not attempt it, if it were to be the means of inconvenience to the Highbury people, but if you call to mind exactly the present line of the path – the only way of proving it, however, will be to turn to our maps. I shall see you at the Abbey tomorrow morning, I hope, and then we will look them over, and you shall give me your opinion.'

Mr Woodhouse was rather agitated by such harsh reflections on his friend Perry, to whom he had in fact, though unconsciously, been attributing many of his own feelings and expressions; but the soothing attentions of his daughters gradually removed the present evil, and the immediate alertness of one brother, and better recollections of the other, prevented any renewal of it.

Chapter 13

There could hardly be a happier creature in the world than Mrs John Knightley, in this short visit to Hartfield, going about every morning among her old acquaintance with her five children, and talking over what she had done every evening with her father and sister. She had nothing to wish otherwise, but that the days did not pass so swiftly. It was a delightful visit – perfect, in being much too short.

In general their evenings were less engaged with friends than their mornings; but one complete dinner engagement, and out of the house too, there was no avoiding, though at Christmas. Mr Weston would take no denial; they must all dine at Randalls one day; even Mr Woodhouse was persuaded to think it a possible thing in preference to a division of the party.

How they were all to be conveyed, he would have made a difficulty if he could, but as his son and daughter's carriage and horses were actually at Hartfield, he was not able to make more than a simple question on that head; it hardly amounted to a doubt, nor did it occupy Emma long to convince him that they might in one of the carriages find room for Harriet also.

Harriet, Mr Elton, and Mr Knightley, their own especial set, were the only persons invited to meet them – the hours were to be early as well as the numbers few; Mr Woodhouse's habits and inclinations being consulted in everything.

The evening before this great event (for it was a very great event that Mr Woodhouse should dine out on the 24th of December) had been spent by Harriet at Hartfield, and she had gone home so much indisposed with a cold, that, but for her own earnest wish of being nursed by Mrs Goddard, Emma could not have allowed her to leave the house. Emma called on her the next day, and found her doom already signed with regard to Randalls. She was very feverish and had a bad sore throat. Mrs Goddard was full of care and affection, Mr Perry was talked of, and Harriet herself was too ill and low to resist the authority which excluded her from this delightful engagement, though she could not speak of her loss without many tears.

Emma sat with her as long as she could, to attend her in Mrs Goddard's unavoidable absences, and raise her spirits by representing how much Mr Elton's would be depressed when he knew her state; and left her at last tolerably comfortable, in the sweet dependence of his having a most comfortless visit, and of their all missing her very much. She had not advanced many yards from Mrs Goddard's door, when she was met by Mr Elton himself, evidently coming towards it, and as they walked on slowly together in conversation about the invalid – of whom he, on the rumour of considerable illness, had been going to enquire, that he might carry some report of her to Hartfield – they were overtaken by Mr John Knightley, returning from the daily visit to Donwell, with his two eldest boys, whose healthy glowing faces showed all the benefit of a country run, and seemed to ensure a quick despatch of the roast mutton and rice pudding they were hastening home for. They joined company and proceeded together. Emma was just describing the nature of her friend's complaint – 'a throat very much inflamed, with a great deal of heat about her, a quick low pulse, etc., and she was sorry to find from Mrs Goddard that Harriet was liable to very bad sore throats, and had often alarmed her with them.' Mr Elton looked all alarm on the occasion, as he exclaimed: 'A sore throat! – I hope not infectious. I hope not of a putrid infectious sort. Has Perry seen her? Indeed you should take care of yourself as well as of your friend. Let me entreat you to run no risks. Why does not Perry see her?'

Emma, who was not really at all frightened herself, tranquillised this excess of apprehension by assurances of Mrs Goddard's experience and care; but as there must still remain a degree of uneasiness which she could not wish to reason away, which she would rather feed and assist than not, she added soon afterwards – as if quite another subject: 'It is so cold, so very cold, and looks and feels so very much like snow, that if it were to any other place or with any other party, I should really try not to go out today, and dissuade my father from venturing; but as he has made up his mind, and does not seem to feel the cold himself, I do not like to interfere, as I know it would be so great a disappointment to Mr and Mrs Weston. But upon my word, Mr Elton, in your case, I should certainly excuse myself. You appear to me a little hoarse already; and when you consider what demand of voice and what fatigues tomorrow will bring, I think it would be no more than common prudence to stay at home and take care of yourself tonight.'

Mr Elton looked as if he did not very well know what answer to make; which was exactly the case; for though very much gratified by the kind care of such a fair lady, and not liking to resist any advice of her, he had not really the least inclination to give up the visit; but Emma, too eager and busy in her own previous conceptions and views to hear him impartially, or see him with clear vision, was very well satisfied with his muttering acknowledgement of its being 'very cold, certainly very cold,' and walked on, rejoicing in having extricated himself from Randalls, and secured him the power of sending to enquire after Harriet every hour of the evening.

'You do quite right,' said she; 'we will make your apologies to Mr and Mrs Weston.'

But hardly had she so spoken, when she found her brother was civilly offering a seat in his carriage, if the weather were Mr Elton's only objection, and Mr Elton actually accepting the offer with much prompt satisfaction. It was a done thing; Mr Elton was to go, and never had his broad handsome face expressed more pleasure than at this moment; never had his smile been stronger, nor his eyes more exulting than when he next looked at her.

'Well,' said she to herself, 'this is most strange! After I had got him off so well, to choose to go into company, and leave Harriet ill behind! Most strange indeed! But there is, I believe, in many men, especially single men, such an inclination – such a passion for dining out; a dinner engagement is so high in the class of their pleasures, their employments, their dignities, almost their duties, that anything gives way to it, and this must be the case with Mr Elton – a most valuable, amiable, pleasing young man undoubtedly, and very much in love with Harriet; but still he cannot refuse an invitation, he must dine out wherever he is asked. What a strange thing love is! he can see ready wit in Harriet, but will not dine alone for her.'

Soon afterwards Mr Elton quitted them, and she could not but do him the justice of feeling that there was a great deal of sentiment in his manner of naming Harriet at parting; in the tone of his voice, while assuring her that he should call at Mrs Goddard's for news of her fair friend, the last thing before he prepared for the happiness of meeting her again, when he hoped to be able to give a better report; and he sighed and smiled himself off in a way that left the balance of approbation much in his favour.

After a few minutes of entire silence between them, John Knightley began with: 'I never in my life saw a man more intent on being agreeable than Mr Elton. It is downright labour to him where ladies are concerned. With men he can be rational and unaffected, but when he has ladies to please, every feature works.'

'Mr Elton's manners are not perfect,' replied Emma; 'but where there is a wish to please, one ought to overlook, and one does overlook a great deal. Where a man does his best with only moderate powers, he will have the advantage over negligent superiority. There is such perfect good temper and goodwill in Mr Elton, as one cannot but value.'

'Yes,' said Mr John Knightley presently, with some slyness, 'he seems to have a great deal of goodwill towards *you*.'

'Me!' she replied, with a smile of astonishment; 'are you imagining me to be Mr Elton's object?'

'Such an imagination has crossed me, I own, Emma; and if it never occurred to you before, you may as well take it into consideration now.'

'Mr Elton in love with me! What an idea!'

'I do not say it is so; but you will do well to consider whether it is so or not, and to regulate your behaviour accordingly. I think your manners to him encouraging. I speak as a friend, Emma. You had better look about you, and ascertain what you do, and what you mean to do.'

'I thank you; but I assure you, you are quite mistaken. Mr Elton and I are very good friends, and nothing more;' and she walked on, amusing herself in the consideration of the blunders which often arise from a partial knowledge of circumstances, of the mistakes which people of high pretensions to judgement are for ever falling into; and not very well pleased with her brother for imagining her blind and ignorant, and in want of counsel. He said no more.

Mr Woodhouse had so completely made up his mind to the visit, that in spite of the increasing coldness, he seemed to have no idea of shrinking from it, and set forward at last most punctually with his eldest daughter in his own carriage, with less apparent consciousness of the weather than either of the others; too full of the wonder of his own going, and the pleasure it was to afford at Randalls, to see that it was cold, and too well wrapped up to feel it. The cold, however, was severe; and by the time the second carriage was in motion, a few flakes of snow were finding their way down, and the sky had the appearance of being so overcharged as to want only a milder air to produce a very white world in a very short time.

Emma soon saw that her companion was not in the happiest humour. The preparing and the going abroad in such weather, with the sacrifice of his children after dinner, were evils, were disagreeables at least, which Mr John Knightley did not by any means like; he anticipated nothing in the visit that could be at all worth the purchase; and the whole of their drive to the vicarage was spent by him in expressing his discontent.

'A man,' said he, 'must have a very good opinion of himself when he asks people to leave their own fireside, and encounter such a day as this, for the sake of coming to see him. He must think himself a most agreeable fellow; I could not do such a thing. It is the greatest absurdity – actually snowing at this moment! The folly of not allowing people to be comfortable at home, and the folly of people's not staying comfortably at home when they can! If we were obliged to go out such an evening as this, by any call of duty or business, what a hardship we should deem it; and here are we, probably with rather thinner clothing than usual, setting forward voluntarily, without excuse, in defiance of the voice of nature, which tells man, in everything given to his view or his feelings, to stay at home himself, and keep all under shelter that he can; here are we setting forward to spend five dull hours in another man's house, with nothing to say or to hear that was not said and heard yesterday, and may not be said and heard again tomorrow. Going in dismal weather, to return probably in worse; four horses and four servants taken out for nothing but to convey five idle, shivering creatures into colder rooms and worse company than they might have had at home.'

Emma did not find herself equal to give the pleased assent, which no doubt he was in the habit of receiving, to emulate the 'Very true, my love,' which must have been usually administered by his travelling companion; but she had resolution enough to refrain from making any answer at all. She could not be complying; she dreaded being quarrelsome; her heroism reached only to silence. She allowed him to talk, and arranged the glasses, and wrapped herself up without opening her lips.

They arrived, the carriage turned, the step was let down, and Mr Elton, spruce, black, and smiling, was with them instantly. Emma thought with pleasure of some change of subject. Mr Elton was all obligation and cheerfulness; he was so very cheerful in his civilities indeed, that she began to think he must have received a different account of Harriet from what had reached her. She had sent while dressing and the answer had been, 'Much the same – not better.'

'*My* report from Mrs Goddard's,' said she, presently, 'was not so pleasant as I had hoped; "not better", was my answer.'

His face lengthened immediately, and his voice was the voice of sentiment as he answered: 'Oh no – I am grieved to find – I was on the point of telling you, that when I called at Mrs Goddard's door, which I did the very last thing before I returned to dress, I was told that Miss Smith was not better, by no means better, rather worse. Very much grieved and concerned – I had flattered myself that she must be better after such a cordial as I knew had been given her in the morning.'

Emma smiled and answered: 'My visit was of use to the nervous part of her complaint, I hope; but not even I can charm away a sore throat; it is a most severe cold, indeed. Mr Perry has been with her, as you probably heard.'

'Yes – I imagined – that is – I did not – '

'He has been used to her in these complaints, and I hope tomorrow morning will bring us both a more comfortable report. But it is impossible not to feel uneasiness. Such a sad loss to our party today!'

'Dreadful! Exactly so, indeed. She will be missed every moment.'

This was very proper; the sigh which accompanied it was really estimable; but it should have lasted longer. Emma was rather in dismay when only half a minute afterwards he began to speak of other things, and in a voice of the greatest alacrity and enjoyment.

'What an excellent device,' said he, 'the use of a sheep-skin for carriages. How very comfortable they make it; impossible to feel cold with such precautions. The contrivances of modern days, indeed, have rendered a gentleman's carriage perfectly complete. One is so fenced and guarded from the weather that not a breath of air can find its way unpermitted. Weather becomes absolutely of no consequence. It is a very cold afternoon – but in this carriage we know nothing of the matter. Ha! snows a little, I see.'

'Yes,' said John Knightley, 'and I think we shall have a good deal of it.'

'Christmas weather,' observed Mr Elton. 'Quite seasonable; and extremely fortunate we may think ourselves that it did not begin yesterday, and prevent this day's party, which it might very possibly have done, for Mr Woodhouse would hardly have ventured had there been much snow on the ground; but now it is of no consequence. This is quite the season, indeed, for friendly meetings. At Christmas everybody invites their friends about them, and people think little of even the worst weather. I was snowed up at a friend's house once for a week. Nothing could be pleasanter. I went for only one night, and could not get away till that very day sennight.'

Mr John Knightley looked as if he did not comprehend the pleasure, but said only, coolly: 'I cannot wish to be snowed up a week at Randalls.'

At another time Emma might have been amused, but she was too much astonished now at Mr Elton's spirits for other feelings. Harriet seemed quite forgotten in the expectation of a pleasant party.

'We are sure of excellent fires,' continued he, 'and everything in the greatest comfort. Charming people Mr and Mrs Weston; Mrs Weston indeed is much beyond praise, and he is exactly what one values, so hospitable, and so fond of society; it will be a small party, but where small parties are select, they are, perhaps, the most agreeable of any. Mr Weston's dining-room does not accommodate more than ten comfortably; and, for my part, I would rather, under such circumstances, fall short by two than exceed by two. I think you will agree with me (turning with a soft air to Emma), I think I shall certainly have your approbation, though Mr Knightley, perhaps, from being used to the large parties of London, may not quite enter into our feelings.'

'I know nothing of the large parties of London, sir – I never dine with anybody.'

'Indeed!' (in a tone of wonder and pity) 'I had no idea that the law had been so great a slavery. Well, sir, the time must come when you will be paid for all this, when you will have little labour and great enjoyment.'

'My first enjoyment,' replied John Knightley, as they passed through the sweep-gate, 'will be to find myself safe at Hartfield again.'

Chapter 14

Some change of countenance was necessary for each gentleman as they walked into Mrs Weston's drawing-room; Mr Elton must compose his joyous looks, and Mr John Knightley disperse his ill humour. Mr Elton must smile less, and Mr John Knightley more, to fit them for the place. Emma only might be as nature prompted, and show herself just as happy as she was. To her, it was real enjoyment to be with the Westons. Mr Weston was a great favourite, and there was not a creature in the world to whom she spoke with such unreserve as to his wife; not anyone, to whom she related with such conviction of being listened to, and understood, of being always interesting and always intelligible, the little affairs, arrangements, perplexities, and pleasures of her father and herself. She could tell nothing of Hartfield, in which Mrs Weston had not a lively concern; and half an hour's uninterrupted communication of all those little matters on which the daily happiness of private life depends, was one of the first gratifications of each.

This was a pleasure which perhaps the whole day's visit might not afford, which certainly did not belong to the present half hour; but the very sight of Mrs Weston, her smile, her touch, her voice, was grateful to Emma, and she determined to think as little as possibile of Mr Elton's oddities, or of anything else unpleasant and enjoy all that was enjoyable to the utmost.

The misfortune of Harriet's cold had been pretty well gone through before her arrival. Mr Woodhouse had been safely seated long enough to give the history of it, besides all the history of his own and Isabella's coming, and of Emma's being to follow; and had, indeed, just got to the end of his satisfaction that James should come and see his daughter, when the others appeared, and Mrs Weston, who had been almost wholly engrossed by her attentions to him, was able to turn away and welcome her dear Emma.

Emma's project of forgetting Mr Elton for a while made her rather sorry to find, when they had all taken their places, that he was close to her. The difficulty was great of driving his strange sensibility towards Harriet from her mind, while he not only sat at her elbow, but was continually obtruding his happy countenance on her notice, and solicitously addressing her upon every occasion. Instead of forgetting him, his behaviour was such that she could not avoid the internal suggestion of 'Can it really be as my brother imagined? can it be possible for this man to be beginning to transfer his affections from Harriet to me? – Absurd and insufferable!' Yet he would be so anxious for her being perfectly warm, would be so interested about her father, and so delighted with Mrs Weston; and, at last, would begin admiring her drawings with so much zeal and so little knowledge, as seemed terribly like a would-be lover, and made it some effort with her to preserve her good manners. For her own sake she could not be rude; and for Harriet's in the hope that all would yet turn out right, she was even positively civil; but it was an effort, especially as something was going on amongst the others in the most overpowering period of Mr Elton's nonsense, which she particularly wished to listen to.

She heard enough to know that Mr Weston was giving some information about his son; she heard the words 'my son,' and 'Frank,' and 'my son,' repeated several times over; and, from a few other half-syllables, very much suspected that he was announcing an early visit from his son; but before she could quiet Mr Elton, the subject was so completely past, that any reviving question from her would have been awkward.

Now it so happened, that, in spite of Emma's resolution of never marrying, there was something in the name, in the idea, of Mr Frank Churchill, which always interested her. She had frequently thought – especially since his father's marriage with Miss Taylor – that if she were to marry, he was the very person to suit her in age, character and condition. He seemed by this connection between the families, quite to belong to her. She could not but suppose it to be a match that everybody who knew them must think of. That Mr and Mrs Weston did think of it, she was very strongly persuaded; and though not meaning to be induced by him, or by anybody else, to give up a situation which she believed more replete with good than any she could change it for, she had a great curiosity to see him, a decided intention of finding him pleasant, of being liked by him to a certain degree, and a sort of pleasure in the idea of their being coupled in their friends' imaginations.

With such sensations, Mr Elton's civilities were dreadfully ill-timed; but she had the comfort of appearing very polite, while feeling very cross; and of thinking that the rest of the visit could not possibly pass without bringing forward the same information again, or the substance of it, from the open-hearted Mr Weston. So it proved; for, when happily released from Mr Elton, and seated by Mr Weston at dinner, he made use of the very first interval in the cares of hospitality, the very first leisure from the saddle of mutton, to say to her: 'We want only two more to be just the right number. I should like to see two more here – your pretty little friend, Miss Smith, and my son – and then I should say we were quite complete. I believe you did not hear me telling the others in the drawing-room that we are expecting Frank. I had a letter from him this morning, and he will be with us within a fortnight.'

Emma spoke with a very proper degree of pleasure, and fully assented to his proposition, of Mr Frank Churchill and Miss Smith making their party quite complete.

'He has been wanting to come to us,' continued Mr Weston, 'ever since September; every letter has been full of it; but he cannot command his own time. He has those to please who must be pleased, and who (between ourselves) are sometimes to be pleased only by a good many sacrifices. But now I have no doubt of seeing him here about the second week in January.'

'What a very great pleasure it will be to you! and Mrs Weston is so anxious to be acquainted with him, that she must be almost as happy as yourself.'

'Yes, she would be, but that she thinks there will be another put off. She does not depend upon his coming so much as I do; but she does not know the parties so well as I do. The case, you see, is – (but this is quite between ourselves. I did not mention a syllable of it in the other room. There are secrets in all families, you know) – the case is, that a party of friends are invited to pay a visit at Enscombe in January, and that Frank's coming depends upon their being put off. If they are not put off, he cannot stir. But I know they will, because it is a family that a certain lady, of some consequence at Enscombe, had a particular dislike to; and though it is thought necessary to invite them once in two or three years, they always are put off when it comes to the point. I have not the smallest doubt of the issue. I am as confident of seeing Frank here before the middle of January, as I am of being here myself; but your good friend there (nodding towards the upper end of the table) has so few vagaries herself, and has been so little used to them at Hartfield, that she cannot calculate on their effects, as I have been long in the practice of doing.'

'I am sorry there should be anything like doubt in the case,' replied Emma; 'but am disposed to side with you, Mr Weston. If you think he will come, I shall think so too; for you know Enscombe.'

'Yes – I have some right to that knowledge, though I have never been at the place in my life. She is an odd woman! But I never allow myself to speak ill of her, on Frank's account for I do believe her to be very fond of him. I used to think she was not capable of being fond of anybody except herself; but she has always been kind to him (in her way – allowing for little whims and caprices, and expecting everything to be as she likes). And it is no small credit, in my opinion, to him, that he should excite such an affection; for, though I would not say it to anybody else, she has no more heart than a stone to people in general, and the devil of a temper.'

Emma liked the subject so well, that she began upon it to Mrs Weston, very soon after their moving into the drawing-room, wishing her joy – yet observing that she knew the first meeting must be rather alarming. Mrs Weston agreed to it; but added that she should be very glad to besecure of undergoing the anxiety of a first meeting at the time talked of; 'for I cannot depend upon his coming. I cannot be so sanguine as Mr Weston. I am very much afraid that it will all end in nothing. Mr Weston, I dare say, has been telling you exactly how the matter stands?'

'Yes; it seems to depend upon nothing but the ill humour of Mrs Churchill, which I imagine to be the most certain thing in the world.'

'My Emma!' replied Mrs Weston, smiling, 'what is the certainty of caprice?' Then turning to Isabella, who had not been attending before – 'You must know, my dear Mrs Knightley, that we are by no means so sure of seeing Mr Frank Churchill, in my opinion, as his father thinks. It depends entirely upon his aunt's spirits and pleasure; in short, upon her temper. To you – to my two daughters – I may venture on the truth. Mrs Churchill rules at Enscombe, and is a very odd-tempered woman; and his coming now depends upon her being willing to spare him.'

'Oh, Mrs Churchill! everybody knows Mrs Churchill,' replied Isabella, 'and I am sure I never think of that poor young man without the greatest compassion. To be constantly living with an ill-tempered person must be dreadful. It is what we happily have never known anything of; but, it must be a life of misery. What a blessing that she never had any children! Poor little creatures, how unhappy she would have made them!'

Emma wished she had been alone with Mrs Weston. She should then have heard more. Mrs Weston would speak to her with a degree of unreserve which she would not hazard with Isabella; and she really believed, would scarcely try to conceal anything relative to the Churchills from her, excepting those views on the young man, of which her own imagination had already given her such instinctive knowledge. But at present there was nothing more to be said. Mr Woodhouse very soon followed them into the drawing-room. To be sitting long after dinner was a confinement that he could not endure. Neither wine nor conversation was anything to him; and gladly did he move to those with whom he was always comfortable.

While he talked to Isabella, however, Emma found an opportunity of saying: 'And so you do not consider this visit from your son as by any means certain. I am sorry for it. The introduction must be unpleasant, whenever it takes place; and the sooner it could be over the better.'

'Yes; and every delay makes one more apprehensive of other delays. Even if this family, the Braithwaites, are put off, I am still afraid that some excuse may be found for disappointing us. I cannot bear to imagine any reluctance on his side; but I am sure there is a great wish on the Churchills' to keep him to themselves. There is jealousy. They are jealous even of his regard for his father. In short, I can feel no dependence on his coming, and I wish Mr Weston were less sanguine.'

'He ought to come,' said Emma. 'If he could stay only a couple of days, he ought to come; and one can hardly conceive a young man's not having it in his power to do as much as that. A young *woman,* if she fall into bad hands, may be teased, and kept at a distance from those she wants to be with; but one cannot comprehend a young *man's* being under such restraint as not to be able to spend a week with his father, if he likes to.'

'One ought to be at Enscombe, and know the ways of the family, before one decides upon what he can do,' replied Mrs Weston. 'One ought to use the same caution, perhaps, in judging of the conduct of any one individual of any one family; but Enscombe, I believe, certainly must not be judged by general rules; *she* is so very unreasonable; and everything gives way to her.'

'But she is so fond of the nephew; he is so very great a favourite. Now, according to my idea of Mrs Churchill, it would be most natural, that while she makes no sacrifice for the comfort of the husband, to whom she owes everything, while she exercises incessant caprice towards him, she should frequently be governed by the nephew, to whom she owes nothing at all.'

'My dearest Emma, do not pretend, with your sweet temper, to understand a bad one, or to lay down rules for it; you must let it go its own way. I have no doubt of his having, at times, considerable influence; but it may be perfectly impossible for him to know beforehand *when* it will be.'

Emma listened, and then coolly said, 'I shall not be satisfied unless he comes.'

'He may have a great deal of influence on some points,' continued Mrs Weston, 'and on others, very little; and among those, on which she is beyond his reach, it is but too likely may be this very circumstance of his coming away from them to visit us.'

Chapter 15

Mr Woodhouse was soon ready for his tea; and when he had drank his tea, he was quite ready to go home, and it was as much as his three companions could do, to entertain away his notice of the lateness of the hour, before the other gentlemen appeared. Mr Weston was chatty and convivial, and no friend to early separations of any sort; but at last the drawing-room party did receive an augmentation. Mr Elton, in very good spirits, was one of the first to walk in. Mrs Weston and Emma were sitting together on a sofa. He joined them immediately, and with scarcely an invitation, seated himself between them.

Emma, in good spirits too, from the amusement afforded her mind by the expectation of Mr Frank Churchill, was willing to forget his late improprieties, and be as well satisfied with him as before, and on his making Harriet his very first subject, was ready to listen with most friendly smiles.

He professed himself extremely anxious about her fair friend – her fair, lovely, amiable friend. 'Did she know? – had she heard anything about her since their being at Randalls? – he felt much anxiety – he must confess that the nature of her complaint alarmed him considerably.' And in this style he talked on for some time very properly, not much attending to any answer, but altogether sufficiently awake to the terror of a bad sore throat; and Emma was quite in charity with him.

But at last there seemed a perverse turn; it seemed all at once as if he were more afraid of its being a bad sore throat on her account than on Harriet's – more anxious that she should escape the infection, than that there should be no infection in the complaint. He began with great earnestness to entreat her to refrain from visiting the sick-chamber again, for the present, to entreat her to *promise him* not to venture into such hazard till he had seen Mr Perry and learnt his opinion, and though she tried to laugh it off and bring the subject back into its proper course, there was no putting an end to his extreme solicitude about her. She was vexed. It did appear – there was no concealing it – exactly like the pretence of being in love with her instead of Harriet; an inconstancy, if real, the most contemptible and abominable! and she had difficulty in behaving with temper. He turned to Mrs Weston to implore her assistance; 'Would not she give him her support? – would not she add her persuasions to his, to induce Miss Woodhouse not to go to Mrs Goddard's till it were certain that Miss Smith's disorder had no infection? He could not be satisfied without a promise – would not she give him her influence in procuring it?'

'So scrupulous for others,' he continued, 'and yet so careless for herself! She wanted me to nurse my cold by staying at home today, and yet will not promise to avoid the danger of catching an ulcerated sore throat herself. Is this fair, Mrs Weston? Judge between us. Have not I some right to complain? I am sure of your kind support and aid.'

Emma saw Mrs Weston's surprise, and felt that it must be great, at an address which, in words and manner, was assuming to himself the right of first interest in her; and as for herself, she was too much provoked and offended to have the power of directly saying anything to the purpose. She could only give him a look; but it was such a look as she thought must restore him to his senses, and then left the sofa, removing to a seat by her sister, and giving her all her attention.

She had not time to know how Mr Elton took the reproof, so rapidly did another subject succeed; for Mr John Knightley now came into the room from examining the weather, and opened on them all with the information of the ground being covered with snow, and of its still snowing fast, with a strong drifting wind; concluding with these words to Mr Woodhouse: 'This will prove a spirited beginning of your winter engagements, sir. Something new for your coachman and horses to be making their way through a storm of snow.'

Poor Mr Woodhouse was silent from consternation; but everybody else had something to say; everybody was either surprised, or not surprised, and had some question to ask, or some comfort to offer. Mrs Weston and Emma tried earnestly to cheer him and turn his attention from his son-in-law, who was pursuing his triumph rather unfeelingly.

'I admired your resolution very much, sir,' said he, 'in venturing out in such weather, for of course you saw there would be snow very soon. Everybody must have seen the snow coming on. I admired your spirit; and I dare say we shall get home very well. Another hour or two's snow can hardly make the road impassable; and we are two carriages; if *one* is blown over in the bleak part of the common field there will be the other at hand. I dare say we shall be all safe at Hartfield before midnight.'

Mr Weston, with triumph of a different sort, was confessing that he had known it to be snowing some time, but had not said a word, lest it should make Mr Woodhouse uncomfortable, and be an excuse for his hurrying away. As to there being any quantity of snow fallen or likely to fall to impede their return, that was a mere joke; he was afraid they would find no difficulty. He wished the road might be impassable, that he might be able to keep them all at Randalls; and with the utmost goodwill was sure that accommodation might be found for everybody, calling on his wife to agree with him, that, with a little contrivance, everybody might be lodged, which she hardly knew how to do, from the consciousness of there being but two spare rooms in the house.

'What is to be done, my dear Emma? what is to be done?' was Mr Woodhouse's first exclamation, and all that he could say for some time. To her he looked for comfort; and her assurances of safety, her representation of the excellence of the horses, and of James, and of their having so many friends about them, revived him a little.

His eldest daughter's alarm was equal to his own. The horror of being blocked up at Randalls, while her children were at Hartfield, was full in her imagination; and fancying the road to be now just passable for adventurous people, but in a state that admitted no delay, she was eager to have it settled, that her father and Emma should remain at Randalls, while she and her husband set forward instantly, through all the possible accumulations of drifted snow that might impede them.

'You had better order the carriage directly, my love,' said she; 'I dare say we shall be able to get along, if we set off directly; and if we do come to anything very bad, I can get out and walk. I am not at all afraid. I should not mind walking half the way. I could change my shoes, you know, the moment I got home; and it is not the sort of thing that gives me cold.'

'Indeed!' replied he. 'Then, my dear Isabella, it is the most extraordinary sort of thing in the world, for in general everything does give you cold. Walk home! you are prettily shod for walking home, I dare say. It will be bad enough for the horses.'

Isabella turned to Mrs Weston for her approbation of the plan. Mrs Weston could only approve. Isabella then went to Emma; but Emma could not so entirely give up the hope of their being all able to get away; and they were still discussing the point, when Mr Knightley, who had left the room immediately after his brother's first report of the snow, came back again, and told them that he had been out-of-doors to examine, and could answer for there not being the smallest difficulty in their getting home, whenever they liked it, either now or an hour hence. He had gone beyond the sweep – some way along the Highbury Road – the snow was nowhere above half an inch deep – in many places hardly enough to whiten the ground; a very few flakes were falling at present, but the clouds were parting, and there was every appearance of its being soon over. He had seen the coachmen, and they both agreed with him in there being nothing to apprehend.

To Isabella the relief of such tidings was very great, and they were scarcely less acceptable to Emma on her father's account, who was immediately set as much at ease on the subject as his nervous constitution allowed; but the alarm that had been raised could not be appeased, so as to admit of any comfort for him while he continued at Randalls. He was satisfied of there being no present danger in returning home, but no assurances could convince him that it was safe to stay; and while the others were variously urging and recommending, Mr Knightley and Emma settled it in a few brief sentences: thus: 'Your father will not be easy; why do not you go?'

'I am ready, if the others are.'

'Shall I ring the bell?'

'Yes, do.'

And the bell was rung and the carriages spoken for. A few minutes more, and Emma hoped to see one troublesome companion deposited in his own house, to get sober and cool, and the other recover his temper and happiness when this visit of hardship were over.

The carriage came; and Mr Woodhouse, always the first object on such occasions, was carefully attended to his own by Mr Knightley and Mr Weston; but not all that either could say could prevent some renewal of alarm at the sight of the snow which had actually fallen, and the discovery of a much darker night than he had been prepared for. 'He was afraid they should have a very bad drive. He was afraid poor Isabella would not like it. And there would be poor Emma in the carriage behind. He did not know what they had best do. They must keep as much together as they could;' and James was talked to, and given a charge to go very slow, and wait for the other carriage.

Isabella stepped in after her father; John Knightley forgetting that he did not belong to their party, stepped in after his wife very naturally; so that Emma found, on being escorted and followed into the second carriage by Mr Elton, that the door was to be lawfully shut on them, and that they were to have a tête-à-tête drive. It would not have been the awkwardness of a moment, it would have been rather a pleasure, previous to the suspicions of this very day; she could have talked to him of Harriet, and the three-quarters of a mile would have seemed but one. But now, she would rather it had not happened. She believed he had been drinking too much of Mr Weston's good wine, and felt sure that he would want to be talking nonsense.

To restrain him as much as might be, by her own manners, she was immediately preparing to speak, with exquisite calmness and gravity, of the weather and the night; but scarcely had she begun, scarcely had they passed the sweep-gate and joined the other carriage, than she found her subject cut up – her hand seized – her attention demanded, and Mr Elton actually making violent love to her: availing himself of the precious opportunity, declaring sentiments which must be already well known, hoping – fearing – adoring – ready to die if she refused him; but flattering himself that his ardent attachment and unequalled love and unexampled passion could not fail of having some effect, and, in short, very much resolved on being seriously accepted as soon as possible. It really was so. Without scruple – without apology – without much apparent diffidence, Mr Elton, the lover of Harriet, was professing himself her lover. She tried to stop him; but vainly; he would go on, and say it all. Angry as she was, the thought of the moment made her resolve to restrain herself when she did speak. She felt that half this folly must be drunkenness, and therefore could hope that it might belong only to the passing hour. Accordingly, with a mixture of the serious and the playful, which she hoped would best suit his half-and-half state, she replied: 'I am very much astonished, Mr Elton. This to *me*! You forget yourself; you take me for my friend; any message to Miss Smith I shall be happy to deliver; but no more of this to *me*, if you please.'

'Miss Smith! message to Miss Smith! What could she possibly mean?' And he repeated her words with such assurance of accent, such boastful pretence of amazement, that she could not help replying with quickness: 'Mr Elton, this is the most extraordinary conduct! and I can account for it only in one way; you are not yourself, or you could not speak either to me or of

Harriet in such a manner. Command yourself enough to say no more, and I will endeavour to forget it.'

But Mr Elton had only drunk wine enough to elevate his spirits, not at all to confuse his intellects. He perfectly knew his own meaning; and having warmly protested against her suspicion as most injurious, and slightly touched upon his respect for Miss Smith as her friend, but acknowledging his wonder that Miss Smith should be mentioned at all, he resumed the subject of his own passion, and was very urgent for a favourable answer.

As she thought less of his inebriety, she thought more of his inconstancy and presumption, and with fewer struggles for politeness, replied: 'It is impossible for me to doubt any longer. You have made yourself too clear. Mr Elton, my astonishment is much beyond anything I can express. After such behaviour as I have witnessed during the last month, to Miss Smith – such attentions as I have been in the daily habit of observing – to be addressing me in this manner: this is an unsteadiness of character, indeed, which I had not supposed possible. Believe me, sir, I am far, very far, from gratified in being the object of such professions.'

'Good Heaven!' cried Mr Elton, 'what can be the meaning of this? Miss Smith! I never thought of Miss Smith in the whole course of my existence; never paid her any attentions, but as your friend; never cared whether she were dead or alive, but as your friend. If she has fancied otherwise, her own wishes have misled her, and I am very sorry, extremely sorry. But, Miss Smith, indeed! Oh, Miss Woodhouse, who can think of Miss Smith when Miss Woodhouse is near? No, upon my honour, there is no unsteadiness of character. I have thought only of you. I protest against having paid the smallest attention to anyone else. Everything that I have said or done, for many weeks past, has been with the sole view of marking my adoration of yourself. You cannot really seriously doubt it. No' (in an accent meant to be insinuating), 'I am sure you have seen and understood me.'

It would be impossible to say what Emma felt on hearing this; which of all her unpleasant sensations was uppermost. She was too completely overpowered to be immediately able to reply; and two moments of silence being ample encouragement for Mr Elton's sanguine state of mind, he tried to take her hand again, as he joyously exclaimed: 'Charming Miss Woodhouse! allow me to interpret this interesting silence. It confesses that you have long understood me.'

'No, sir,' cried Emma, 'it confesses no such thing. So far from having long understood you I have been in a most complete error with respect to your views, till this moment. As to myself, I am very sorry that you should have been giving way to any feelings. Nothing could be further from my wishes – your attachment to my friend Harriet – your pursuit of her (pursuit it appeared) gave me great pleasure, and I have been very earnestly wishing you success; but had I supposed that she were not your attraction to Hartfield, I should certainly have thought you judged ill in making your visits so frequent. Am I to believe that you have never sought to recommend yourself particularly to Miss Smith – that you have never thought seriously of her?'

'Never, madam,' cried he, affronted in his turn; 'never, I assure you. I think seriously of Miss Smith! Miss Smith is a very good sort of girl: and I should be happy to see her respectably settled. I wish her extremely well; and, no doubt, there are men who might not object to – Everybody has their level; but as for myself, I am not, I think, quite so much at a loss. I need not so totally despair of an equal alliance as to be addressing myself to Miss Smith! No, madam, my visits to Hartfield have been for yourself only; and the encouragement I received – '

'Encouragement! I give you encouragement! Sir, you have been entirely mistaken in supposing it. I have seen you only as the admirer of my friend. In no other light could you have been more to me than a common acquaintance. I am exceedingly sorry; but it is well that the mistake ends where it does. Had the same behaviour continued, Miss Smith might have been led into a misconception of your views; not being aware, probably, any more than myself, of the very great inequality which you are so sensible of. But, as it is, the disappointment is single, and, I trust, will not be lasting. I have no thoughts of matrimony at present.'

He was too angry to say another word, her manner too decided to invite supplication; and in this state of swelling resentment, and mutually deep mortification, they had to continue together a few minutes longer, for the fears of Mr Woodhouse had confined them to a foot-pace. If there had not been so much anger, there would have been desperate awkwardness; but their straightforward emotions left no room for the little zigzags of embarrassment. Without knowing when the carriage turned into Vicarage Lane, or when it stopped, they found themselves, all at once, at the door of his house; and he was out before another syllable passed. Emma then felt it indispensable to wish him a good night. The compliment was just returned, coldly and proudly; and, under indescribable irritation of spirits, she was then conveyed to Hartfield.

There she was welcomed, with the utmost delight, by her father, who had been trembling for the dangers of a solitary drive from Vicarage Lane – turning a corner which he could never bear to think of – and in strange hands – a mere common coachman – no James; and there it seemed as if her return only were wanted to make everything go well: for Mr John Knightley, ashamed of his ill humour, was now all kindness and attention; and so particularly solicitous for the comfort of her father, as to seem – if not quite ready to join him in a basin of gruel – perfectly sensible of its being exceedingly wholesome; and the day was concluding in peace and comfort to all their little party, except herself. But her mind had never been in such perturbation; and it needed a very strong effort to appear attentive and cheerful till the usual hour of separating allowed her the relief of quiet reflection.

Chapter 16

The hair was curled, and the maid sent away, and Emma sat down to think and be miserable. It was a wretched business indeed. Such an overthrow of everything she had been wishing for. Such a development of everything most unwelcome! Such a blow for Harriet – that was the worst of all. Every part of it brought pain and humiliation of some sort or other; but, compared with the evil to Harriet, all was light; and she would gladly have submitted to feel yet more mistaken – more in error – more disgraced by misjudgement than she actually was, could the effects of her blunders have been confined to herself.

'If I had not persuaded Harriet into liking the man, I could have borne anything. He might have doubled his presumption to me – but poor Harriet!'

How she could have been so deceived! He protested that he had never thought seriously of Harriet – never! She looked back as well as she could; but it was all confusion. She had taken up the idea, she supposed, and made everything bend to it. His manners, however, must have been unmarked, wavering, dubious, or she could not have been so misled.

The picture! How eager he had been about the picture! and the charade! and an hundred other circumstances; how clearly they had seemed to point at Harriet! To be sure, the charade, with its 'ready wit' – but then, the 'soft eyes' – in fact, it suited neither; it was a jumble without taste or truth. Who could have seen through such thick-headed nonsense?

Certainly she had often, especially of late, thought his manners to herself unnecessarily gallant; but it had passed as his way, as a mere error of judgement, of knowledge, of taste, as one proof, among others, that he had not always lived in the best society; that, with all the gentleness of his address, true elegance was sometimes wanting; but, till this very day, she had never for an instant suspected it to mean anything but grateful respect to her as Harriet's friend.

To Mr John Knightley was she indebted for her first idea on the subject, for the first start of its possibility. There was no denying that those brothers had penetration. She remembered what Mr Knightley had once said to her about Mr Elton, the caution he had given, the conviction he had professed that Mr Elton would never marry indiscreetly; and blushed to think how much truer a knowledge of his character had been there shown than any she had reached herself. It was dreadfully mortifying; but Mr Elton was proving himself, in many respects, the very reverse of what she had meant and believed him – proud, assuming, conceited; very full of his own claims, and little concerned about the feelings of others.

Contrary to the usual course of things, Mr Elton's wanting to pay his addresses to her had sunk him in her opinion. His professions and his proposals did him no service. She thought nothing of his attachment, and was insulted by his hopes. He wanted to marry well, and having the arrogance to raise his eyes to her, pretended to be in love; but she was perfectly easy as to his not suffering any disappointment that need be cared for. There had been no real affection either in his language or manners. Sighs and fine words had been given in abundance; but she would hardly devise any set of expressions, or fancy any tone of voice, less allied with real love. She need not trouble herself to pity him. He only wanted to aggrandise and enrich himself; and if Miss Woodhouse of Hartfield, the heiress of thirty thousand pounds, were not quite so easily obtained as he had fancied, he would soon try for Miss Somebody Else with twenty, or with ten.

But, that he should talk of encouragement, should consider her as aware of his views, accepting his attentions, meaning, in short, to marry him – should suppose himself her equal in

connection or mind – look down upon her friend, so well understanding the gradations of rank below him, and be so blind to
what rose above, as to fancy himself showing no presumption in
addressing her! – it was most provoking.

Perhaps it was not fair to expect him to feel how very much he
was her inferior in talent, and all the elegancies of mind. The very
want of such equality might prevent his perception of it; but he
must know that in fortune and consequence she was greatly his
superior. He must know that the Woodhouses had been settled
for several generations at Hartfield, the younger branch of a very
ancient family, and that the Eltons were nobody. The landed
property of Hartfield certainly was inconsiderable, being but a
sort of notch in the Donwell Abbey estate, to which all the rest of
Highbury belonged; but their fortune, from other sources, was
such as to make them scarcely secondary to Donwell Abbey itself,
in every other kind of consequence; and the Woodhouses had
long held a high place in the consideration of the neighbourhood
which Mr Elton had first entered not two years ago, to make his
way as he could, without any alliances but in trade, or anything to
recommend him to notice but his situation and his civility. But he
had fancied her in love with him; that evidently must have been
his dependence; and after raving a little about the seeming incon-
gruity of gentle manners and a conceited head, Emma was
obliged, in common honesty, to stop and admit that her own
behaviour to him had been so complaisant and obliging, so full of
courtesy and attention, as (supposing her real motive unperceived) might warrant a man of ordinary observation and delicacy,
like Mr Elton, in fancying himself a very decided favourite. If *she*
had so misinterpreted his feelings, she had little right to wonder
that *he*, with self-interest to blind him, should have mistaken
hers.

The first error, and the worst, lay at her door. It was foolish, it
was wrong, to take so active a part in bringing any two people
together. It was adventuring too far, assuming too much, making
light of what ought to be serious – a trick of what ought to be

simple. She was quite concerned and ashamed, and resolved to do such things no more.

'Here have I,' said she, 'actually talked poor Harriet into being very much attached to this man. She might never have thought of him but for me; and certainly never would have thought of him with hope, if I had not assured her of his attachment, for she is as modest and humble as I used to think him. Oh that I had been satisfied with persuading her not to accept young Martin. There I was quite right: that was well done of me; but there I should have stopped, and left the rest to time and chance. I was introducing her into good company, and giving her the opportunity of pleasing some one worth having; I ought not to have attempted more. But now, poor girl! her peace is cut up for some time. I have been but half a friend to her! and if she were not to feel this disappointment so very much, I am sure I have not an idea of anybody else who would be at all desirable for her. William Coxe – oh no, I could not endure William Coxe – a pert young lawyer.'

She stopped to blush and laugh at her own relapse, and then resumed a more serious, more dispiriting cogitation upon what had been, and might be, and must be. The distressing explanation she had to make to Harriet, and all that poor Harriet would be suffering with the awkwardness of future meetings, the difficulties of continuing or discontinuing the acquaintance, of subduing feelings, concealing resentment, and avoiding clat, were enough to occupy her in most unmirthful reflections some time longer, and she went to bed at last with nothing settled but the conviction of her having blundered most dreadfully.

To youth and natural cheerfulness like Emma's, though under temporary gloom at night, the return of day will hardly fail to bring return of spirits. The youth and cheerfulness of morning are in happy analogy, and of powerful operation; and if the distress be not poignant enough to keep the eyes unclosed, they will be sure to open to sensations of softened pain and brighter hope.

Emma got up on the morrow more disposed for comfort than she had gone to bed; more ready to see alleviations of the evil before her, and to depend on getting tolerably out of it.

It was a great consolation that Mr Elton should not be really in love with her, or so particularly amiable as to make it shocking to disappoint him; that Harriet's nature should not be of that superior sort in which the feelings are most acute and retentive; and that there could be no necessity for anybody's knowing what had passed except the three principals, and especially for her father's being given a moment's uneasiness about it.

These were very cheering thoughts; and the sight of a great deal of snow on the ground did her further service, for anything was welcome that might justify their all three being quite asunder at present.

The weather was most favourable for her; though Christmas Day, she could not go to church. Mr Woodhouse would have been miserable had his daughter attempted it, and she was therefore safe from either exciting or receiving unpleasant and most unsuitable ideas. The ground covered with snow, and the atmosphere in that unsettled taste between frost and thaw which is, of all others, the most unfriendly for exercise, every morning beginning in rain or snow, and every evening setting in to freeze, she was for many days a most honourable prisoner. No intercourse with Harriet possible but by note; no church for her on Sunday any more than on Christmas Day; and no need to find excuses for Mr Elton's absenting himself.

It was weather which might fairly confine everybody at home; and though she hoped and believed him to be really taking comfort in some society or other, it was very pleasant to have her father so well satisfied with his being all alone in his own house, too wise to stir out; and to hear him say to Mr Knightley, whom no weather could keep entirely from them: 'Ah, Mr Knightley, why do not you stay at home like poor Mr Elton?'

These days of confinement would have been, but for her private perplexities, remarkably comfortable, as such seclusion exactly suited her brother, whose feelings must always be of great importance to his companions; and he had, besides, so thoroughly cleared off his ill humour at Randalls, that his amiableness never failed him during the rest of his stay at Hartfield. He was always agreeable and obliging, and speaking pleasantly of everybody. But with all the hopes of cheerfulness, and all the present comfort of delay, there was still such an evil hanging over her in the hour of explanation with Harriet, as made it impossible for Emma to be ever perfectly at ease.

Chapter 17

Mr and Mrs John Knightley were not detained long at Hartfield. The weather soon improved enough for those to move who must move; and Mr Woodhouse having, as usual, tried to persuade his daughter to stay behind with all her children, was obliged to see the whole party set off, and return to his lamentations over the destiny of poor Isabella – which poor Isabella, passing her life with those she doted on, full of their merits, blind to their faults, and always innocently busy, might have been a model of right feminine happiness.

The evening of the very day on which they went brought a note from Mr Elton to Mr Woodhouse, a long, civil, ceremonious note, to say, with Mr Elton's best compliments, 'that he was proposing to leave Highbury the following morning in his way to Bath; where, in compliance with the pressing entreaties of some friends, he had engaged to spend a few weeks; and very much regretted the impossibility he was under, from various circumstances of weather and business, of taking a personal leave of Mr

Woodhouse, of whose friendly civilities he should ever retain a grateful sense; and had Mr Woodhouse any commands, should be happy to attend to them.'

Emma was most agreeably surprised. Mr Elton's absence just at this time was the very thing to be desired. She admired him for contriving it, though not able to give him much credit for the manner in which it was announced. Resentment could not have been more plainly spoken than in a civility to her father, from which she was so pointedly excluded. She had not even a share in his opening compliments. Her name was not mentioned; and there was so striking a change in all this, and such an ill-judged solemnity of leave-taking in his graceful acknowledgements, as she thought, at first, could not escape her father's suspicion.

It did, however. Her father was quite taken up with the surprise of so sudden a journey, and his fears that Mr Elton might never get safely to the end of it, and saw nothing extraordinary in his language. It was a very useful note, for it supplied them with fresh matter for thought and conversation during the rest of their lonely evening. Mr Woodhouse talked over his alarms, and Emma was in spirits to persuade them away with all her usual promptitude.

She now resolved to keep Harriet no longer in the dark. She had reason to believe her nearly recovered from her cold, and it was desirable that she should have as much time as possible for getting the better of her other complaint before the gentleman's return. She went to Mrs Goddard's, accordingly, the very next day, to undergo the necessary penance of communication; and a severe one it was. She had to destroy all the hopes which she had been so industriously feeding, to appear in the ungracious character of the one preferred, and acknowledge herself grossly mistaken and misjudging in all her ideas on one subject, all her observations, all her convictions, all her prophecies for the last six weeks.

The confession completely renewed her first shame, and the sight of Harriet's tears made her think that she should never be in charity with herself again.

Harriet bore the intelligence very well, blaming nobody, and in everything testifying such an ingenuousness of disposition and lowly opinion of herself as must appear with particular advantage at that moment to her friend.

Emma was in the humour to value simplicity and modesty to the utmost; and all that was amiable, all that ought to be attaching, seemed on Harriet's side, not her own. Harriet did not consider herself as having anything to complain of. The affection of such a man as Mr Elton would have been too great a distinction. She never could have deserved him; and nobody but so partial and kind a friend as Miss Woodhouse would have thought it possible.

Her tears fell abundantly; but her grief was so truly artless that no dignity could have made it more respectable in Emma's eyes; and she listened to her, and tried to console her with all her heart and understanding – really for the time convinced that Harriet was the superior creature of the two, and that to resemble her would be more for her own welfare and happiness than all that genius or intelligence could do.

It was rather too late in the day to set about being simple-minded and ignorant; but she left her with every previous resolution confirmed of being humble and discreet, and repressing imagination all the rest of her life. Her second duty now, inferior only to her father's claims, was to promote Harriet's comfort, and endeavour to prove her own affection in some better method than by match-making. She got her to Hartfield, and showed her the most unvarying kindness, striving to occupy and amuse her, and by books and conversation to drive Mr Elton from her thoughts.

Time, she knew, must be allowed for this being thoroughly done; and she could suppose herself but an indifferent judge of such matters in general, and very inadequate to sympathise in an attachment to Mr Elton in particular; but it seemed to her reasonable that at Harriet's age, and with the entire extinction of all

hope, such a progress might be madetowards a state of composure by the time of Mr Elton's return, as to allow them all to meet
again in the common routine of acquaintance, without any
danger of betraying sentiments or increasing them.

Harriet did think him all perfection, and maintain the non-
existence of anybody equal to him in person or goodness, and did,
in truth, prove herself more resolutely in love than Emma had
foreseen; but yet it appeared to her so natural, so inevitable to
strive against an inclination of that sort *unrequited,* that she could
not comprehend its continuing very long in equal force.

If Mr Elton, on his return, made his own indifference as
evident and indubitable as she could not doubt he would
anxiously do, she could not imagine Harriet's persisting to place
her happiness in the sight or the recollection of him.

Their being fixed, so absolutely fixed, in the same place, was
bad for each, for all three. Not one of them had the power of
removal, or of effecting any material change of society. They must
encounter each other, and make the best of it.

Harriet was further unfortunate in the tone of her companions at Mrs Goddard's, Mr Elton being the adoration of all the
teachers and great girls in the school; and it must be at Hartfield
only that she could have any chance of hearing him spoken of
with cooling moderation or repellant truth. Where the wound had
been given, there must the cure be found, if anywhere; and Emma
felt that till she saw her in the way of cure, there could be no true
peace for herself.

Chapter 18

Mr Frank Churchill did not come. When the time proposed drew near, Mrs Weston's fears were justified in the arrival of a letter of excuse. For the present, he could not be spared to his 'very great mortification and regret; but still he looked forward with the hope of coming to Randalls at no distant period.'

Mrs Weston was exceedingly disappointed – much more disappointed, in fact, than her husband, though her dependence on seeing the young man had been so much more sober; but a sanguine temper, though for ever expecting more good than occurs, does not always pay for its hopes by any proportionate depression. It soon flies over the present failure, and begins to hope again. For half an hour Mr Weston was surprised and sorry; but then he began to perceive that Frank's coming two or three months later would be a much better plan, better time of year, better weather; and that he would be able, without any doubt, to stay considerably longer with them than if he had come sooner.

These feelings rapidly restored his comfort, while Mrs Weston, of a more apprehensive disposition, foresaw nothing but a repetition of excuses and delays; and after all her concern for what her husband was to suffer, suffered a great deal more herself.

Emma was not, at this time, in a state of spirits to care really about Mr Frank Churchill's not coming, except as a disappointment at Randalls. The acquaintance, at present, had no charm for her. She wanted rather to be quiet and out of temptation; but still, as it was desirable that she should appear, in general like her usual self, she took care to express as much interest in the circumstance, and enter as warmly into Mr and Mrs Weston's disappointment as might naturally belong to their friendship.

She was the first to announce it to Mr Knightley; and exclaimed quite as much as was necessary (or, being acting a part, perhaps rather more), at the conduct of the Churchills in keeping him away. She then proceeded to say a good deal more than she felt of the advantage of such an addition to their confined society in Surrey; the pleasure of looking at somebody new; the gala-day to Highbury entire, which the sight of him would have made; and ending with reflections on the Churchills again, found herself directly involved in a disagreement with Mr Knightley. And, to her great amusement, perceived that she was taking the other side of the question from her real opinion, and making use of Mrs Weston's arguments against herself.

'The Churchills are very likely in fault,' said Mr Knightley coolly; 'but I dare say he might come if he would.'

'I do not know why you should say so. He wishes exceedingly to come; but his uncle and aunt will not spare him.'

'I cannot believe that he has not the power of coming, if he made a point of it. It is too unlikely for me to believe it without proof.'

'How odd you are! What has Mr Frank Churchill done, to make you suppose him such an unnatural creature?'

'I am not supposing him at all an unnatural creature, in suspecting that he may have learnt to be above his connections, and to care very little for anything but his own pleasure, from living with those who have always set him the example of it. It is a great deal more natural than one could wish, that a young man, brought up by those who are proud, luxurious, and selfish, should be proud, luxurious, and selfish too. If Frank Churchill had wanted to see his father, he would have contrived it between September and January. A man at his age – what is he? three- or four-and-twenty – cannot be without the means of doing as much as that. It is impossible.'

'That's easily said, and easily felt by you, who have always been your own master. You are the worst judge in the world, Mr

Knightley, of the difficulties of dependence. You do not know what it is to have tempers to manage.'

'It is not to be conceived that a man of three or four-and-twenty should not have liberty of mind or limb to that amount. He cannot want money, he cannot want leisure. We know, on the contrary, that he has so much of both, that he is glad to get rid of them at the idlest haunts in the kingdom. We hear of him for ever at some watering-place or other; a little while ago he was at Weymouth. This proves that he can leave the Churchills.'

'Yes, sometimes he can.'

'And those times are, whenever he thinks it worth his while; whenever there is any temptation of pleasure.'

'It is very unfair to judge of anybody's conduct without an intimate knowledge of their situation. Nobody, who has not been in the interior of a family, can say what the difficulties of any individual of that family may be. We ought to be acquainted with Enscombe, and with Mrs Churchill's temper before we pretend to decide upon what her nephew can do. He may, at times, be able to do a great deal more than he can at others.'

'There is one thing, Emma, which a man can always do, if he chooses, and that is, his duty; not by manoeuvring and finessing, but by vigour and resolution. It is Frank Churchill's duty to pay this attention to his father. He knows it to be so, by his promises and messages; but if he wished to do it, it might be done. A man who felt rightly would say at once, simply and resolutely, to Mrs Churchill: "Every sacrifice of mere pleasure you will always find me ready to make to your convenience; but I must go and see my father immediately. I know he would be hurt by my failing in such a mark of respect to him on the present occasion. I shall, therefore, set off tomorrow." If he would say so to her at once in the tone of decision becoming a man, there would be no opposition made to his going.'

'No,' said Emma, laughing; 'but perhaps there might be some made to his coming back again. Such language for a young man entirely dependent to use! Nobody but you, Mr Knightley, would imagine it possible; but you have not an idea of what is requisite in situations directly opposite to your own. Mr Frank Churchill to be making such a speech as that to the uncle and aunt who have brought him up, and are to provide for him! standing up in the middle of the room, I suppose, and speaking as loud as he could! How can you imagine such conduct practicable?'

'Depend upon it, Emma, a sensible man would find no difficulty in it. He would feel himself in the right; and the declaration, made, of course, as a man of sense would make it, in a proper manner, would do him more good, raise him higher, fix his interest stronger with the people he depended on, than all that a line of shifts and expedients can ever do. Respect would be added to affection. They would feel that they could trust him; that the nephew who had done rightly by his father would do rightly by them; for they know as well as he does as well as all the world must know, that he ought to pay this visit to his father; and while meanly exerting their power to delay it, are in their hearts not thinking the better of him for submitting to their whims. Respect for right conduct is felt by everybody: if he would act in this sort of manner on principle, consistently, regularly, their little minds would bend to his.'

'I rather doubt that. You are very fond of bending little minds; but where little minds belong to rich people in authority, I think they have a knack of swelling out till they are quite as unmanageable as great ones. I can imagine that if you, as you are, Mr Knightley, were to be transported and placed all at once in Mr Frank Churchill's situation, you would be able to say and do just what you have been recommending for him; and it might have a very good effect. The Churchills might not have a word to say in return; but then you would have no habits of early obedience and long observance to break through. To him who has, it might not be so easy to burst forth at once into perfect independence, and set all their claims on his gratitude and regard at naught. He may have as strong a sense of what would be right as you can have, without being so equal, under particular circumstances, to act up to it.'

'Then it would not be so strong a sense. If it failed to produce equal exertion, it could not be an equal conviction.'

'Oh the difference of situation and habit! I wish you would try to understand what an amiable young man may be likely to feel in directly opposing those whom, as child and boy, he has been looking up to all his life.'

'Your amiable young man is a very weak young man, if this be the first occasion of his carrying through a resolution to do right against the will of others. It ought to have been a habit with him, by this time, of following his duty, instead of consulting expediency. I can allow for the fears of the child, but not of the man. As he became rational, he ought to have roused himself, and shaken off all that was unworthy in their authority. He ought to have opposed the first attempt on their side to make him slight his father. Had he begun as he ought, there would have been no difficulty now.'

'We shall never agree about him,' cried Emma; 'but that is nothing extraordinary. I have not the least idea of his being a weak young man; I feel sure that he is not. Mr Weston would not be blind to folly, though in his own son; but he is very likely to have a more yielding, complying, mild disposition than would suit your notions of man's perfection. I dare say he has; and though it may cut him off from some advantages, it will secure him many others.'

'Yes; all the advantages of sitting still when he ought to move, and of leading a life of mere idle pleasure, and fancying himself extremely expert in finding excuses for it. He can sit down and write a fine flourishing letter, full of professions and falsehoods, and persuade himself that he has hit upon the very best method in the world of preserving peace at home, and preventing his father's having any right to complain. His letters disgust me.'

'Your feelings are singular. They seem to satisfy everybody else.'

'I suspect they do not satisfy Mrs Weston. They hardly can satisfy a woman of her good sense and quick feelings: standing in a mother's place, but without a mother's affection to blind her. It is on her account that attention to Randalls is doubly due, and she must doubly feel the omission. Had she been a person of consequence herself he would have come, I dare say; and it would not have signified whether he did or no. Can you think your friend behindhand in these sort of considerations? Do you suppose she does not often say all this to herself? No, Emma; your amiable young man can be amiable only in French, not in English. He may be very "amiable", have very good manners, and be very agreeable; but he can have no English delicacy towards the feelings of other people – nothing really amiable about him.'

'You seem determined to think ill of him.'

'Me! not at all,' replied Mr Knightley, rather displeased; 'I do not want to think ill of him. I should be as ready to acknowledge his merits as any other man; but I hear of none, except what are merely personal – that he is well-grown and good-looking, with smooth, plausible manners.'

'Well, if he have nothing else to recommend him, he will be a treasure at Highbury. We do not often look upon fine young men, well-bred and agreeable. We must not be nice, and ask for all the virtues into the bargain. Cannot you imagine, Mr Knightley, what a *sensation* his coming will produce? There will be but one subject throughout the parishes of Donwell and Highbury; but one interest – one object of curiosity; it will be all Mr Frank Churchill; we shall think and speak of nobody else.'

'You will excuse my being so much overpowered. If I find him conversable, I shall be glad of his acquaintance; but if he is only a chattering coxcomb, he will not occupy much of my time or thoughts.'

'My idea of him is, that he can adapt his conversation to the taste of everybody, and has the power as well as the wish of being universally agreeable. To you, he will talk of farming; to me, of drawing or music; and so on to everybody, having that general information on all subjects which will enable him to follow the lead, or take the lead, just as propriety may require, and to speak extremely well on each; that is my idea of him.'

'And mine,' said Mr Knightley warmly, 'is, that if he turn out anything like it, he will be the most insufferable fellow breathing! What! at three-and-twenty to be the king of his company – the great man – the practised politician, who is to read everybody's character, and make everybody's talents conduce to the display of his own superiority; to be dispensing his flatteries around, that he may make all appear like fools compared with himself! My dear Emma, your own good sense could not endure such a puppy when it came to the point.'

'I will say no more about him,' cried Emma – 'you turn everything to evil. We are both prejudiced! you against, I for him; and we have no chance of agreeing till he is really here.'

'Prejudiced! I am not prejudiced.'

'But I am very much, and without being at all ashamed of it. My love for Mr and Mrs Weston gives me a decided prejudice in his favour.'

'He is a person I never think of from one month's end to another,' said Mr Knightley, with a degree of vexation, which made Emma immediately talk of something else, though she could not comprehend why he should be angry.

To take a dislike to a young man, only because he appeared to be of a different disposition from himself, was unworthy the real liberality of mind which she was always used to acknowledge in him; for, with all the high opinion of himself which she had often laid to his charge, she had never before for a moment supposed it could make him unjust to the merit of another.

Chapter 19

Emma and Harriet had been walking together one morning, and, in Emma's opinion, had been talking enough of Mr Elton for that day. She could not think that Harriet's solace or her own sins required more; and she was therefore industriously getting rid of the subject as they returned, but it burst out again when she thought she had succeeded, and after speaking some time of what the poor must suffer in winter, and receiving no other answer than a very plaintive – 'Mr Elton is so good to the poor!' she found something else must be done.

They were just approaching the house where lived Mrs and Miss Bates. She determined to call upon them, and seek safety in numbers. There was always sufficient reason for such an attention; Mrs and Miss Bates loved to be called on; and she knew she was considered by the very few who presumed ever to see imperfection in her, as rather negligent in that respect, and as not contributing what she ought to the stock of their scanty comforts.

She had had many a hint from Mr Knightley, and some from her own heart, as to her deficiency, but none were equal to counteract the persuasion of its being very disagreeable – a waste of time – tiresome women – and all the horror of being in danger of falling in with the second rate and third rate of Highbury, who were calling on them for ever, and therefore she seldom went near them. But now she made the sudden resolution of not passing their door without going in; observing, as she proposed it to Harriet, that, as well as she could calculate, they were just now quite safe from any letter from Jane Fairfax.

The house belonged to people in business. Mrs and Miss Bates occupied the drawing-room floor; and there, in the very moderate-sized apartment, which was everything to them, the visitors were most cordially and even gratefully welcomed; the quiet neat old lady, who with her knitting was seated in the warmest corner, wanting even to give up her place to Miss Woodhouse, and her more active, talking daughter almost ready to overpower them with care and kindness, thanks for their visit, solicitude for their shoes, anxious enquiries after Mr Woodhouse's health, cheerful communications about her mother's, and sweet-cake from the beaufet: 'Mrs Cole had just been there, just called in for ten minutes, and had been so good as to sit an hour with them, and she had taken a piece of cake, and been so kind as to say she liked it very much; and, therefore, she hoped Miss Woodhouse and Miss Smith would do them the favour to eat a piece too.'

The mention of the Coles was sure to be followed by that of Mr Elton. There was intimacy between them, and Mr Cole had heard from Mr Elton since his going away. Emma knew what was coming: they must have the letter over again, and settle how long he had been gone, and how much he was engaged in company, and what a favourite he was wherever he went, and how full the Master of the Ceremonies' ball had been; and she went through it very well, with all the interest and all the commendation that could be requisite, and always putting forward to prevent Harriet's being obliged to say a word.

This she had been prepared for when she entered the house; but meant, having once talked him handsomely over, to be no further incommoded by any troublesome topic, and to wander at large amongst all the Mistresses and Misses of Highbury, and their card-parties. She had not been prepared to have Jane Fairfax succeed Mr Elton; but he was actually hurried off by Miss Bates; she jumped away from him at last abruptly to the Coles, to usher in a letter from her niece.

'Oh yes – Mr Elton, I understand – certainly as to dancing – Mrs Cole was telling me that dancing at the rooms at Bath was – Mrs Cole was so kind as to sit some time with us, talking of Jane; for as soon as she came in she began enquiring after her, Jane is so very great a favourite there. Whenever she is with us, Mrs Cole does not know how to show her kindness enough; and I must say that Jane deserves it as much as anybody can. And so she began enquiring after her directly, saying, "I know you cannot have heard from Jane lately, because it is not her time for writing;" and when I immediately said, "But indeed we have, we had a letter this very morning," I do not know that I ever saw anybody more surprised. "Have you, upon your honour?" said she; "well, that is quite unexpected. Do let me hear what she says." '

Emma's politeness was at hand directly, to say, with smiling interest: 'Have you heard from Miss Fairfax so lately? I am extremely happy. I hope she is well?'

'Thank you. You are so kind!' replied the happily deceived aunt, while eagerly hunting for the letter. 'Oh, here it is. I was sure it could not be far off; but I had put my huswife upon it, you see, without being aware, and so it was quite hid; but I had it in my hand so very lately that I was almost sure it must be on the table. I was reading it to Mrs Cole, and, since she went away, I was reading it again to my mother, for it is such a pleasure to her – a letter from Jane – that she can never hear it often enough; so I knew it could not be far off, and here it is, only just under my huswife – and since you are so kind as to wish to hear what she says – but, first of all, I really must, in justice to Jane, apologise for her writing so short a letter – only two pages, you see, hardly two, and in general she fills the whole paper and crosses half. My mother often wonders that I can make it out so well. She often says, when the letter is first opened, "Well, Hetty, now I think you will be put to it to make out all that checker-work" – don't you, ma'am? And then I tell her, I am sure she would contrive to make it out herself, if she had nobody to do it for her, every word of it – I am sure she would pore over it till she had made out every word. And, indeed, though my mother's eyes are not so good as they were, she can see amazingly well still, thank God! with the help of spectacles. It is such a blessing! My mother's are really very good indeed. Jane often says, when she is here, "I am sure, grandmamma, you must have had very strong eyes to see as you do, and so much fine work as you have done too! I only wish my eyes may last me as well." '

All this, spoken extremely fast, obliged Miss Bates to stop for breath; and Emma said something very civil about the excellence of Miss Fairfax's handwriting.

'You are extremely kind,' replied Miss Bates, highly gratified; 'you, who are such a judge, and write so beautifully yourself. I am sure there is nobody's praise that could give us so much pleasure as Miss Woodhouse's. My mother does not hear; she is a little deaf, you know. Ma'am,' addressing her, 'do you hear what Miss Woodhouse is so obliging to say about Jane's handwriting?'

And Emma had the advantage of hearing her own silly compliment repeated twice over before the good old lady could comprehend it. She was pondering, in the meanwhile, upon the possibility, without seeming very rude, of making her escape from Jane Fairfax's letter, and had almost resolved on hurrying away directly, under some slight excuse, when Miss Bates turned to her again and seized her attention.

'My mother's deafness is very trifling, you see, just nothing at all. By only raising my voice, and saying anything two or three times over, she is sure to hear; but then she is used to my voice. But it is very remarkable that she should always hear Jane better than she does me. Jane speaks so distinct! However, she will not find her grandmamma at all deafer than she was two years ago; which is saying a great deal at my mother's time of life; and it really is full two years, you know, since she was here. We never were so long without seeing her before; and, as I was telling Mrs Cole, we shall hardly know how to make enough of her now.'

'Are you expecting Miss Fairfax here soon?'

'Oh, yes; next week.'

'Indeed! that must be a very great pleasure.'

'Thank you. You are very kind. Yes, next week. Everybody is so surprised; and everybody says the same obliging things. I am sure she will be as happy to see her friends at Highbury as they can be to see her. Yes, Friday or Saturday; she cannot say which, because Colonel Campbell will be wanting the carriage himself one of those days. So very good of them to send her the whole way! But they always do, you know. Oh, yes, Friday or Saturday next. That is what she writes about. That is the reason of her writing out of rule, as we call it; for, in the common course, we should not have heard from her before next Tuesday or Wednesday.'

'Yes, so I imagined. I was afraid there could be little chance of my hearing anything of Miss Fairfax today.'

'So obliging of you! No, we should not have heard, if it had not been for this particular circumstance, of her being to come here so soon. My mother is so delighted! for she is to be three months with us at least. Three months, she says so, positively, as I am going to have the pleasure of reading to you. The case is, you see, that the Campbells are going to Ireland. Mrs Dixon has persuaded her father and mother to come over and see her directly. They had not intended to go over till the summer, but she is so impatient to see them again; for till she married, last October, she was never away from them so much as a week, which must make it very strange to be in different kingdoms, I was going to say, but, however, different countries, and so she wrote a very urgent letter to her mother, or her father – I declare I do not know which it was, but we shall see presently in Jane's letter – wrote in Mr Dixon's name as well as her own, to press their coming over directly; and they would give them the meeting in Dublin, and take them back to their country-seat, Baly-craig – a beautiful place, I fancy. Jane has heard a great deal of its beauty – from Mr Dixon I mean – I do not know that she ever heard about it from anybody else – but it was very natural, you know, that he should like to speak of his own place while he was paying his addresses – and as Jane used to be very often walking out with them – for Colonel and Mrs Campbell were very particular about their daughter's not walking out often with only Mr Dixon, for which I do not at all blame them; of course she heard everything he might be telling Miss Campbell about his own home in Ireland; and I think she wrote us word that

141

he had shown them some drawings of the place, views that he had taken himself. He is a most amiable, charming young man, I believe. Jane was quite longing to go to Ireland, from his account of things.'

At this moment, an ingenious and animating suspicion entering Emma's brain with regard to Jane Fairfax, this charming Mr Dixon, and the not going to Ireland, she said, with the insidious design of further discovery: 'You must feel it very fortunate that Miss Fairfax should be allowed to come to you at such a time. Considering the very particular friendship between her and Mrs Dixon you could hardly have expected her to be excused from accompanying Colonel and Mrs Campbell.'

'Very true, very true, indeed. The very thing that we have always been rather afraid of; for we should not have liked to have her at such a distance from us, for months together – not able to come if anything was to happen; but you see everything turns out for the best. They want her (Mr and Mrs Dixon) excessively to come over with Colonel and Mrs Campbell; quite depend upon it; nothing can be more kind or pressing than their joint invitation, Jane says, as you will hear presently. Mr Dixon does not seem in the least backward in any attention. He is a most charming young man. Ever since the service he rendered Jane at Weymouth, when they were out in that party on the water, and she, by the sudden whirling round of something or other among the sails, would have been dashed into the sea at once, and actually was all but gone, if he had not with the greatest presence of mind caught hold of her habit – I can never think of it without trembling! But ever since we had the history of that day, I have been so fond of Mr Dixon!'

'But, in spite of all her friends' urgency, and her own wish of seeing Ireland, Miss Fairfax prefers devoting the time to you and Mrs Bates?'

'Yes – entirely her own doing, entirely her own choice; and Colonel and Mrs Campbell think she does quite right, just what they should recommend; and indeed they particularly wish her to try her native air, as she has not been quite so well as usual lately.'

'I am concerned to hear of it. I think they judge wisely; but Mrs Dixon must be very much disappointed. Mrs Dixon, I understand, has no remarkable degree of personal beauty – is not, by any means, to be compared with Miss Fairfax?'

'Oh, no. You are very obliging to say such things, but certainly not. There is no comparison between them. Miss Campbell always was absolutely plain, but extremely elegant and amiable.'

'Yes, that of course.'

'Jane caught a bad cold, poor thing! so long ago as the 7th of November (as I am going to read to you), and has never been well since. A long time, is not it, for a cold to hang upon her? She never mentioned it before, because she would not alarm us. Just like her! so considerate! But, however, she is so far from well, that her kind friends the Campbells think she had better come home, and try an air that always agrees with her: and they have no doubt that three or four months at Highbury will entirely cure her; and it is certainly a great deal better that she should come here than go to Ireland, if she is unwell. Nobody could nurse her as we should do.'

'It appears to me the most desirable arrangement in the world.'

'And so she is to come to us next Friday or Saturday, and the Campbells leave town in their way to Holyhead the Monday following, as you will find from Jane's letter. So sudden! You may guess, dear Miss Woodhouse, what a flurry it has thrown me in. If it was not for the drawback of her illness – but I am afraid we must expect to see her grown thin, and looking very poorly. I must tell you what an unlucky thing happened to me as to that. I always make a point of reading Jane's letters through to myself first, before I read them aloud to my mother, you know, for fear of there being anything in them to distress her. Jane desired me to do it, so I always do! and so I began today with my usual caution: but no sooner did I come to the mention of her being unwell, than I burst out, quite frightened, with "Bless me! poor Jane is ill!" which my mother, being on the watch, heard distinctly, and was sadly alarmed at. However, when I read on, I found it was not near so bad as I had fancied at first; and I make so light of it now to her that she does not think much about it: but I cannot imagine how I could be so off my guard. If Jane does not get well soon, we will call in Mr Perry. The expense shall not be thought of; and though he is so liberal and so fond of Jane, that I dare say he would not mean to charge anything for attendance, we could not suffer it to be so, you know. He has a wife and family to maintain, and is not to be giving away his time. Well, now I have just given you a hint of what Jane writes about, we will turn to her letter, and I am sure she tells her own story a great deal better than I can tell it for her.'

'I am afraid we must be running away,' said Emma, glancing at Harriet, and beginning to rise, 'my father will be expecting us. I had no intention, I thought I had no power, of staying more than five minutes, when I first entered the house. I merely called because I would not pass the door without enquiring after Mrs Bates; but I have been so pleasantly detained. Now, however, we must wish you and Mrs Bates good morning.'

And not all that could be urged to detain her succeeded. She regained the street, happy in this, that though much had been forced on her against her will; though she had, in fact, heard the whole substance of Jane Fairfax's letter, she had been able to escape the letter itself.

Chapter 20

Jane Fairfax was an orphan, the only child of Mrs Bates's youngest daughter.

The marriage of Lieut. Fairfax of the — regiment of infantry, and Miss Jane Bates, had had its day of fame and pleasure, hope and interest; but nothing now remained of it save the melancholy remembrance of him dying in action abroad, of his widow sinking under consumption and grief soon afterwards, and this girl.

By birth she belonged to Highbury; and when, at three years old, on losing her mother she became the property, the charge, the consolation, the fondling of her grandmother and aunt, there had seemed every probability of her being permanently fixed there; of her being taught only what very limited means could command, and growing up with no advantages of connection or improvement, to be engrafted on what nature had given her in a pleasing person, good understanding, and warm-hearted, well-meaning relations.

But the compassionate feelings of a friend of her father gave a change to her destiny. This was Colonel Campbell, who had very highly regarded Fairfax, as an excellent officer and most deserving young man; and further had been indebted to him for such attentions, during a severe camp-fever, as he believed had saved his life. These were claims which he did not learn to overlook, though some years passed away from the death of poor Fairfax before his own return to England put anything in his power. When he did return, he sought out the child and took notice of her. He was a married man, with only one living child, a girl, about Jane's age; and Jane became their guest, paying them long visits and growing a favourite with all, and before she was nine years old, his daughter's great fondness for her, and his own wish of being a real friend, united to produce an offer from Colonel Campbell of undertaking the whole charge of her education. It was accepted; and from that period Jane had belonged to Colonel Campbell's family, and had lived with them entirely, only visting her grandmother from time to time.

The plan was that she should be brought up for educating others; the very few hundred pounds which she inherited from her father making independence impossible. To provide for her otherwise was out of Colonel Campbell's power; for though his income, by pay and appointments, was handsome, his fortune was moderate, and must be all his daughter's; but, by giving her an education, he hoped to be supplying the means of respectable subsistence hereafter.

Such was Jane Fairfax's history. She had fallen into good hands, known nothing but kindness from the Campbells, and been given an excellent education. Living constantly with right-minded and well-informed people, her heart and understanding had received every advantage of discipline and culture; and Colonel Campbell's residence being in London, every lighter talent had been done full justice to, by the attendance of first-rate masters. Her disposition and abilities were equally worthy of all that friendship could do; and at eighteen or nineteen she was, as far as such an early age can be qualified for the care of children, fully competent to the office of instruction herself; but she was too much beloved to be parted with. Neither father nor mother could promote, and the daughter could not endure it. The evil day was put off. It was easy to decide that she was still too young; and Jane remained with them, sharing as another daughter, in all the rational pleasures of an elegant society, and a judicious mixture of home and amusement, with only the drawback of the future – the sobering suggestions of her own good understanding – to remind her that all this might soon be over.

The affection of the whole family, the warm attachment of Miss Campbell in particular, was the more honourable to each party from the circumstance of Jane's decided superiority, both in beauty and acquirements. That nature had given it in feature could not be unseen by the young woman, nor could her higher powers of mind be unfelt by the parents. They continued together with unabated regard, however, till the marriage of Miss Campbell, who, by that chance, that luck which so often defies anticipation in matrimonial affairs, giving attraction to what is moderate rather than to what is superior, engaged the affections of Mr Dixon, a young man, rich and agreeable, almost as soon as they were acquainted; and was eligibly and happily settled, while Jane Fairfax had yet her bread to earn.

This event had very lately taken place; too lately for anything to be yet attempted by her less fortunate friend towards entering on her path of duty, though she had now reached the age which her own judgement had fixed on for beginning. She had long resolved that one-and-twenty should be the period. With the fortitude of a devoted noviciate, she had resolved at one-and-twenty to complete the sacrifice, and retire from all the pleasures of life, of rational intercourse, equal society, peace and hope, to penance and mortification for ever.

The good sense of Colonel and Mrs Campbell could not oppose such a resolution, though their feelings did. As long as they lived, no exertions would be necessary, their home might be hers for ever; and for their own comfort they would have retained her wholly; but this would be selfishness: what must be at last had better be soon. Perhaps they began to feel it might have been kinder and wiser to have resisted the temptation of any delay, and spared her from a taste of such enjoyments of ease and leisure as must now be relinquished. Still, however, affection was glad to catch at any reasonable excuse for not hurrying on the wretched moment. She had never been quite well since the time of their daughter's marriage; and till she should have completely recovered her usual strength, they must forbid her engaging in duties which, so far from being compatible with a weakened frame and varying spirits, seemed, under the most favourable circumstances, to require something more than human perfection of body and mind to be discharged with tolerable comfort.

With regard to her not accompanying them to Ireland, her account to her aunt contained nothing but truth, though there might be some truths not told. It was her own choice to give the time of their absence to Highbury; to spend, perhaps, her last months of perfect liberty with those kind relations to whom she was so very dear; and the Campbells, whatever might be their motive or motives, whether single, or double, or treble, gave the arrangement their ready sanction, and said that they depended more on a few months spent in her native air, for the recovery of her health, than on anything else. Certain it was that she was to come, and that Highbury, instead of welcoming that perfect novelty which had been so long promised it – Mr Frank Churchill – must put up for the present with Jane Fairfax, who could bring only the freshness of a two years' absence.

Emma was sorry to have to pay civilities to a person she did not like through three long months – to be always doing more than she wished, and less than she ought! Why she did not like Jane Fairfax might be a difficult question to answer; Mr Knightley had once told her it was because she saw in her the really accomplished young woman which she wanted to be thought herself; and though the accusation had been eagerly refuted at the time, there were moments of self-examination in which her conscience could not quite acquit her. But 'she could never get acquainted with her; she did not know how it was, but there was such coldness and reserve; such apparent indifference whether she pleased or not; and then, her aunt was such an eternal talker! and she was made such a fuss with by everybody! and it had been always imagined that they were to be intimate; because their ages were the same, everybody had supposed they must be so fond of each other.' These were her reasons; she had no better.

It was a dislike so little just – every imputed fault was so magnified by fancy – that she never saw Jane Fairfax, the first time after any considerable absence, without feeling that she had injured her; and now, when the due visit was paid on her arrival, after a two years' interval, she was particularly struck with the very appearance and manners which for those two whole years she had been depreciating. Jane Fairfax was very elegant, remarkably elegant, and she had herself the highest value for elegance. Her height was pretty, just such as almost everybody would think tall, and nobody could think very tall; her figure particularly graceful: her size a most becoming medium, between fat and thin, though a slight appearance of ill health seemed to point out the likeliest evil of the two. Emma could not but feel all this; and then, her face – her features – there was more beauty in them all together than she had remembered; it was not regular, but it was very pleasing beauty. Her eyes, a deep gray, with dark eyelashes and eyebrows, had never been denied their praise; but the skin, which she had been used to cavil at, as wanting colour, had a clearness and delicacy which really needed no fuller bloom. It was a style of beauty of which elegance was the reigning character, and as such, she must, in honour, by all her principles, admire it; elegance which, whether of person or of mind, she saw so little in Highbury. There, not to be vulgar, was distinction and merit.

In short, she sat, during the first visit, looking at Jane Fairfax with twofold complacency – the sense of pleasure and the sense of rendering justice, and was determining that she would dislike her no longer. When she took in her history, indeed, her situation, as well as her beauty; when she considered what all this elegance was destined to, what she was going to sink from, how she was going to live, it seemed impossible to feel anything but compassion and respect; especially, if to every well-known particular, entitling her to interest, were added the highly probable circumstance of an attachment to Mr Dixon, which she had so naturally started to herself. In that case, nothing could be more pitiable or more honourable than the sacrifices she had resolved on. Emma was very willing now to acquit her of having seduced Mr Dixon's affections from his wife, or of anything mischievous which her imagination had suggested at first. If it were love, it might be simple, single, successless love on her side alone. She might have been unconsciously sucking in the sad poison, while a sharer of his conversation with her friend; and from the best, the purest of motives, might now be denying herself this visit to Ireland, and resolving to divide herself effectually from him and his connections by soon beginning her career of laborious duty.

Upon the whole, Emma left her with such softened, charitable feelings, as made her look around in walking home, and lament that Highbury afforded no young man worthy of giving her independence – nobody that she could wish to scheme about for her.

These were charming feelings, but not lasting. Before she had committed herself by any public profession of eternal friendship for Jane Fairfax, or done more towards a recantation of past prejudices and errors, than saying to Mr Knightley, 'She certainly is handsome: she is better than handsome!' Jane had spent an evening at Hartfield with her grandmother and aunt, and everything was relapsing much into its usual state. Former provocations reappeared. The aunt was as tiresome as ever; more tiresome, because anxiety for her health was now added to admiration of her powers; and they had to listen to the description of exactly how little bread and butter she ate for breakfast, and how small a slice of mutton for dinner, as well as to see exhibitions of new caps and new workbags for her mother and herself; and Jane's offences rose again. They had music: Emma was obliged to play; and the thanks and praise which necessarily followed appeared to her an affection of candour, an air of greatness, meaning only to show off in higher style her own very superior performance. She was, besides, which was the worst of all, so cold, so cautious! There was no getting at her real opinion. Wrapt up in a cloak of politeness, she seemed determined to hazard nothing. She was disgustingly, was suspiciously reserved.

If anything could be more, where all was most, she was more reserved on the subject of Weymouth and the Dixons than anything. She seemed bent on giving no real insight into Mr

Dixon's character, or her own value for his company, or opinion of the suitableness of the match. It was all general approbation and smoothness; nothing delineated or distinguished. It did her no service, however. Her caution was thrown away. Emma saw its artifice, and returned to her first surmises. There probably *was* something more to conceal than her own preference; Mr Dixon, perhaps, had been very near changing one friend for the other, or been fixed only to Miss Campbell, for the sake of the future twelve thousand pounds.

The like reserve prevailed on other topics. She and Mr Frank Churchill had been at Weymouth at the same time. It was known that they were a little acquainted, but not a syllable of real information could Emma procure as to what he truly was. 'Was he handsome?' 'She believed he was reckoned a very fine young man.' 'Was he agreeable?' 'He was generally thought so.' 'Did he appear a sensible young man; a young man of information?' 'At a watering-place, or in a common London acquaintance, it was difficult to decide on such points. Manners were all that could be safely judged of, under a much longer knowledge than they had yet had of Mr Churchill. She believed everybody found his manners pleasing.' Emma could not forgive her.

Chapter 21

Emma could not forgive her; but as neither provocation nor resentment were discerned by Mr Knightley, who had been of the party, and had seen only proper attention and pleasing behaviour on each side, he was expressing the next morning, being at Hartfield again on business with Mr Woodhouse, his approbation of the whole; not so openly as he might have done had her father been out of the room, but speaking plain enough to be very intelligible to Emma. He had been used to think her unjust to Jane, and had now great pleasure in marking an improvement.

'A very pleasant evening,' he began, as soon as Mr Woodhouse had been talked into what was necessary, told that he understood, and the papers swept away – 'particularly pleasant. You and Miss Fairfax gave us some very good music. I do not know a more luxurious state, sir, sitting at one's ease to be entertained a whole evening by two such young women; sometimes with music and sometimes with conversation. I am sure Miss Fairfax must have found the evening pleasant, Emma. You left nothing undone. I was glad you made her play so much, for having no instrument at her grandmother's, it must have been a real indulgence.'

'I am happy you approved,' said Emma, smiling; 'but I hope I am not often deficient in what is due to guests at Hartfield.'

'No, my dear,' said her father instantly; '*that* I am sure you are not. There is nobody half so attentive and civil as you are. If anything you are too attentive. The muffin last night – if it had been handed round once, I think it would have been enough.'

'No,' said Mr Knightley, nearly at the same time; 'you are not often deficient; not often deficient, either in manner or comprehension. I think you understand me, therefore.'

An arch look expressed – 'I understand you well enough'; but she said only, 'Miss Fairfax is reserved.'

'I always told you she was – a little; but you will soon overcome all that part of her reserve which ought to be overcome, all that has its foundation in diffidence. What arises from discretion must be honoured.'

'You think her diffident. I do not see it.'

'My dear Emma,' said he, moving from his chair into one close by her, 'you are not going to tell me, I hope, that you had not a pleasant evening?'

'Oh no; I was pleased with my own perseverance in asking questions; and amused to think how little information I obtained.'

'I am disappointed,' was his only answer.

'I hope everybody had a pleasant evening,' said Mr Woodhouse, in his quiet way. 'I had. Once, I felt the fire rather too much; but then I moved back my chair a little, a very little, and it did not disturb me. Miss Bates was very chatty and good-humoured, as she always is, though she speaks rather too quick. However, she is very agreeable, and Mrs Bates, too, in a different way. I like old friends; and Miss Jane Fairfax is a very pretty sort of young lady; a very pretty and a very well-behaved young lady indeed. She must have found the evening agreeable, Mr Knightley, because she had Emma.'

'True, sir; and Emma, because she had Miss Fairfax.'

Emma saw his anxiety, and wishing to appease it, at least for the present, said, and with a sincerity which no one could question: 'She is a sort of elegant creature that one cannot keep one's eyes from. I am always watching her to admire; and I do pity her from my heart.'

Mr Knightley looked as if he were more gratified than he cared to express; and before he could make any reply, Mr Woodhouse, whose thoughts were on the Bates's, said: 'It is a great pity that their circumstances should be so confined! a great pity indeed! and I have often wished – but it is so little one can venture to do – small, trifling presents, of anything uncommon. Now, we have killed a porker, and Emma thinks of sending them a loin or a leg; it is very small and delicate – Hartfield pork is not like any other pork – but still it is pork – and, my dear Emma, unless one could be sure of their making it into steaks, nicely fried, as ours are fried, without the smallest grease, and not roast it, for no stomach can bear roast pork – I think we had better send the leg – do not you think so, my dear?'

'My dear papa, I sent the whole hind-quarter. I knew you would wish it. There will be the leg to be salted, you know, which is so very nice, and the loin to be dressed directly, in any manner they like.'

'That's right, my dear – very right. I had not thought of it before, but that is the best way. They must not over-salt the leg; and then, if it is not over-salted, and if it is very thoroughly boiled, just as Serle boils ours, and eaten very moderately of, with a boiled turnip, and a little carrot or parsnip, I do not consider it unwholesome.'

'Emma,' said Mr Knightley presently, 'I have a piece of news for you. You like news – and I heard an article on my way hither that I think will interest you.'

'News! Oh yes, I always like news. What is it? why do you smile so? where did you hear it? at Randalls?'

He had time only to say: 'No, not at Randalls; I have not been near Randalls' – when the door was thrown open, and Miss Bates and Miss Fairfax walked into the room. Full of thanks, and full of news, Miss Bates knew not which to give quickest. Mr Knightley soon saw that he had lost his moment, and that not another syllable of communication could rest with him.

'Oh, my dear sir, how are you this morning? My dear Miss Woodhouse – I come quite overpowered. Such a beautiful hind-quarter of pork! You are too bountiful! Have you heard the news? Mr Elton is going to be married.'

Emma had not had time even to think of Mr Elton, and she was so completely surprised, that she could not avoid a little start, and a little blush, at the sound.

'There is my news – I thought it would interest you,' said Mr Knightley, with a smile, which implied a conviction of some part of what had passed between them.

'But where could you hear it?' cried Miss Bates. 'Where could you possibly hear it, Mr Knightley? For it is not five minutes since I received Mrs Cole's note – no, it cannot be more than five – or at least ten – for I had got my bonnet and spencer on, just ready to come out – I was only gone down to Patty again about the pork – Jane was standing in the passage (were not you, Jane?) for my mother was so afraid that we had not any salting-pan large enough. So I said I would go down and see, and Jane said, "Shall I go down instead? for I think you have a little cold, and Patty has been washing the kitchen." "Oh, my dear" – said I – well, and just then came the note. A Miss Hawkins – that's all I know. A Miss Hawkins of Bath. But, Mr Knightley, how could you possibly have heard it? for the very moment Mr Cole told Mrs Cole of it, she sat down and wrote to me. A Miss Hawkins – '

'I was with Mr Cole on business an hour and a half ago. He had just read Elton's letter as I was shown in, and handed it to me directly.'

'Well! that is quite – I suppose there never was a piece of news more generally interesting. My dear sir, you really are too bountiful. My mother desires her very best compliments and regards, and a thousand thanks, and says you really quite oppress her.'

'We consider our Hartfield pork,' replied Mr Woodhouse – 'indeed, it certainly is, so very superior to all other pork, that Emma and I cannot have a greater pleasure than – '

'Oh, my dear sir, as my mother says, our friends are only too good to us. If ever there were people who, without having great wealth themselves, had everything they could wish for, I am sure it is us. We may well say, that "our lot is cast in a goodly heritage." Well, Mr Knightley, and so you actually saw the letter – well – '

'It was short – merely to announce – but cheerful, exulting, of course.' Here was a sly glance at Emma. 'He had been so fortunate as to – I forget the precise words – one has no business to remember them. The information was, as you state, that he was going to be married to a Miss Hawkins. By his style I should imagine it just settled.'

'Mr Elton going to be married!' said Emma, as soon as she could speak. 'He will have everybody's wishes for his happiness.'

'He is very young to settle,' was Mr Woodhouse's observation. 'He had better not be in a hurry. He seemed to me very well off as he was. We were always glad to see him at Hartfield.'

'A new neighbour for us all, Miss Woodhouse!' said Miss Bates joyfully; 'my mother is so pleased! she says she cannot bear to have the poor old Vicarage without a mistress. This is great news, indeed. Jane, you have never seen Mr Elton; no wonder that you have such a curiosity to see him.'

Jane's curiosity did not appear of that absorbing nature as wholly to occupy her.

'No, I have never seen Mr Elton,' she replied, starting on this appeal: 'is he – is he a tall man?'

'Who shall answer that question?' cried Emma. 'My father would say, "Yes"; Mr Knightley, "No"; and Miss Bates and I, that he is just the happy medium. When you have been here a little longer, Miss Fairfax, you will understand that Mr Elton is the standard of perfection in Highbury, both in person and mind.'

'Very true, Miss Woodhouse, so she will. He is the very best young man; but, my dear Jane, if you remember, I told you yesterday he was precisely the height of Mr Perry. Miss Hawkins? I dare say, an excellent young woman. His extreme attention to my mother – wanting her to sit in the vicarage-pew, that she might hear the better, for my mother is a little deaf, you know – it is not much, but she does not hear quite quick. Jane says that Colonel Campbell is a little deaf. He fancied bathing might be good for it – the warm bath – but she says it did him no lasting benefit. Colonel Campbell, you know, is quite our angel. And Mr Dixon seems a very charming young man, quite worthy of him. It is such a happiness when good people get together – and they always do. Now, here will be Mr Elton and Miss Hawkins; and there are the Coles, such very good people; and the Perrys – I suppose there never was a happier or a better couple than Mr and Mrs Perry. I say, sir,' turning to Mr Woodhouse, 'I think there are few places with such society as Highbury. I always say, we are quite blessed in our neighbours. My dear sir, if there is one thing my mother loves better than another, it is pork – a roast loin of pork – '

'As to who, or what, Miss Hawkins is, or how long he has been acquainted with her,' said Emma, 'nothing, I suppose, can be known. One feels that it cannot be a very long acquaintance. He has been gone only four weeks.'

Nobody had any information to give; and, after a few more wonderings, Emma said: 'You are silent, Miss Fairfax – but I hope you mean to take an interest in this news. You, who have been hearing and seeing so much of late on these subjects, who must have been so deep in the business on Miss Campbell's account – we shall not excuse your being indifferent about Mr Elton and Miss Hawkins.'

'When I have seen Mr Elton,' replied Jane, 'I dare say I shall be interested – but I believe it requires *that* with me. And as it is some months since Miss Campbell married, the impression may be a little worn off.'

'Yes, he has been gone just four weeks, as you observe, Miss Woodhouse,' said Miss Bates, 'four weeks yesterday. A Miss Hawkins! Well, I had always rather fancied it would be some young lady hereabouts; not that I ever – Mrs Cole once whispered to me – but I immediately said: "No, Mr Elton is a most worthy young man – but –" In short, I do not think I am particularly quick at those sort of discoveries. I do not pretend to it. What is before me, I see. At the same time, nobody could wonder if Mr Elton should have aspired – Miss Woodhouse lets me chatter on, so good-humouredly. She knows I would not offend for the world. How does Miss Smith do? She seems quite recovered now. Have you heard from Mrs John Knightley lately? Oh, those dear little children. Jane, do you know I always fancy Mr Dixon like Mr John Knightley. I mean in person – tall, and with that sort of look – and not very talkative.'

'Quite wrong, my dear aunt; there is no likeness at all.'

'Very odd! but one never does form a just idea of anybody beforehand. One takes up a notion and runs away with it. Mr Dixon, you see, is not, strictly speaking, handsome.'

'Handsome! Oh no – far from it – certainly plain. I told you he was plain.'

'My dear, you said that Miss Campbell would not allow him to be plain, and that you yourself – '

'Oh, as for me, my judgement is worth nothing. Where I have a regard, I always think a person well-looking. But I gave what I believed the general opinion, when I called him plain.'

'Well, my dear Jane. I believe we must be running away. The weather does not look well, and grandmamma will be uneasy. You are too obliging, my dear Miss Woodhouse; but we really must take leave. This has been a most agreeable piece of news indeed. I shall just go round by Mrs Cole's; but I shall not stop three minutes; and, Jane, you had better go home directly – I would not have you out in a shower. We think she is the better for Highbury already. Thank you – we do indeed. I shall not attempt calling on Mrs Goddard, for I really do not think she cares for anything but *boiled* pork; when we dress the leg it will be another thing. Good morning to you, my dear sir. Oh, Mr Knightley is coming too. Well, that is so very – I am sure if Jane is tired, you will be so kind as to give her your arm. Mr Elton and Miss Hawkins! Good morning to you.'

Emma, alone with her father, had half her attention wanted by him, while he lamented that young people would be in such a hurry to marry – and to marry strangers too – and the other half she could give to her own view of the subject. It was to herself an amusing and a very welcome piece of news, as proving that Mr Elton could not have suffered long; but she was sorry for Harriet – Harriet must feel it – and all that she could hope was, by giving the first information herself, to save her from hearing it abruptly from others. It was now about the time that she was likely to call. If she were to meet Miss Bates in her way! and upon its beginning to rain, Emma was obliged to expect that the weather would be detaining her at Mrs Goddard's, and that the intelligence would undoubtedly rush upon her without preparation.

The shower was heavy, but short; and it had not been over five minutes, when in came Harriet, with just the heated, agitated look which hurrying thither with a full heart was likely to give; and the 'Oh, Miss Woodhouse, what do you think has happened?' which instantly burst forth, had all the evidence of corresponding perturbation. As the blow was given, Emma felt that she could not now show greater kindness than in listening; and Harriet, unchecked, ran eagerly through what she had to tell. 'She had set out from Mrs Goddard's half an hour ago – she had been afraid it would rain – she had been afraid it would pour down every moment – but she thought she might get to Hartfield first – she had hurried on as fast as possible; but then, as she was passing by the house where a young woman was making up a gown for her, she thought she would just step in and see how it went on; and though she did not seem to stay half a moment there, soon after she came out it began to rain, and she did not know what to do; so she ran on directly, as fast as she could, and took shelter at Ford's.'

Ford's was the principal woollen-draper, linen-draper, and haberdasher's shop united – the shop first in size and fashion in the place. 'And so there she had set, without an idea of anything in the world, full ten minutes perhaps – when, all of a sudden, who should come in – to be sure it was so very odd! but they always dealt at Ford's – who should come in, but Elizabeth Martin and her brother! Dear Miss Woodhouse! only think. I thought I should have fainted. I did not know what to do. I was sitting near the door – Elizabeth saw me directly; but he did not; he was busy with the umbrella. I am sure she saw me, but she looked away directly, and took no notice; and they both went to quite the farther end of the shop; and I kept sitting near the door. Oh dear, I was so miserable! I am sure I must have been as white as my gown. I could not go away, you know, because of the rain; but I did so wish myself anywhere in the world but there. Oh dear, Miss Woodhouse! Well, at last, I fancy, he looked round and saw me; for instead of going on with her buyings, they began whispering to one another. I am sure they were talking of me, and I could not help thinking that he was persuading her to speak to me – (do you think he was, Miss Woodhouse?) – for presently she came forward – came quite up to me, and asked me how I did, and seemed ready to shake hands, if I would. She did not do any of it in the same way that she used: I could see she was altered; but, however, she seemed to try to be very friendly, and we shook hands, and stood talking some time; but I know no more what I said – I was in such a tremble! I remember she said she was sorry we never met now, which I thought almost too kind! Dear Miss Woodhouse, I was absolutely miserable! By that time, it was beginning to hold up, and I was determined that nothing should stop me from getting away – and then – only think! I found he was coming up towards me too – slowly, you know, and as if he did not quite know what to do; and so he came and spoke, and I answered – and I stood for a minute, feeling dreadfully, you know, one can't tell how; and then I took courage, and said it did not rain, and I must go; and so off I set; and I had not got three yards from the door, when he came after me, only to say, if I was going to Hartfield, he thought I had much better go round by Mr Cole's stables, for I should find the near way quite floated by this rain. Oh dear, I thought it would have been the death of me! So I said I was very much obliged to him: you know I could not do less; and then he went back to Elizabeth, and I came round by the stables – I believe I did – but I hardly knew where I was, or anything about it. Oh, Miss Woodhouse, I would rather have done anything than have had it happen; and yet, you know, there was a sort of satisfaction in seeing him behave so pleasantly and so kindly. And Elizabeth, too. Oh, Miss Woodhouse, do talk to me, and make me comfortable again.'

Very sincerely did Emma wish to do so; but it was not immediately in her power. She was obliged to stop and think. She was not thoroughly comfortable herself. The young man's conduct, and his sister's, seemed the result of real feeling, and she could not but pity them. As Harriet described it, there had been an interesting mixture of wounded affection and genuine delicacy in their behaviour; but she had believed them to be well-meaning, worthy people before; and what difference did this make in the evils of the connection? It was folly to be disturbed by it. Of course, he must be sorry to lose her – they must be all sorry – ambition, as well as love, had probably been mortified. They might all have hoped to rise by Harriet's acquaintance; and besides, what was the value of Harriet's description? So easily pleased – so little discerning – what signified her praise!

She exerted herself, and did try to make her comfortable, by considering all that had passed as a mere trifle, and quite unworthy of being dwelt on.

'It might be distressing for the moment,' said she, 'but you seem to have behaved extremely well; and it is over, and may never – can never, as a first meeting – occur again, and therefore you need not think about it.'

Harriet said, 'Very true,' and she 'would not think about it'; but still she talked of it – still she could talk of nothing else; and Emma, at last, in order to put the Martins out of her head, was obliged to hurry on the news, which she had meant to give with so much tender caution, hardly knowing herself whether to rejoice or be angry, ashamed, or only amused, at such a state of mind in poor Harriet – such a conclusion of Mr Elton's importance with her!

Mr Elton's rights, however, gradually revived. Though she did not feel the first intelligence as she might have done the day before, or an hour before, its interest soon increased; and before their first conversation was over, she had talked herself into all the sensations of curiosity, wonder, and regret, pain and pleasure, as to this fortunate Miss Hawkins, which could conduce to place the Martins under proper subordination in her fancy.

Emma learned to be rather glad that there had been such a meeting. It had been serviceable in deadening the first shock, without retaining any influence to alarm. As Harriet now lived, the Martins could not get at her, without seeking her where hitherto they had wanted either the courage or the condescension to seek her; for since her refusal of the brother, the sisters never had been at Mrs Goddard's; and a twelvemonth might pass without their being thrown together again, with any necessity, or even any power of speech.

Chapter 22

Human nature is so well disposed towards those who are in interesting situations, that a young person, who either marries or dies, is sure of being kindly spoken of.

A week had not passed since Miss Hawkins's name was first mentioned in Highbury, before she was, by some means or other, discovered to have every recommendation of person and mind – to be handsome, elegant, highly accomplished, and perfectly amiable; and when Mr Elton himself arrived to triumph in his happy prospects, and circulate the fame of her merits, there was very little more for him to do than to tell her Christian name, and say whose music she principally played.

Mr Elton returned, a very happy man. He had gone away rejected and mortified, disappointed in a very sanguine hope, after a series of what appeared to him strong encouragement; and not only losing the right lady, but finding himself debased to the level of a very wrong one. He had gone away deeply offended, he came back engaged to another; and to another as superior, of course, to the first, as under such circumstances what is gained always is to what is lost. He came back gay and self-satisfied, eager and busy, caring nothing for Miss Woodhouse, and defying Miss Smith.

The charming Augusta Hawkins, in addition to all the usual advantages of perfect beauty and merit, was in possession of an independent fortune, of so many thousands as would always be called ten – a point of some dignity, as well as some convenience. The story told well: he had not thrown himself away – he had gained a woman of £10,000, or thereabouts, and he had gained her with such delightful rapidity; the first hour of introduction had been so very soon followed by distinguishing notice; the history which he had to give Mrs Cole of the rise and progress of the affair was so glorious; the steps so quick, from the accidental rencontre, to the dinner at Mr Green's, and the party at Mrs Brown's – smiles and blushes rising in importance – with consciousness and agitation richly scattered; the lady had been so easily impressed – so sweetly disposed – had, in short, to use a most intelligible phrase, been so very ready to have him, that vanity and prudence were equally contented.

He had caught both substance and shadow, both fortune and affection, and was just the happy man he ought to be; talking only of himself and his own concerns – expecting to be congratulated – ready to be laughed at – and, with cordial, fearless smiles, now addressing all the young ladies of the place, to whom, a few weeks ago, he would have been more cautiously gallant.

The wedding was no distant event, as the parties had only themselves to please, and nothing but the necessary preparations to wait for; and when he set out for Bath again, there was a general expectation, which a certain glance of Mrs Cole's did not seem to contradict, that when he next entered Highbury he would bring his bride.

During his present short stay, Emma had barely seen him; but just enough to feel that the first meeting was over, and to give her the impression of his not being improved by the mixture of pique and pretension now spread over his air. She was, in fact, beginning very much to wonder that she had ever thought him pleasing at all; and his sight was so inseparably connected with some very disagreeable feelings, that, except in a moral light, as a penance, a lesson, a source of profitable humiliation to her own mind, she would have been thankful to be assured of never seeing him again. She wished him very well; but he gave her pain; and his welfare twenty miles off would administer most satisfaction.

The pain of his continued residence in Highbury, however, must certainly be lessened by his marriage. Many vain solicitudes would be prevented – many awkwardnesses smoothed by it. A *Mrs Elton* would be an excuse for any change of intercourse; former intimacy might sink without remark. It would be almost beginning their life of civility again.

Of the lady individually, Emma thought very little. She was good enough for Mr Elton, no doubt; accomplished enough for Highbury – handsome enough – to look plain, probably, by Harriet's side. As to connection, there Emma was perfectly easy; persuaded that, after all his own vaunted claims and disdain of Harriet, he had done nothing. On that article, truth seemed attainable. *What* she was, must be uncertain; but *who* she was, might be found out; and setting aside the £10,000 it did not appear that she was at all Harriet's superior. She brought no name, no blood, no alliance. Miss Hawkins was the youngest of the two daughters of a Bristol – merchant, of course, he must be called; but, as the whole of the profits of his mercantile life appeared so very moderate, it was not unfair to guess the dignity of his line of trade had been very moderate also. Part of every winter she had been used to spend in Bath; but Bristol was her home, the very heart of Bristol; for though the father and mother had died some years ago, an uncle remained – in the law line: nothing more distinctly honourable was hazarded of him, than that he was in the law line; and with him the daughter had lived. Emma guessed him to be the drudge of some attorney, and too stupid to rise. And all the grandeur of the connection seemed dependent on the elder sister, who was *very well married*, to a gentleman in a *great way*, near Bristol, who kept two carriages! That was the wind-up of the history; that was the glory of Miss Hawkins.

Could she but have given Harriet her feelings about it all! She had talked her into love; but, alas! she was not so easily to be talked out of it. The charm of an object to occupy the many vacancies of Harriet's mind was not to be talked away. He might be super-seded by another; he certainly would, indeed; nothing could be clearer; even a Robert Martin would have been sufficient; but nothing else, she feared, would cure her. Harriet was one of those, who, having once begun, would be always in love. And now, poor girl, she was considerably worse from this reappearance of Mr Elton – she was always having a glimpse of him somewhere or other. Emma saw him only once; but two or three times every day Harriet was sure *just* to meet with him, or *just* to miss him, *just* to hear his voice, or see his shoulder, *just* to have something occur to preserve him in her fancy, in all the favouring warmth of surprise and conjecture. She was, moreover, perpetually hearing about him; for, excepting when at Hartfield, she was always among those who saw no fault in Mr Elton, and found nothing so inter-esting as the discussion of his concerns; and every report, there-fore, every guess – all that had already occurred, all that might occur in the arrangement of his affairs, comprehending income, servants, and furniture – was continually in agitation around her. Her regard was receiving strength by invariable praise of him, and her regrets kept alive, and feelings irritated by ceaseless repe-titions of Miss Hawkins's happiness, and continual observation of how much he seemed attached! his air as he walked by the house, the very sitting of his hat, being all in proof of how much he was in love.

Had it been allowable entertainment, had there been no pain to her friend, or reproach to herself, in the waverings of Harriet's mind, Emma would have been amused by its variations. Some-times Mr Elton predominated, sometimes the Martins; and each was occasionally useful as a check to the other. Mr Elton's engage-ment had been the cure of the agitation of meeting Mr Martin. The unhappiness produced by the knowledge of that engagement had been a little put aside by Elizabeth Martin's calling at Mrs

Goddard's a few days afterwards. Harriet had not been at home; but a note had been prepared and left for her, written in the very style to touch – a small mixture of reproach with a great deal of kindness; and till Mr Elton himself appeared, she had been much occupied by it, continually pondering over what could be done in return, and wishing to do more than she dared to confess. But Mr Elton, in person, had driven away all such cares. While he stayed, the Martins were forgotten; and on the very morning of his setting off for Bath again, Emma, to dissipate some of the distress it occasioned, judged it best for her to return Elizabeth Martin's visit.

How that visit was to be acknowledged, what would be necessary, and what might be safest, had been a point of some doubtful consideration. Absolute neglect of the mother and sisters, when invited to come, would be ingratitude. It must not be; and yet the danger of a renewal of the acquaintance!

After much thinking, she could determine on nothing better than Harriet's returning the visit; but in a way that, if they had understanding, should convince them that it was to be only a formal acquaintance. She meant to take her in the carriage, leave her at the Abbey Mill, while she drove a little farther, and call for her again so soon as to allow no time for insidious applications or dangerous recurrences to the past, and give the most decided proof of what degree of intimacy was chosen for the future.

She could think of nothing better; and though there was something in it which her own heart could not approve – something of ingratitude, merely glossed over – it must be done, or what would become of Harriet?

Chapter 23

Small heart had Harriet for visiting. Only half an hour before her friend called for her at Mrs Goddard's, her evil stars had led her to the very spot where, at that moment, a trunk, directed to *The Revd Philip Elton, White Hart, Bath,* was to be seen under the operation of being lifted into the butcher's cart, which was to convey it to where the coaches passed; and everything in this world, except that trunk and the direction, was consequently a blank.

She went, however; and when they reached the farm, and she was to be put down, at the end of the broad, neat gravel-walk, which led between espalier apple trees to the front door, the sight of everything which had given her so much pleasure the autumn before was beginning to revive a little local agitation; and when they parted, Emma observed her to be looking around with a sort of fearful curiosity, which determined her not to allow the visit to exceed the proposed quarter of an hour. She went on herself, to give that portion of time to an old servant who was married, and settled in Donwell.

The quarter of an hour brought her punctually to the white gate again; and Miss Smith, receiving her summons, was with her without delay, and unattended by any alarming young man. She came solitarily down the gravel-walk – a Miss Martin just appearing at the door, and parting with her seemingly with ceremonious civility.

Harriet could not very soon give an intelligible account. She was feeling too much; but at last Emma collected from her enough to understand the sort of meeting, and the sort of pain it was creating. She had seen only Mrs Martin and the two girls. They had received her doubtingly, if not coolly; and nothing beyond the merest commonplace had been talked almost all the time – till just at last, when Mrs Martin's saying all of a sudden, that she thought Miss Smith was grown, had brought on a more interesting subject, and a warmer manner. In that very room she had been measured last September with her two friends. There were the pencilled marks and memorandums in the wainscot by the window. *He* had done it. They all seemed to remember the day, the hour, the party, the occasion – to feel the same conscious-ness, the same regrets – to be ready to return to the same good understanding; and they were just growing again like themselves (Harriet, as Emma must suspect, as ready as the best of them to be cordial and happy) when the carriage reappeared, and all was over. The style of the visit, and the shortness of it, were then felt to be decisive. Fourteen minutes to be given to those with whom she had thankfully passed six weeks not six months ago! Emma could not but picture it all, and feel how justly they might resent, how naturally Harriet must suffer. It was a bad business. She would have given a great deal, or endured a great deal, to have had the Martins in a higher rank of life. They were so deserving, that a *little* higher should have been enough; but as it was, how could she have done otherwise? Impossible! She could not repent. They must be separated. but there was a great deal of pain in the process – so much to herself at this time, that she soon felt the necessity of a little consolation, and resolved on going home by way of Randalls to procure it. Her mind was quite sick of Mr Elton and the Martins. The refreshment of Randalls was absolutely necessary.

It was a good scheme; but on driving to the door they heard that neither 'master nor mistress was at home'; they had both been out some time; the man believed they were gone to Hartfield.

'This is too bad!' cried Emma, as they turned away. 'And now we shall just miss them; too provoking. I do not know when I have been so disappointed.' And she leaned back in the corner, to indulge her murmurs, or to reason them away; probably a little of both – such being the commonplace process of a not ill-disposed mind. Presently the carriage stopped: she looked up; it was stopped by Mr and Mrs Weston, who were standing to speak to her. There was instant pleasure in the sight of them, and still greater pleasure was conveyed in sound; for Mr Weston immediately accosted her with: 'How d'ye do? how d'ye do? We have been sitting with your father – glad to see him so well. Frank comes tomorrow – I had a letter this morning – we see him tomorrow by dinner-time to a certainty – he is at Oxford today, and he comes for a whole fortnight – I knew it would be so. If he had come at Christmas he could not have stayed three days. I was always glad he did not come at Christmas; now we are going to have just the right weather for him – fine, dry, settled weather. We shall enjoy him completely; everything has turned out exactly as we could wish.'

There was no resisting such news, no possibility of avoiding the influence of such a happy face as Mr Weston's, confirmed as it all was by the words and the countenance of his wife, fewer and quieter, but not less to the purpose. To know that she thought his coming certain was enough to make Emma consider it so, and sincerely did she rejoice in their joy. It was a most delightful re-animation of exhausted spirits. The worn-out past was sunk in the freshness of what was coming; and in the rapidity of half a moment's thought she hoped Mr Elton would now be talked of no more.

Mr Weston gave her the history of the engagements at Enscombe, which allowed his son to answer for having an entire fortnight at his command, as well as the route and the method of his journey; and she listened, and smiled, and congratulated.

'I shall soon bring him over to Hartfield,' said he, at the conclusion.

Emma could imagine she saw a touch of the arm at this speech, from his wife.

'We had better move on, Mr Weston,' said she; 'we are detaining the girls.'

'Well, well, I am ready;' and turning again to Emma – 'but you must not be expecting such a *very* fine young man; you have only had *my* account, you know; I dare say he is really nothing extraordinary,' though his own sparkling eyes at the moment were speaking a very different conviction.

Emma could look perfectly unconscious and innocent, and answer in a manner that appropriated nothing.

'Think of me tomorrow, my dear Emma, about four o'clock,' was Mrs Weston's parting injunction, spoken with some anxiety, and meant only for her.

'Four o'clock! depend upon it, he will be here by three,' was Mr Weston's quick amendment; and so ended a most satisfactory meeting. Emma's spirits were mounted quite up to happiness. Everything wore a different air. James and his horses seemed not half so sluggish as before. When she looked at the hedges, she thought the elder, at least, must soon be coming out; and when she turned round to Harriet she saw something like a look of spring, a tender smile even there.

'Will Mr Frank Churchill pass through Bath as well as Oxford?' was a question, however, which did not augur much.

But neither geography nor tranquillity could come all at once; and Emma was now in a humour to resolve that they should both come in time.

The morning of the interesting day arrived, and Mrs Weston's faithful pupil did not forget either at ten, or eleven, or twelve o'clock, that she was to think of her at four.

'My dear, dear anxious friend,' said she, in mental soliloquy, while walking downstairs from her own room, 'always over-careful for everybody's comfort but your own; I see you now in all your little fidgets, going again and again into his room, to be sure that all is right.' The clock struck twelve as she passed through the hall. ' 'Tis twelve; I shall not forget to think of you four hours hence; and by this tomorrow, perhaps, or a little later, I may be thinking of the possibility of their all calling here. I am sure they will bring him soon.'

She opened the parlour door, and saw two gentlemen sitting with her father – Mr Weston and his son. They had been arrived only a few minutes; and Mr Weston had scarcely finished his explanation of Frank's being a day before his time, and her father was yet in the midst of his very civil welcome and congratulations, when she appeared, to have her share of surprise, introduction, and pleasure.

The Frank Churchill so long talked of, so high in interest, was actually before her. He was presented to her, and she did not think too much had been said in his praise. He was a *very* good-looking young man – height, air, address, all were unexceptionable, and his countenance had a great deal of the spirit and liveliness of his father's – he looked quick and sensible. She felt immediately that she should like him; and there was a well-bred ease of manner, and a readiness to talk, which convinced her that he came intending to be acquainted with her, and that acquainted they soon must be.

He had reached Randalls the evening before. She was pleased with the eagerness to arrive which had made him alter his plan, and travel earlier, later, and quicker, that he might gain half a day.

'I told you yesterday,' cried Mr Weston, with exultation, 'I told you all that he would be here before the time named. I remembered what I used to do myself. One cannot creep upon a journey; one cannot help getting on faster than one has planned: and the pleasure of coming in upon one's friends before the look-out begins is worth a great deal more than any little exertion it needs.'

'It is a great pleasure where one can indulge in it,' said the young man, 'though there are not many houses that I should presume on so far; but in coming *home* I felt I might do anything.'

The word *home* made his father look on him with fresh complacency. Emma was directly sure that he knew how to make himself agreeable; the conviction was strengthened by what followed. He was very much pleased with Randalls, thought it a most admirably-arranged house, would hardly allow it even to be very small, admired the situation, the walk to Highbury,

Highbury itself, Hartfield still more, and professed himself to have always felt the sort of interest in the country, which none but one's *own* country gives, and the greatest curiosity to visit it. That he should never have been able to indulge so amiable a feeling before passed suspiciously through Emma's brain; but still if it were a falsehood, it was a pleasant one, and pleasantly handled. His manner had no air of study or exaggeration. He did really look and speak as if in a state of no common enjoyment.

Their subjects, in general, were such as belong to an opening acquaintance. On his side were the enquiries – 'Was she a horse-woman? Pleasant rides? Pleasant walks? Had they a large neighbourhood? Highbury, perhaps, afforded society enough? There were several very pretty houses in and about it. Balls – had they balls? Was it a musical society?'

But when satisfied on all these points, and their acquaintance proportionately advanced, he contrived to find an opportunity while their two fathers were engaged with each other, of introducing his mother-in-law, and speaking of her with so much handsome praise, so much warm admiration, so much gratitude for the happiness she secured to his father, and her very kind reception of himself, as was an additional proof of his knowing how to please – and of his certainly thinking it worth while to try to please her. He did not advance a word of praise beyond what she knew to be thoroughly deserved by Mrs Weston; but, undoubtedly, he could know very little of the matter. He understood what would be welcome; he could be sure of little else. 'His father's marriage,' he said, 'had been the wisest measure: every friend must rejoice in it; and the family from whom he had received such a blessing must be ever considered as having conferred the highest obligations on him.'

He got as near as he could to thanking her for Miss Taylor's merits, without seeming quite to forget that, in the common course of things, it was to be rather supposed that Miss Taylor had formed Miss Woodhouse's character, than Miss Woodhouse Miss Taylor's. And at last, as if resolved to qualify his opinion completely for travelling round to its object, he wound it all up with astonishment at the youth and beauty of her person.

'Elegant, agreeable manners, I was prepared for,' said he; 'but I confess that, considering everything, I had not expected more than a very tolerably well-looking woman of a certain age; I did not know that I was to find a pretty young woman in Mrs Weston.'

'You cannot see too much perfection in Mrs Weston, for my feelings,' said Emma; 'were you to guess her to be *eighteen, I* should listen with pleasure; but *she* would be ready to quarrel with you for using such words. Don't let her imagine that you have spoken of her as a pretty young woman.'

'I hope I should know better,' he replied; 'no, depend upon it' (with a gallant bow), 'that in addressing Mrs Weston, I should understand whom I might praise without any danger of being thought extravagant in my terms.'

Emma wondered whether the same suspicion of what might be expected from their knowing each other, which had taken strong possession of her mind, had ever crossed his; and whether his compliments were to be considered as marks of acquiescence or proofs of defiance. She must see more of him to understand his ways; at present she only felt they were agreeable.

She had no doubt of what Mr Weston was often thinking about. His quick eye she detected again and again glancing towards them with a happy expression; and even when he might have determined not to look she was confident that he was often listening.

Her own father's perfect exemption from any thought of the kind, the entire deficiency in him of all such sort of penetration or suspicion, was a most comfortable circumstance. Happily he was not further from approving matrimony than from foreseeing it. Though always objecting to every marriage that was arranged he never suffered beforehand from the apprehension of any; it seemed as if he could not think so ill of any two persons' understanding as to suppose they meant to marry till it were proved against them. She blessed the favouring blindness. He could now, without the drawback of a single unpleasant surmise, without a glance forward at any possible treachery in his guest, give way to all his natural kind-hearted civility, in solicitous enquiries after Mr Frank Churchill's accommodation on his journey, through the sad evils of sleeping two nights on the road, and express very genuine unmixed anxiety to know that he had certainly escaped catching cold – which, however, he could not allow him to feel quite assured of himself, till after another night.

A reasonable visit paid, Mr Weston began to move. 'He must be going. He had business at the Crown about his hay, and a great many errands for Mrs Weston at Ford's; but he need not hurry anybody else.' His son, too well bred to hear the hint, rose immediately also, saying: 'As you are going farther on business, sir, I will take the opportunity of paying a visit, which must be paid some day or other, and therefore may as well be paid now. I have the honour of being acquainted with a neighbour of yours' (turning to Emma), 'a lady residing in or near Highbury; a family of the name of Fairfax. I shall have no difficulty, I suppose, in finding the house; though Fairfax, I believe, is not the proper name – I should rather say Barnes or Bates. Do you know any family of that name?'

'To be sure we do,' cried his father; 'Mrs Bates – we passed her house – I saw Miss Bates at the window. True, true, you are acquainted with Miss Fairfax; I remember you knew her at Weymouth, and a fine girl she is. Call upon her, by all means.'

'There is no necessity for my calling this morning,' said the young man; 'another day would do as well; but there was that degree of acquaintance at Weymouth, which – '

'Oh, go today, go today. Do not defer it. What is right to be done cannot be done too soon. And, besides, I must give you a hint, Frank – any want of attention to her *here* should be carefully avoided. You saw her with the Campbells, when she was the equal of everybody she mixed with, but here she is with a poor old grandmother, who has barely enough to live on. If you do not call early it will be a slight.'

The son looked convinced.

'I have heard her speak of the acquaintance,' said Emma; 'she is a very elegant young woman.'

He agreed to it, but with so quiet a 'Yes,' as inclined her almost to doubt his real concurrence; and yet there must be a very distinct sort of elegance for the fashionable world if Jane Fairfax could be thought only ordinarily gifted with it.

'If you were never particularly struck by her manners before,' said she, 'I think you will today. You will see her to advantage; see her and hear her – no, I am afraid you will not hear her at all, for she has an aunt who never holds her tongue.'

'You are acquainted with Miss Jane Fairfax, sir, are you?' said Mr Woodhouse, always the last to make his way in conversation; 'then give me leave to assure you that you will find her a very agreeable young lady. She is staying here on a visit to her grand-mamma and aunt, very worthy people; I have known them all my life. They will be extremely glad to see you, I am sure; and one of my servants shall go with you to show you the way.'

'My dear sir, upon no account in the world; my father can direct me.'

'But your father is not going so far; he is only going to the Crown, quite on the other side of the street, and there are a great many houses; you might be very much at a loss, and it is a very dirty walk, unless you keep on the footpath; but my coachman can tell you where you had best cross the street.'

Mr Frank Churchill still declined it, looking as serious as he could: and his father gave his hearty support, by calling out: 'My good friend, this is quite unnecessary; Frank knows a puddle of water when he sees it, and as to Mrs Bates's, he may get there from the Crown in a hop, step, and jump.'

They were permitted to go alone; and with a cordial nod from one, and a graceful bow from the other, the two gentlemen took leave. Emma remained very well pleased with this beginning of the acquaintance, and could now engage to think of them all at Randalls any hour of the day, with full confidence in their comfort.

Chapter 24

🌿 🌿 🌿

The next morning brought Mr Frank Churchill again. He came with Mrs Weston, to whom and to Highbury he seemed to take very cordially. He had been sitting with her, it appeared, most companionably at home, till her usual hour of exercise: and on being desired to choose their walk, immediately fixed on Highbury. 'He did not doubt there being very pleasant walks in every direction, but if left to him, he should always choose the same. Highbury, that airy, cheerful, happy-looking Highbury, would be his constant attraction.' Highbury, with Mrs Weston, stood for Hartfield, and she trusted to its bearing the same construction with him. They walked thither directly.

Emma had hardly expected them: for Mr Weston, who had called in for half a minute, in order to hear that his son was very handsome, knew nothing of their plans; and it was an agreeable surprise to her, therefore, to perceive them walking up to the house together, arm in arm. She was wanting to see him again; and especially to see him in company with Mrs Weston, upon his behaviour to whom her opinion of him was to depend. If he were deficient there, nothing should make amends for it. But on seeing them together she became perfectly satisfied. It was not merely in fine words or hyperbolical compliment that he paid his duty; nothing could be more proper or pleasing than his whole manner to her – nothing could more agreeably denote his wish of considering her as a friend, and securing her affection. And there was time enough for Emma to form a reasonable judgement, as their visit included all the rest of the morning. They were all three walking about together for an hour or two – first round the shrubberies of Hartfield, and afterwards in Highbury. He was delighted with everything; admired Hartfield sufficiently for Mr Woodhouse's ear; and when their going farther was resolved on, confessed his wish to be made acquainted with the whole village, and found matter of commendation and interest much oftener than Emma could have supposed.

Some of the objects of his curiosity spoke very amiable feelings. He begged to be shown the house which his father had lived in so long, and which had been the home of his father's father, and on recollecting that an old woman who had nursed him was still living, walked in quest of her cottage, from one end of the street to the other; and though in some points of pursuit or observation there was no positive merit, they showed altogether a good will towards Highbury in general, which must be very like a merit to those he was with.

Emma watched, and decided that with such feelings as were now shown it could not be fairly supposed that he had been ever voluntarily absenting himself; that he had not been acting a part, or making a parade of insincere professions; and that Mr Knightley certainly had not done him justice.

Their first pause was at the Crown Inn, an inconsiderable house, though the principal one of the sort, where a couple of pair of post-horses were kept, more for the convenience of the neighbourhood than from any run on the road; and his companions had not expected to be detained by any interest excited there; but in passing it they gave the history of the large room visibly added. It had been built many years ago for a ballroom and while the neighbourhood had been in a particularly populous, dancing state, had been occasionally used as such; but such brilliant days had long passed away; and now the highest purpose for which it was ever wanted was to accommodate a whist-club, established among the gentlemen and half-gentlemen of the place. He was immediately interested. Its character as a ballroom caught him; and instead of passing on, he stopped for several minutes at the two superior sashed windows which were open, to look in and contemplate its capabilities, and lament that its original purpose should have ceased. He saw no fault in the room; he would acknowledge none which they suggested. No; it was long enough, broad enough, handsome enough. It would hold the very number for comfort. They ought to have balls there at least every fortnight through the winter. Why had not Miss Woodhouse revived the former good old days of the room? She who could do anything in Highbury! The want of proper families in the place, and the conviction that none beyond the place and its immediate environs could be tempted to attend, were mentioned: but he was not satisfied. He could not be persuaded that so many good-looking houses as he saw around him could not furnish numbers enough for such a meeting; and even when particulars were given and families described, he was still unwilling to admit that the inconvenience of such a mixture would be anything, or that there would be the smallest difficulty in everybody's returning into their proper place the next morning. He argued like a young man very much bent on dancing; and Emma was rather surprised to see the constitution of the Westons prevail so decidedly against the habits of the Churchills. He seemed to have all the life and spirit, cheerful feelings, and social inclinations of his father, and nothing of the pride or reserve of Enscombe. Of pride, indeed, there was, perhaps, scarcely enough; his indifference to a confusion of rank bordered too much on inelegance of mind. He could be no judge, however, of the evil he was holding cheap. It was but an effusion of lively spirits.

At last he was persuaded to move on from the front of the Crown; and being now almost facing the house where the Bates lodged, Emma recollected his intended visit the day before, and asked him if he had paid it.

'Yes, oh yes!' he replied; 'I was just going to mention it. A very successful visit. I saw all the three ladies; and felt very much obliged to you for your preparatory hint. If the talking aunt had taken me quite by surprise, it must have been the death of me. As it was, I was only betrayed into paying a most unreasonable visit. Ten minutes would have been all that was necessary, perhaps all that was proper; and I had told my father I should certainly be at home before him, but there was no getting away, no pause; and, to my utter astonishment, I found, when he (finding me nowhere else) joined me there at last, that I had been actually sitting with them very nearly three quarters of an hour. The good lady had not given me the possibility of escape before.'

'And how did you think Miss Fairfax looking?'

'Ill, very ill – that is, if a young lady can ever be allowed to look ill; but the expression is hardly admissible, Mrs Weston, is it? Ladies can never look ill; and seriously, Miss Fairfax is naturally so pale as almost always to give the appearance of ill health – a most deplorable want of complexion.'

Emma would not agree to this, and began a warm defence of Miss Fairfax's complexion. 'It was certainly never brilliant, but she would not allow it to have a sickly hue in general, and there was a softness and delicacy in her skin which gave peculiar elegance to the character of her face.' He listened with all due deference; acknowledged that he had heard many people say the same; but yet he must confess that to him nothing could make amends for the want of the fine glow of health. Where features were indifferent, a fine complexion gave beauty to them all; and where they were good, the effect was – fortunately he need not attempt to describe what the effect was.

'Well,' said Emma, 'there is no disputing about taste. At least you admire her, except her complexion.'

He shook his head and laughed. 'I cannot separate Miss Fairfax and her complexion.'

'Did you see her often at Weymouth? Were you often in the same society?'

At this moment they were approaching Ford's, and he hastily exclaimed: 'Ha! this must be the very shop that everybody attends every day of their lives, as my father informs me. He comes to Highbury himself, he says, six days out of the seven, and has always business at Ford's. If it be not inconvenient to you, pray let us go in, that I may prove myself to belong to the place – to be a true citizen of Highbury. I must buy something at Ford's. It will be taking out my freedom. I dare say they sell gloves.'

'Oh yes, gloves and everything. I do admire your patriotism. You will be adored in Highbury. You were very popular before you came, because you were Mr Weston's son; but lay out half a guinea at Ford's, and your popularity will stand upon your own virtues.'

They went in; and while the sleek, well-tied parcels of 'Men's Beavers' and 'York Tan' were bringing down and displaying on the counter, he said: 'But I beg your pardon, Miss Woodhouse; you were speaking to me, you were saying something at the very moment of this burst of my *amor patriae*. Do not let me lose it. I assure you the utmost stretch of public fame would not make me amends for the loss of any happiness in private life.'

'I merely asked, whether you had known much of Miss Fairfax and her party at Weymouth?'

'And now that I understand your question I must pronounce it to be a very unfair one. It is always the lady's right to decide on the degree of acquaintance. Miss Fairfax must already have given her account. I shall not commit myself by claiming more than she may choose to allow.'

'Upon my word, you answer as discreetly as she could do herself. But her account of everything leaves so much to be guessed; she is so very reserved, so very unwilling to give the least information about anybody, that I really think you may say what you like of your acquaintance with her.'

'May I, indeed? Then I will speak the truth, and nothing suits me so well. I met her frequently at Weymouth. I had known the Campbells a little in town; and at Weymouth we were very much in the same set. Colonel Campbell is a very agreeable man, and Mrs Campbell a friendly warm-hearted woman. I like them all.'

'You know Miss Fairfax's situation in life, I conclude – what she is destined to be?'

'Yes' – (rather hesitatingly) – 'I believe I do.'

'You get upon delicate subjects, Emma,' said Mrs Weston, smiling; 'remember that I am here. Mr Frank Churchill hardly knows what to say when you speak of Miss Fairfax's situation in life. I will move a little farther off.'

'I certainly do forget to think of her,' said Emma, 'as having ever been anything but my friend and my dearest friend.'

He looked as if he fully understood and honoured such a sentiment.

When the gloves were bought, and they had quitted the shop again – 'Did you ever hear the young lady we were speaking of play?' said Frank Churchill.

'Ever hear her?' repeated Emma. 'You forget how much she belongs to Highbury. I have heard her every year of our lives since we both began. She plays charmingly.'

'You think so, do you? I wanted the opinion of some one who would really judge. She appeared to me to play well, that is, with considerable taste, but I know nothing of the matter myself. I am excessively fond of music, but without the smallest skill or right of judging of anybody's performance. I have been used to hear hers admired; and I remember one proof of her being thought to play well: a man, a very musical man, and in love with another woman – engaged to her on the point of marriage – would yet never ask that other woman to sit down to the instrument, if the lady in question could sit down instead – never seemed to like to hear one if he could hear the other. That, I thought, in a man of known musical talent, was some proof.'

'Proof, indeed!' said Emma, highly amused. 'Mr Dixon is very musical, is he? We shall know more about them all, in half an hour, from you, than Miss Fairfax would have vouchsafed in half a year.'

'Yes, Mr Dixon and Miss Campbell were the persons; and I thought it a very strong proof.'

'Certainly, very strong it was; to own the truth, a great deal stronger than, if I had been Miss Campbell, would have been at all agreeable to me. I could not excuse a man's having more music than love – more ear than eye – a more acute sensibility to fine sounds than to my feelings. How did Miss Campbell appear to like it?'

'It was her very particular friend, you know.'

'Poor comfort!' said Emma, laughing. 'One would rather have a stranger preferred than one's very particular friend, with a stranger it might not recur again, but the misery of having a very particular friend always at hand, to do everything better than one does oneself. Poor Mrs Dixon! Well, I am glad she is gone to settle in Ireland!'

'You are right. It was not very flattering to Miss Campbell; but she really did not seem to feel it.'

'So much the better, or so much the worse. I do not know which. But be it sweetness, or be it stupidity in her – quickness of friendship, or dullness of feeling – there was one person, I think, who must have felt it – Miss Fairfax herself. *She* must have felt the improper and dangerous distinction.'

'As to that – I do not – '

'Oh, do not imagine that I expect an account of Miss Fairfax's sensations from you, or from anybody else. They are known to no human being, I guess, but herself; but if she continued to play whenever she was asked by Mr Dixon, one may guess what one chooses.'

'There appeared such a perfectly good understanding among them all – ' he began rather quickly, but checking himself, added: 'however, it is impossible for me to say on what terms they really were – how it might all be behind the scenes. I can only say that there was smoothness outwardly. But you, who have known Miss Fairfax from a child, must be a better judge of her character, and of how she is likely to conduct herself in critical situations, than I can be.'

'I have known her from a child, undoubtedly; we have been children and women together; and it is natural to suppose that we should be intimate – that we should have taken to each other whenever she visited her friends. But we never did. I hardly know how it has happened; a little, perhaps, from that wickedness on my side which was prone to take disgust towards a girl so idolised and so cried up as she always was, by her aunt and grandmother, and all their set. And then, her reserve! I never could attach myself to anyone so completely reserved.'

'It is a most repulsive quality, indeed,' said he. 'Oftentimes very convenient, no doubt, but never pleasing. There is safety in reserve, but no attraction. One cannot love a reserved person.'

'Not till the reserve ceases toward oneself; and then the attraction may be the greater. But I must be more in want of a friend, or an agreeable companion, than I have yet been, to take the trouble of conquering anybody's reserve to procure one. Intimacy between Miss Fairfax and me is quite out of the question. I have no reason to think ill of her – not the least – except that such extreme and perpetual cautiousness of word and manner, such a dread of giving a distinct idea about anybody, is apt to suggest suspicions of there being something to conceal.'

He perfectly agreed with her; and after walking together so long, and thinking so much alike, Emma felt herself so well acquainted with him that she could hardly believe it to be only their second meeting. He was not exactly what she had expected; less of the man of the world in some of his notions, less of the spoiled child of fortune, therefore better than she had expected. His ideas seemed more moderate – his feelings warmer. She was particularly struck by his manner of considering Mr Elton's house, which, as well as the church, he would go and look at, and would not join them in finding much fault with. No, he could not believe it a bad house; not such a house as a man was to be pitied for having. If it were to be shared with the woman he loved, he could not think any man to be pitied for having that house. There must be ample room in it for every real comfort. The man must be a blockhead who wanted more. Mrs Weston laughed, and said he did not know what he was talking about. Used only to a large house himself, and without ever thinking how many advantages and accommodations were attached to its size, he could be no judge of the privations inevitably belonging to a small one. But Emma, in her own mind, determined that he *did* know what he was talking about, and that he showed a very amiable inclination to settle early in life, and to marry from worthy motives. He might not be aware of the inroads on domestic peace to be occasioned by no housekeeper's room, or a bad butler's pantry; but no doubt he did perfectly feel that Enscombe could not make him happy, and that whenever he were attached he would willingly give up much of wealth to be allowed an early establishment.

Chapter 25

Emma's very good opinion of Frank Churchill was a little shaken the following day by hearing that he was gone off to London, merely to have his hair cut. A sudden freak seemed to have seized him at breakfast, and he had sent for a chaise and set off, intending to return to dinner, but with no more important view that appeared than having his hair cut. There was certainly no harm in his travelling sixteen miles twice over on such an errand; but there was an air of foppery and nonsense in it which she could not approve. It did not accord with the rationality of plan, the moderation in expense, or even the unselfish warmth of heart, which she had believed herself to discern in him yesterday.

Vanity, extravagance, love of change, restlessness of temper, which must be doing something, good or bad; heedlessness as to the pleasure of his father and Mrs Weston, indifference as to how his conduct might appear in general; he became liable to all these charges. His father only called him a coxcomb, and thought it a very good story; but that Mrs Weston did not like it was clear enough by her passing it over as quickly as possible, and making no other comment than that 'all young people would have their little whims.'

With the exception of this little blot, Emma found that his visit hitherto had given her friend only good ideas of him. Mrs Weston was very ready to say how attentive and pleasant a companion he made himself – how much she saw to like in his disposition altogether. He appeared to have a very open temper – certainly a very cheerful and lively one; she could observe nothing wrong in his notions – a great deal decidedly right; he spoke of his uncle with warm regard – was fond of talking of him; said he would be the best man in the world if he were left to himself; and though there was no being attached to the aunt, he acknowledged her kindness with gratitude, and seemed to mean always to speak of her with respect. This was all very promising; and but for such an unfortunate fancy for having his hair cut, there was nothing to denote him unworthy of the distinguished honour which her imagination had given him; the honour, if not of being really in love with her, of being at least very near it, and saved only by her own indifference – (for still her resolution held of never marrying) – the honour, in short, of being marked out for her by all their joint acquaintance.

Mr Weston, on his side, added a virtue to the account which must have some weight. He gave her to understand that Frank admired her extremely – thought her very beautiful and very charming; and with so much to be said for him altogether, she found she must not judge him harshly. As Mrs Weston observed: 'All young people would have their little whims.'

There was one person among his new acquaintance in Surrey not so leniently disposed. In general, he was judged, throughout the parishes of Donwell and Highbury with great candour; liberal allowances were made for the little excesses of such a handsome young man – one who smiled so often and bowed so well; but there was one spirit among them not to be softened, from its power of censure, by bows or smiles – Mr Knightley. The circumstance was told him at Hartfield; for the moment he was silent. but Emma heard him almost immediately afterwards say to himself, over a newspaper he held in his hand: 'Hum! just the trifling, silly fellow I took him for.' She had half a mind to resent; but an instant's observation convinced her that it was really said only to relieve his own feelings, and not meant to provoke; and therefore she let it pass.

Although in one instance the bearers of not good tidings, Mr and Mrs Weston's visit this morning was in another respect particularly opportune. Something occurred while they were at Hartfield to make Emma want their advice; and, which was still more lucky, she wanted exactly the advice they gave.

This was the occurrence. The Coles had been settled some years in Highbury, and were very good sort of people, friendly, liberal, and unpretending; but, on the other hand, they were of low origin, in trade, and only moderately genteel. On their first coming into the country they had lived in proportion to their income, quietly, keeping little company, and that little unexpensively; but the last year or two had brought them a considerable increase of means – the house in town had yielded greater profits, and fortune in general had smiled on them. With their wealth their views increased; their want of a larger house, their inclination for more company. They added to their house, to their number of servants, to their expenses of every sort; and by this time were, in fortune and style of living, second only to the family at Hartfield. Their love of society, and their new dining-room, prepared everybody for their keeping dinner-company; and a few parties, chiefly among the single men, had already taken place. The regular and best families Emma could hardly suppose they would presume to invite – neither Donwell, nor Hartfield, nor Randalls. Nothing should tempt *her* to go, if they did; and she regretted that her father's known habits would be giving her refusal less meaning than she could wish. The Coles were very respectable in their way, but they ought to be taught that it was not for them to arrange the terms on which the superior families would visit them. This lesson, she very much feared, they would receive only from herself; she had little hope of Mr Knightley, none of Mr Weston.

But she had made up her mind how to meet this presumption so many weeks before it appeared, that when the insult came at last it found her very differently affected. Donwell and Randalls had received their invitation, and none had come for her father and herself; and Mrs Weston's accounting for it with, 'I suppose they will not take the liberty with you; they know you do not dine out,' was not quite sufficient. She felt that she should like to have had the power of refusal; and afterwards, as the idea of the party to be assembled there, consisting precisely of those whose society was dearest to her, occurred again and again, she did not know that she might not have been tempted to accept. Harriet was to be there in the evening, and the Bateses. They had been speaking of it as they walked about Highbury the day before, and Frank Churchill had most earnestly lamented her absence. Might not the evening end in a dance? had been a question of his. The bare possibility of it acted as a further irritation on her spirits; and her being left in solitary grandeur, even supposing the omission to be intended as a compliment, was but poor comfort.

It was the arrival of this very invitation, while the Westons were at Hartfield, which made their presence so acceptable; for though her first remark on reading it was, that 'of course it must be declined,' she so very soon proceeded to ask them what they advised her to do, that their advice for her going was most prompt and successful.

She owned that, considering everything, she was not absolutely without inclination for the party. The Coles expressed themselves so properly – there was so much real attention in the manner of it – so much consideration for her father. 'They would have solicited the honour earlier, but had been waiting the arrival of a folding-screen from London, which they hoped might keep Mr Woodhouse from any draught of air, and, therefore, induce him the more readily to give them the honour of his company.' Upon the whole, she was very persuadable; and it being chiefly settled among themselves how it might be done without neglecting his comfort – how certainly Mrs Goddard, if not Mrs Bates, might be depended on for bearing him company – Mr Woodhouse was to be talked into an acquiescence of his daughter's going out to dinner on a day now near at hand, and spending the whole evening away from him. As for *his* going, Emma did not wish him to think it possible; the hours would be too late, and the party too numerous. He was soon pretty well resigned.

'I am not fond of dinner-visiting,' said he; 'I never was. No more is Emma. Late hours do not agree with us. I am sorry Mr and Mrs Cole should have done it. I think it would be much better if they would come in one afternoon next summer and take their tea with us; take us in their afternoon walk, which they might do, as our hours are so reasonable, and yet get home without being out in the damp of the evening. The dews of a summer evening are what I would not expose anybody to. However, as they are so very desirous to have dear Emma dine with them, and as you will both be there, and Mr Knightley too, to take care of her, I cannot wish to prevent it, provided the weather be what it ought, neither damp, nor cold, nor windy.' Then turning to Mrs Weston, with a look of gentle reproach – 'Ah, Miss Taylor, if you had not married, you would have stayed at home with me.'

'Well, sir,' cried Mr Weston, 'as I took Miss Taylor away, it is incumbent on me to supply her place, if I can; and I will step to Mrs Goddard in a moment, if you wish it.'

But the idea of anything to be done in a *moment* was increasing, not lessening, Mr Woodhouse's agitation. The ladies knew better how to allay it. Mr Weston must be quiet, and everything deliberately arranged.

With this treatment Mr Woodhouse was soon composed enough for talking as usual. 'He should be happy to see Mrs Goddard. He had a great regard for Mrs Goddard; and Emma should write a line and invite her. James could take the note. But first of all there must be an answer written to Mrs Cole.'

'You will make my excuses, my dear, as civilly as possible. You will say that I am quite an invalid, and go nowhere, and therefore must decline their obliging invitation; beginning with my *compliments,* of course. But you will do everything right. I need not tell you what is to be done. We must remember to let James know that the carriage will be wanted on Tuesday. I shall have no fears for you with him. We have never been there above once since the new approach was made; but still I have no doubt that James will take you very safely; and when you get there you must tell him at what time you would have him come for you again; and you had better name an early hour. You will not like staying late. You will get very tired when tea is over.'

'But you would not wish me to come away before I am tired, papa?'

'Oh no, my love; but you will soon be tired. There will be a great many people talking at once. You will not like the noise.'

'But, my dear sir,' cried Mr Weston, 'if Emma comes away early it will be breaking up the party.'

'And no great harm if it does,' said Mr Woodhouse. 'The sooner every party breaks up the better.'

'But you do not consider how it may appear to the Coles. Emma's going away directly after tea might be giving offence. They are good-natured people, and think little of their own claims;

but still they must feel that anybody's hurrying away is no great compliment; and Miss Woodhouse's doing it would be more thought of than any other person's in the room. You would not wish to disappoint and mortify the Coles, I am sure, sir; friendly, good sort of people as ever lived, and who have been your neighbours these ten years.'

'No, upon no account in the world, Mr Weston, I am much obliged to you for reminding me. I should be extremely sorry to be giving them any pain. I know what worthy people they are. Perry tells me that Mr Cole never touches malt liquor. You would not think it to look at him, but he is bilious – Mr Cole is very bilious. No, I would not be the means of giving them any pain. My dear Emma, we must consider this. I am sure rather than run the risk of hurting Mr and Mrs Cole you would stay a little longer than you might wish. You will not regard being tired. You will be perfectly safe, you know, among your friends.'

'Oh yes, papa. I have no fears at all for myself; and I should have no scruples of staying as late as Mrs Weston, but on your account. I am only afraid of your sitting up for me. I am not afraid of your not being exceedingly comfortable with Mrs Goddard. She loves piquet, you know; but when she is gone home I am afraid you will be sitting up by yourself, instead of going to bed at your usual time; and the idea of that would entirely destroy my comfort. You must promise me not to sit up.'

He did, on the condition of some promises on her side; such as that, if she came home cold, she would be sure to warm herself thoroughly; if hungry, that she would take something to eat; that her own maid should sit up for her; and that Serle and the butler should see that everything were safe in the house as usual.

Chapter 26

Frank Churchill came back again; and if he kept his father's dinner waiting it was not known at Hartfield; for Mrs Weston was too anxious for his being a favourite with Mr Woodhouse, to betray any imperfection which could be concealed.

He came back, had had his hair cut, and laughed at himself with a very good grace, but without seeming really at all ashamed of what he had done. He had no reason to wish his hair longer to conceal any confusion of face; no reason to wish the money unspent to improve his spirits. He was quite as undaunted and as lively as ever; and, after seeing him, Emma thus moralised to herself: 'I do not know whether it ought to be so, but certainly silly things do cease to be silly if they are done by sensible people in an impudent way. Wickedness is always wickedness, but folly is not always folly. It depends upon the character of those who handle it. Mr Knightley, he is not a trifling, silly young man. If he were, he would have done this differently. He would either have gloried in the achievement, or been ashamed of it. There would have been either the ostentation of a coxcomb, or the evasions of a mind too weak to defend its own vanities. No, I am perfectly sure that he is not trifling or silly.'

With Tuesday came the agreeable prospect of seeing him again, and for a longer time than hitherto; of judging of his general manners, and, by inference, of the meaning of his manners towards herself; of guessing how soon it might be necessary for her to throw coldness into her air; and of fancying what the observations of all those might be, who were now seeing them together for the first time.

She meant to be very happy, in spite of the scene being laid at Mr Cole's; and without being able to forget that among the failings of Mr Elton, even in the days of his favour, none had disturbed her more than his propensity to dine with Mr Cole.

Her father's comfort was amply secured, Mrs Bates as well as Mrs Goddard being able to come; and her last pleasing duty, before she left the house, was to pay her respects to them as they sat together after dinner; and while her father was fondly noticing the beauty of her dress, to make the two ladies all the amends in her power, by helping them to large slices of cake and full glasses of wine, for whatever unwilling self-denial his care of their constitution might have obliged them to practise during the meal. She had provided a plentiful dinner for them; she wished she could know that they had been allowed to eat it.

She followed another carriage to Mr Cole's door; and was pleased to see that it was Mr Knightley's; for Mr Knightley, keeping no horses, having little spare money and a great deal of health, activity, and independence, was too apt, in Emma's opinion, to get about as he could, and not use his carriage so often as became the owner of Donwell Abbey. She had an opportunity now of speaking her approbation while warm from her heart, for he stopped to hand her out.

'This is coming as you should do,' said she; 'like a gentleman. I am quite glad to see you.'

He thanked her, observing, 'How lucky that we should arrive at the same moment; for, if we had met first in the drawing-room, I doubt whether you would have discerned me to be more of a gentleman than usual. You might not have distinguished how I came by my look or manner.'

'Yes I should. I am sure I should. There is always a look of consciousness or bustle when people come in a way which they know to be beneath them. You think you carry it off very well, I dare say; but with you it is a sort of bravado, an air of affected unconcern; I always observe it whenever I meet you under those circumstances. *Now* you have nothing to try for. You are not afraid of being supposed ashamed. You are not striving to look taller than anybody else. *Now* I shall be very happy to walk into the same room with you.'

'Nonsensical girl!' was his reply, but not at all in anger.

Emma had as much reason to be satisfied with the rest of the party as with Mr Knightley. She was received with a cordial respect which could not but please, and given all the consequence she could wish for. When the Westons arrived, the kindest looks of love, the strongest of admiration, were for her, from both husband and wife; the son approached her with a cheerful eagerness, which marked her as his peculiar object, and at dinner she found him seated by her; and, as she firmly believed, not without some dexterity on his side.

The party was rather large, as it included one other family – a proper unobjectionable country family, whom the Coles had the advantage of naming among their acquaintance – and the male part of Mr Cox's family, the lawyer of Highbury. The less worthy females were to come in the evening, with Miss Bates, Miss Fairfax, and Miss Smith; but already, at dinner, they were too numerous for any subject of conversation to be general; and, while politics and Mr Elton were talked over, Emma could fairly surrender all her attention to the pleasantness of her neighbour. The first remote sound to which she felt herself obliged to attend was the name of Jane Fairfax. Mrs Cole seemed to be relating something of her that was expected to be very interesting. She listened, and found it well worth listening to. That very dear part of Emma, her fancy, received an amusing supply. Mrs Cole was telling that she had been calling on Miss Bates; and as soon as she entered the room, had been struck by the sight of a pianoforte, a very elegant looking instrument; not a grand, but a large-sized square pianoforte: and the substance of the story, the end of all the dialogue which ensued of surprise, and enquiry, and congratulations on her side, and explanations on Miss Bates's, was that this pianoforte had arrived from Broadwood's the day before, to the great astonishment of both aunt and niece, entirely unexpected; that, at first, by Miss Bates's account, Jane herself was quite at a loss, quite bewildered to think who could possibly have ordered it; but now they were both perfectly satisfied that it could be from only one quarter – of course it must be from Colonel Campbell.

'One can suppose nothing else,' added Mrs Cole; 'and I was only surprised that there could ever have been a doubt. But Jane, it seems, had a letter from them very lately, and not a word was said about it. She knows their ways best; but I should not consider their silence as any reason for their not meaning to make the present. They might choose to surprise her.'

Mrs Cole had many to agree with her; everybody who spoke on the subject was equally convinced that it must come from Colonel Campbell, and equally rejoiced that such a present had been made; and there were enough ready to speak to allow Emma to think her own way, and still listen to Mrs Cole.

'I declare, I do not know when I have heard anything that has given me more satisfaction. It always has quite hurt me that Jane Fairfax, who plays so delightfully, should not have an instrument. It seemed quite a shame, especially considering how many houses there are where fine instruments are absolutely thrown away. This is like giving ourselves a slap, to be sure; and it was but yesterday I was telling Mr Cole I really was ashamed to look at our new grand pianoforte in the drawing-room, while I do not know one note from another, and our little girls, who are but just beginning, perhaps may never make anything of it; and there is poor Jane Fairfax, who is mistress of music, has not anything of the nature of an instrument, not even the pitifullest old spinet in the world, to amuse herself with. I was saying this to Mr Cole but yesterday, and he quite agreed with me; only he is so particularly fond of music that he could not help indulging himself in the purchase, hoping that some of our good neighbours might be so obliging occasionally to put it to a better use than we can; and that really is the reason why the instrument was bought – or else I am sure we ought to be ashamed of it. We are in great hopes that Miss Woodhouse may be prevailed with to try it this evening.'

Miss Woodhouse made the proper acquiescence; and finding that nothing more was to be entrapped from any communication of Mrs Cole's, turned to Frank Churchill.

'Why do you smile?' said she.

'Nay, why do you?'

'Me! I suppose I smile for pleasure at Colonel Campbell's being so rich and so liberal. It is a handsome present.'

'Very.'

'I rather wonder that it was never made before.'

'Perhaps Miss Fairfax has never been staying here so long before.'

'Or that he did not give her the use of their own instrument, which must now be shut up in London, untouched by anybody.'

'That is a grand pianoforte, and he might think it too large for Mrs Bates's house.'

'You may *say* what you choose, but your countenance testifies that your *thoughts* on this subject are very much like mine.'

'I do not know. I rather believe you are giving me more credit for acuteness than I deserve. I smile because you smile, and shall probably suspect whatever I find you suspect; but at present I do not see what there is to question. If Colonel Campbell is not the person, who can be?'

'What do you say to Mrs Dixon?'

'Mrs Dixon! very true, indeed. I had not thought of Mrs Dixon. She must know, as well as her father, how acceptable an instrument would be; and perhaps the mode of it, the mystery, the surprise, is more like a young woman's scheme than an elderly man's. It is Mrs Dixon, I dare say. I told you that your suspicions would guide mine.'

'If so, you must extend your suspicions, and comprehend Mr Dixon in them.'

'Mr Dixon, very well. Yes. I immediately perceive that it must be the joint present of Mr and Mrs Dixon. We were speaking the other day, you know, of his being so warm an admirer of her performance.'

'Yes, and what you told me on that head confirmed an idea which I had entertained before. I do not mean to reflect upon the good intentions of either Mr Dixon or Miss Fairfax; but I cannot help suspecting either that, after making his proposals to her friend, he had the misfortune to fall in love with her, or that he became conscious of a little attachment on her side. One might guess twenty things without guessing exactly the right; but I am sure there must be a particular case for her choosing to come to Highbury, instead of going with the Campbells to Ireland. Here, she must be leading a life of privation and penance; there it would have been all enjoyment. As to the pretence of trying her native air, I look upon that as a mere excuse. In the summer it might have passed; but what can anybody's native air do for them in the months of January, February, and March? Good fires and carriages would be much more to the purpose in most cases of delicate health, and I dare say in hers. I do not require you to adopt all my suspicions, though you make so noble a profession of doing it, but I honestly tell you what they are.'

'And, upon my word, they have an air of great probability. Mr Dixon's preference of her music to her friend's I can answer for being very decided.'

'And then, he saved her life. Did you ever hear of that? A water party; and by some accident she was falling overboard. He caught her.'

'He did. I was there – one of the party.'

'Were you really? Well! But you observed nothing, of course, for it seems to be a new idea to you. If I had been there, I think I should have made some discoveries.'

'I dare say you would; but I, simple I, saw nothing but the fact, that Miss Fairfax was nearly dashed from the vessel, and that Mr Dixon caught her – it was the work of a moment. And though the consequent shock and alarm was very great, and much more durable – indeed I believe it was half an hour before any of us were comfortable again – yet that was too general a sensation for anything of peculiar anxiety to be observable. I do not mean to say, however, that you might not have made discoveries.'

The conversation was here interrupted. They were called on to share in the awkwardness of a rather long interval between the courses, and obliged to be as formal and as orderly as the others; but when the table was again safely covered, when every corner dish was placed exactly right, and occupation and ease were generally restored, Emma said: 'The arrival of this pianoforte is decisive with me. I wanted to know a little more, and this tells me quite enough. Depend upon it, we shall soon hear that it is a present from Mr and Mrs Dixon.'

'And if the Dixons should absolutely deny all knowledge of it, we must conclude it to come from the Campbells.'

'No, I am sure it is not from the Campbells. Miss Fairfax knows it is not from the Campbells, or they would have been guessed at first. She would not have been puzzled had she dared fix on them. I may not have convinced you, perhaps, but I am perfectly convinced myself that Mr Dixon is a principal in the business.'

'Indeed you injure me if you suppose me unconvinced. Your reasonings carry my judgement along with them entirely. At first, while I supposed you satisfied that Colonel Campbell was the giver, I saw it only as paternal kindness, and thought it the most natural thing in the world. But when you mentioned Mrs Dixon, I felt how much more probable that it should be the tribute of warm female friendship. And now I can see it in no other light than as an offering of love.'

There was no occasion to press the matter further. The conviction seemed real; he looked as if he felt it. She said no more – other subjects took their turn, and the rest of the dinner passed away; the dessert succeeded, the children came in, and were talked to and admired amid the usual rate of conversation; a few clever things said, a few downright silly, but by much the larger proportion neither the one nor the other – nothing worse than everyday remarks, dull repetitions, old news, and heavy jokes.

The ladies had not been long in the drawing-room before the other ladies, in their different divisions, arrived. Emma watched the entree of her own particular little friend; and if she could not exult in her dignity and grace she could not only love the blooming sweetness and the artless manner, but could most heartily rejoice in that light, cheerful, unsentimental disposition which allowed her so many alleviations of pleasure in the midst of the pangs of disappointed affection. There she sat – and who would have guessed how many tears she had been lately shedding? To be in company, nicely dressed herself, and seeing others nicely dressed, to sit and smile and look pretty and say nothing, was enough for the happiness of the present hour. Jane Fairfax did look and move superior; but Emma suspected she might have been glad to change feelings with Harriet – very glad to have purchased the mortification of having loved – yes, of having loved even Mr Elton in vain by the surrender of all the dangerous pleasure of knowing herself beloved by the husband of her friend.

In so large a party it was not necessary that Emma should approach her. She did not wish to speak of the pianoforte, she felt too much in the secret herself to think the appearance of curiosity or interest fair, and therefore purposely kept at a distance; but by the others the subject was almost immediately introduced, and she saw the blush of consciousness with which congratulations were received, the blush of guilt which accompanied the name of 'my excellent friend, Colonel Campbell.'

Mrs Weston, kind-hearted and musical, was particularly interested by the circumstance, and Emma could not help being amused at her perseverance in dwelling on the subject; and having so much to ask and to say as to tone, touch, and pedal, totally unsuspicious of that wish of saying as little about it as possible, which she plainly read in the fair heroine's countenance.

They were soon joined by some of the gentlemen; and the very first of the early was Frank Churchill. In he walked, the first and the handsomest; and after paying his compliments, *en passant* to

Miss Bates and her niece, made his way directly to the opposite side of the circle, where sat Miss Woodhouse; and till he could find a seat by her would not sit at all. Emma divined what everybody present must be thinking. She was his object, and everybody must perceive it. She introduced him to her friend Miss Smith, and, at convenient moments afterwards, heard what each thought of the other. 'He had never seen so lovely a face, and was delighted with her *naïveté*.' And she – 'only to be sure it was paying him too great a compliment, but she did think there were some looks a little like Mr Elton.' Emma restrained her indignation, and only turned from her in silence.

Smiles of intelligence passed between her and the gentleman on first glancing towards Miss Fairfax; but it was most prudent to avoid speech. He told her that he had been impatient to leave the dining-room – hated sitting long – was always the first to move when he could – that his father, Mr Knightley, Mr Cox, and Mr Cole, were left very busy over parish business – that as long as he had stayed, however, it had been pleasant enough, as he had found them in general a set of gentlemanlike, sensible men; and spoke so handsomely of Highbury altogether – thought it so abundant in agreeable families – that Emma began to feel she had been used to despise the place rather too much. She questioned him as to the society in Yorkshire, the extent of the neighbourhood about Enscombe, and the sort; and could make out from his answers that, as far as Enscombe was concerned, there was very little going on, that their visitings were among a range of great families, none very near; and that even when days were fixed, and invitations accepted, it was an even chance that Mrs Churchill were not in health and spirits for going; that they made a point of visiting no fresh person; and that, though he had his separate engagements, it was not without difficulty, without considerable address, *at times,* that he could get away, or introduce an acquaintance for a night.

She saw that Enscombe could not satisfy, and that Highbury, taken at its best, might reasonably please a young man who had more retirement at home than he liked. His importance at Enscombe was very evident. He did not boast, but it naturally betrayed itself, that he had persuaded his aunt where his uncle could do nothing, and on her laughing and noticing it he owned that he believed (excepting one or two points) he could *with time* persuade her to anything. One of those points on which his influence failed he then mentioned. He had wanted very much to go abroad – had been very eager indeed to be allowed to travel – but she would not hear of it. This had happened the year before. *Now,* he said, he was beginning to have no longer the same wish.

The unpersuadable point, which he did not mention, Emma guessed to be good behaviour to his father.

'I have made a most wretched discovery,' said he, after a short pause. 'I have been here a week tomorrow – half my time. I never knew days fly so fast. A week tomorrow! and I have hardly begun to enjoy myself. But just got acquainted with Mrs Weston, and others. I hate the recollection.'

'Perhaps you may now begin to regret that you spent one whole day, out of so few, in having your hair cut.'

'No,' said he, smiling, 'that is no subject of regret at all. I have no pleasure in seeing my friends, unless I can believe myself fit to be seen.'

The rest of the gentlemen being now in the room, Emma found herself obliged to turn from him for a few minutes, and listen to Mr Cole. When Mr Cole had moved away, and her attention could be restored as before, she saw Frank Churchill looking intently across the room at Miss Fairfax, who was sitting exactly opposite.

'What is the matter?' said she.

He started. 'Thank you for rousing me,' he replied. 'I believe I have been very rude; but really Miss Fairfax has done her hair in so odd a way – so very odd a way – that I cannot keep my eyes from her. I never saw anything so *outrée*! Those curls! This must be a fancy of her own. I see nobody else looking like her. I must go and ask her whether it is an Irish fashion. Shall I? Yes, I will –

I declare I will; and you shall see how she takes it – whether she colours.'

He was gone immediately; and Emma soon saw him standing before Miss Fairfax, and talking to her; but as to its effect on the young lady, as he had improvidently placed himself exactly between them, exactly in front of Miss Fairfax, she could absolutely distinguish nothing.

Before he could return to his chair it was taken by Mrs Weston.

'This is the luxury of a large party,' said she; 'one can get near everybody, and say everything. My dear Emma, I am longing to talk to you. I have been making discoveries and forming plans, just like yourself, and I must tell them while the idea is fresh. Do you know how Miss Bates and her niece came here?'

'How! They were invited, were not they?'

'Oh yes – but how they were conveyed hither? the manner of their coming?'

'They walked, I conclude. How else could they come?'

'Very true. Well, a little while ago it occurred to me how very sad it would be to have Jane Fairfax walking home again, late at night, and cold as the nights are now. And as I looked at her, though I never saw her appear to more advantage, it struck me that she was heated, and would therefore be particularly liable to take cold. Poor girl! I could not bear the idea of it; so, as soon as Mr Weston came into the room, and I could get at him, I spoke to him about the carriage. You may guess how readily he came into my wishes; and having his approbation, I made my way directly to Miss Bates, to assure her that the carriage would be at her service before it took us home; for I thought it would be making her comfortable at once. Good soul! she was as grateful as possible, you may be sure. "Nobody was ever so fortunate as herself!" – but with many, many thanks – "there was no occasion to trouble us, for Mr Knightley's carriage had brought, and was to take them home again." I was quite surprised – very glad, I am sure; but really quite surprised. Such a very kind attention – and so thoughtful an attention! the sort of thing that so few men would think of. And, in short, from knowing his usual ways, I am very much inclined to think that it was for their accommodation the carriage was used at all. I do suspect he would not have had a pair of horses for himself, and that it was only as an excuse for assisting them.'

'Very likely,' said Emma, 'nothing more likely. I know no man more likely than Mr Knightley to do the sort of thing – to do anything really good-natured, useful, considerate, or benevolent. He is not a gallant man, but he is a very humane one; and this, considering Jane Fairfax's ill health, would appear a case of humanity to him; and for an act of unostentatious kindness there is nobody whom I would fix on more than on Mr Knightley. I know he had horses today, for we arrived together; and I laughed at him about it, but he said not a word that could betray.'

'Well,' said Mrs Weston, smiling, 'you give him credit for more simple, disinterested benevolence in this instance than I do; for while Miss Bates was speaking, a suspicion darted into my head, and I have never been able to get it out again. The more I think of it, the more probable it appears. In short, I have made a match between Mr Knightley and Jane Fairfax. See the consequence of keeping you company! What do you say to it?'

'Mr Knightley and Jane Fairfax!' exclaimed Emma. 'Dear Mrs Weston, how could you think of such a thing? Mr Knightley! Mr Knightley must not marry! You would not have little Henry cut out from Donwell? Oh no, no; Henry must have Donwell. I cannot at all consent to Mr Knightley's marrying; and I am sure it is not at all likely; I am amazed that you should think of such a thing.'

'My dear Emma, I have told you what led me to think of it. I do not want the match – I do not want to injure dear little Henry – but the idea has been given me by circumstances; and if Mr Knightley really wished to marry, you would not have him refrain on Henry's account, a boy of six years old, who knows nothing of the matter?'

'Yes, I would. I could not bear to have Henry supplanted. Mr Knightley marry! No, I have never had such an idea, and I cannot adopt it now. And Jane Fairfax, too, of all women!'

'Nay, she has always been a first favourite with him, as you very well know.'

'But the imprudence of such a match!'

'I am not speaking of its prudence – merely its probability.'

'I see no probability in it, unless you have any better foundation than what you mention. His good nature, his humanity, as I tell you, would be quite enough to account for the horses. He has a great regard for the Bateses, you know, independent of Jane Fairfax – and is always glad to show them attention. My dear Mrs Weston, do not take to match making. You do it very ill. Jane Fairfax mistress of the Abbey? Oh no, no – every feeling revolts. For his own sake, I would not have him do so mad a thing.'

'Imprudent, if you please – but not mad. Excepting inequality of fortune, and perhaps a little disparity of age, I can see nothing unsuitable.'

'But Mr Knightley does not want to marry. I am sure he has not the least idea of it. Do not put it into his head. Why should he marry? He is as happy as possible by himself; with his farm, and his sheep, and his library, and all the parish to manage; and he is extremely fond of his brother's children. He has no occasion to marry, either to fill up his time or his heart.'

'My dear Emma, as long as he thinks so, it is so; but if he really loves Jane Fairfax – '

'Nonsense! He does not care about Jane Fairfax. In the way of love, I am sure he does not. He would do any good to her, or her family; but – '

'Well,' said Mrs Weston, laughing, 'perhaps the greatest good he could do them would be to give Jane such a respectable home.'

'If it would be good to her I am sure it would be evil to himself – a very shameful and degrading connection. How would he bear to have Miss Bates belonging to him? To have her haunting the Abbey, and thanking him all day long for his great kindness in marrying Jane? "So very kind and obliging! But he always had been such a very kind neighbour." And then fly off, through half a sentence, to her mother's old petticoat. "Not that it was such a very old petticoat either – for still it would last a great while – and, indeed, she must thankfully say that their petticoats were all very strong." '

'For shame, Emma! Do not mimic her. You divert me against my conscience. And, upon my word, I do not think Mr Knightley would be much disturbed by Miss Bates. Little things do not irritate him. She might talk on; and if he wanted to say anything himself, he would only talk louder, and drown her voice. But the question is not, whether it would be a bad connection for him, but whether he wishes it; and I think he does. I have heard him speak, and so must you, so very highly of Jane Fairfax! The interest he takes in her – his anxiety about her health – his concern that she should have no happier prospect! I have heard him express himself so warmly on those points. Such an admirer of her performance on the pianoforte, and of her voice. I have heard him say that he could listen to her for ever. Oh! and I had almost forgotten one idea that occurred to me – this pianoforte that has been sent here by somebody – though we have all been so well satisfied to consider it a present from the Campbells, may it not be from Mr Knightley? I cannot help suspecting him. I think he is just the person to do it, even without being in love.'

'Then it can be no argument to prove that he is in love. But I do not think it is at all a likely thing for him to do. Mr Knightley does nothing mysteriously.'

'I have heard him lamenting her having no instrument, repeatedly; oftener than I should suppose such a circumstance would in the common course of things occur to him.'

'Very well; and if he had intended to give her one, he would have told her so.'

'There might be scruples of delicacy, my dear Emma. I have a very strong notion that it comes from him. I am sure he was particularly silent when Mrs Cole told us of it at dinner.'

'You take up an idea, Mrs Weston, and run away with it, as you have many a time reproached me with doing. I see no sign of attachment. I believe nothing of the pianoforte, and proof only shall convince me that Mr Knightley has any thought of marrying Jane Fairfax.'

They combated the point some time longer in the same way, Emma rather gaining ground over the mind of her friend; for Mrs Weston was the most used of the two to yield; till a little bustle in the room showed them that tea was over, and the instrument in preparation; and at the same moment, Mr Cole approaching to entreat Miss Woodhouse would do them the honour of trying it. Frank Churchill, of whom, in the eagerness of her conversation with Mrs Weston, she had been seeing nothing, except that he had found a seat by Miss Fairfax, followed Mr Cole, to add his very pressing entreaties; and as, in every respect, it suited Emma best to lead, she gave a very proper compliance.

She knew the limitation of her own powers too well to attempt more than she could perform with credit; she wanted neither taste nor spirit in the little things which are generally acceptable, and could accompany her own voice well. One accompaniment to her song took her agreeably by surprise; a second, slightly, but correctly taken by Frank Churchill. Her pardon was duly begged at the close of the song, and everything usual followed. He was accused of having a delightful voice, and a perfect knowledge of music, which was properly denied; and that he knew nothing of the matter, and had no voice at all, roundly asserted. They sang together once more: and Emma would then resign her place to Miss Fairfax, whose performance, both vocal and instrumental, she never could attempt to conceal from herself, was infinitely superior to her own.

With mixed feelings she seated herself at a little distance from the numbers round the instrument, to listen. Frank Churchill sang again. They had sung together once or twice, it appeared, at Weymouth. But the sight of Mr Knightley among the most attentive soon drew away half Emma's mind; and she fell into a train of thinking on the subject of Mrs Weston's suspicions, to which the sweet sounds of the united voices gave only momentary interruptions. Her objections to Mr Knightley's marrying did not in the least subside. She could see nothing but evil in it. It would be a great disappointment to Mr John Knightley, consequently to Isabella. A real injury to the children – a most mortifying change and material loss to them all – a very great deduction from her father's daily comfort – and, as to herself, she could not at all endure the idea of Jane Fairfax at Donwell Abbey. A Mrs Knightley for them all to give way to! No – Mr Knightley must never marry. Little Henry must remain the heir of Donwell.

Presently Mr Knightley looked back, and came and sat down by her. They talked at first only of the performance. His admiration was certainly very warm; yet she thought, but for Mrs Weston, it would not have struck her. As a sort of touchstone, however, she began to speak of his kindness in conveying the aunt and niece; and though his answer was in the spirit of cutting the matter short, she believed it to indicate only his disinclination to dwell on any kindness of his own.

'I often feel concern,' said she, 'that I dare not make our carriage more useful on such occasions. It is not that I am without the wish; but you know how impossible my father would deem it that James should put to for such a purpose.'

'Quite out of the question, quite out of the question,' he replied; 'but you must often wish it, I am sure.' And he smiled with such seeming pleasure at the conviction, that she must proceed another step.

'This present from the Campbells,' said she – 'this pianoforte is very kindly given.'

'Yes,' he replied, and without the smallest apparent embarrassment. 'But they would have done better had they given her notice of it. Surprises are foolish things. The pleasure is not enhanced, and the inconvenience is often considerable. I should have expected better judgement in Colonel Campbell.'

From that moment Emma could have taken her oath that Mr Knightley had had no concern in giving the instrument. But whether he were entirely free from peculiar attachment – whether there were no actual preference – remained a little longer doubtful. Towards the end of Jane's second song her voice grew thick.

'That will do,' said he, when it was finished, thinking aloud; 'you have sung quite enough for one evening; now be quiet.'

Another song, however, was begged for. 'One more; they would not fatigue Miss Fairfax on any account, and would only ask for one more.' And Frank Churchill was heard to say, 'I think you could manage this without effort; the first part is so very trifling. The strength of the song falls on the second.'

Mr Knightley grew angry.

'That fellow,' said he, indignantly, 'thinks of nothing but showing off his own voice. This must not be.' And touching Miss Bates, who at that moment passed near, 'Miss Bates, are you mad, to let your niece sing herself hoarse in this manner? Go, and interfere. They have no mercy on her.'

Miss Bates, in her real anxiety for Jane, could hardly stay even to be grateful, before she stepped forward and put an end to all further singing. Here ceased the concert part of the evening, for Miss Woodhouse and Miss Fairfax were the only young lady performers; but soon (within five minutes) the proposal of dancing – originating nobody exactly knew where – was so effectually promoted by Mr and Mrs Cole that everything was rapidly clearing away, to give proper space. Mrs Weston, capital in her country-dances, was seated, and beginning an irresistible waltz; and Frank Churchill, coming up with most becoming gallantry to Emma, had secured her hand, and led her up to the top.

While waiting till the other young people could pair themselves off, Emma found time, in spite of the compliments she was receiving on her voice and her taste, to look about, and see what became of Mr Knightley. This would be a trial. He was no dancer in general. If he were to be very alert in engaging Jane Fairfax now it might augur something. There was no immediate appearance. No; he was talking to Mrs Cole – he was looking on unconcerned; Jane was asked by somebody else, and he was still talking to Mrs Cole.

Emma had no longer an alarm for Henry; his interest was yet safe; and she led off the dance with genuine spirit and enjoyment. Not more than five couples could be mustered; but the rarity and the suddenness of it made it very delightful, and she found herself well matched in a partner. They were a couple worth looking at.

Two dances, unfortunately, were all that could be allowed. It was growing late, and Miss Bates became anxious to get home, on her mother's account. After some attempts, therefore, to be permitted to begin again, they were obliged to thank Mrs Weston, look sorrowful, and have done.

'Perhaps it is as well,' said Frank Churchill, as he attended Emma to her carriage. 'I must have asked Miss Fairfax, and her languid dancing would not have agreed with me after yours.'

Chapter 27

Emma did not repent her condescension in going to the Coles. The visit afforded her many pleasant recollections the next day, and all that she might be supposed to have lost on the side of dignified seclusion must be amply repaid in the splendour of popularity. She must have delighted the Coles – worthy people; who deserved to be made happy! and left a name behind her that would not soon die away.

Perfect happiness, even in memory, is not common; and there were two points on which she was not quite easy. She doubted whether she had not transgressed the duty of woman by woman, in betraying her suspicions of Jane Fairfax's feelings to Frank Churchill. It was hardly right; but it had been so strong an idea that it would escape her, and his submission to all that she told was a compliment to her penetration, which made it difficult for her to be quite certain that she ought to have held her tongue.

The other circumstance of regret related also to Jane Fairfax, and there she had no doubt. She did unfeignedly and unequivocally regret the inferiority of her own playing and singing. She did most heartily grieve over the idleness of her childhood; and sat down and practised vigorously an hour and a half.

She was then interrupted by Harriet's coming in; and if Harriet's praise could have satisfied her, she might soon have been comforted.

'Oh, if I could but play as well as you and Miss Fairfax!'

'Don't class us together, Harriet. My playing is no more like hers than a lamp is like sunshine.'

'O dear, I think you play the best of the two. I think you play quite as well as she does. I am sure I had much rather hear you. Everybody last night said how well you played.'

'Those who knew anything about it must have felt the difference. The truth is, Harriet, that my playing is just good enough to be praised, but Jane Fairfax's is much beyond it.'

'Well, I always shall think that you play quite as well as she does, or that if there is any difference nobody would ever find it out. Mr Cole said how much taste you had, and Mr Frank Churchill talked a great deal about your taste, and that he valued taste much more than execution.'

'Ah, but Jane Fairfax has them both, Harriet.'

'Are you sure? I saw she had execution, but I did not know she had any taste. Nobody talked about it; and I hate Italian singing: there is no understanding a word of it. Besides, if she does play so very well, you know, it is no more than she is obliged to do, because she will have to teach. The Coxes were wondering last night whether she would get into any great family. How did you think the Coxes looked?'

'Just as they always do – very vulgar.'

'They told me something,' said Harriet, rather hesitatingly, 'but it is nothing of any consequence.'

Emma was obliged to ask what they had told her, though fearful of its producing Mr Elton.

'They told me that Mr Martin dined with them last Saturday.'

'Oh!'

'He came to their father upon some business, and he asked him to stay to dinner.'

'Oh!'

'They talked a great deal about him, especially Anne Cox. I do not know what she meant, but she asked me if I thought I should go and stay there again next summer.'

'She meant to be impertinently curious, just as such an Anne Cox should be.'

'She said he was very agreeable the day he dined there. He sat by her at dinner. Miss Nash thinks either of the Coxes would be very glad to marry him.'

'Very likely: I think they are, without exception, the most vulgar girls in Highbury.'

Harriet had business at Ford's. Emma thought it most prudent to go with her. Another accidental meeting with the Martins was possible, and in her present state, would be dangerous.

Harriet, tempted by everything, and swayed by half a word, was always very long at a purchase; and while she was still hanging over muslins and changing her mind Emma went to the door for amusement. Much could not be hoped from the traffic of even the busiest part of Highbury: Mr Perry walking hastily by; Mr William Cox letting himself in at the office-door; Mr Cole's carriage horses returning from exercise; or a stray letter-boy on an obstinate mule, were the liveliest objects she could presume to expect; and when her eyes fell only on the butcher with his tray, a tidy old woman travelling homewards from shop with her full basket, two curs quarrelling over a dirty bone, and a string of dawdling children round the baker's little bow-window eyeing the gingerbread, she knew she had no reason to complain, and was amused enough; quite enough still to stand at the door. A mind lively and at ease can do with seeing nothing, and can see nothing that does not answer.

She looked down the Randalls Road. The scene enlarged: two persons appeared: Mrs Weston and her son-in-law. They were walking into Highbury – to Hartfield of course; they were stopping, however, in the first place at Mrs Bates's, whose house was a little nearer Randalls than Ford's, and had all but knocked when Emma caught their eye. Immediately they crossed the road and came forward to her; and the agreeableness of yesterday's engagement seemed to give fresh pleasure to the present meeting. Mrs Weston informed her that she was going to call on the Bateses, in order to hear the new instrument.

'For my companion tells me,' said she, 'that I absolutely promised Miss Bates last night that I would come this morning. I was not aware of it myself. I did not know that I had fixed a day; but as he says I did I am going now.'

'And while Mrs Weston pays her visit, I may be allowed, I hope,' said Frank Churchill, 'to join your party and wait for her at Hartfield, if you are going home.'

Mrs Weston was disappointed.

'I thought you meant to go with me. They would be very much pleased.'

'Me! I should be quite in the way. But, perhaps, I may be equally in the way here. Miss Woodhouse looks as if she did not want me. My aunt always sends me off when she is shopping. She says I fidget her to death; and Miss Woodhouse looks as if she could almost say the same. What am I to do?'

'I am here on no business of my own,' said Emma, 'I am only waiting for my friend. She will probably have soon done, and then we shall go home. But you had better go with Mrs Weston and hear the instrument.'

'Well, if you advise it. But' (with a smile) 'if Colonel Campbell should have employed a careless friend, and if it should prove to have an indifferent tone, what shall I say? I shall be no support to Mrs Weston. She might do very well by herself. A disagreeable truth would be palatable through her lips, but I am the wretchedest being in the world at a civil falsehood.'

'I do not believe any such thing,' replied Emma; 'I am persuaded that you can be as insincere as your neighbours, when it is necessary; but there is no reason to suppose the instrument is indifferent. Quite otherwise, indeed, if I understood Miss Fairfax's opinion last night.'

'Do come with me,' said Mrs Weston, 'if it be not very disagreeable to you. It need not detain us long. We will go to Hartfield afterwards. We will follow them to Hartfield. I really wish you to call with me: it will be felt so great an attention – and I always thought you meant it.'

He could say no more; and, with the hope of Hartfield to reward him, returned with Mrs Weston to Mrs Bates's door. Emma watched them in, and then joined Harriet at the interesting counter, trying, with all the force of her own mind, to convince her that if she wanted plain muslin, it was of no use to look at figured; and that a blue ribbon, be it ever so beautiful, would still never match her yellow pattern. At last it was all settled, even to the destination of the parcel.

'Should I send it to Mrs Goddard's, ma'am?' asked Mrs Ford. 'Yes – no – yes, to Mrs Goddard's. Only my pattern gown is at Hartfield. No, you shall send it to Hartfield, if you please. But then Mrs Goddard will want to see it. And I could take the pattern gown home any day. But I shall want the ribbon directly; so it had better go to Hartfield – at least the ribbon. You could make it into two parcels, Mrs Ford, could not you?'

'It is not worth while, Harriet, to give Mrs Ford the trouble of two parcels.'

'No more it is.'

'No trouble in the world, ma'am,' said the obliging Mrs Ford.

'Oh, but indeed I would much rather have it only in one. Then, if you please, you shall send it all to Mrs Goddard's – I do not know – no, I think, Miss Woodhouse, I may just as well have it sent to Hartfield, and take it home with me at night. What do you advise?'

'That you do not give another half-second to the subject. To Hartfield, if you please, Mrs Ford.'

'Aye, that will be much best,' said Harriet, quite satisfied; 'I should not at all like to have it sent to Mrs Goddard's.'

Voices approached the shop, or rather, one voice and two ladies; Mrs Weston and Miss Bates met them at the door.

'My dear Miss Woodhouse,' said the latter, 'I am just run across to entreat the favour of you to come and sit down with us a little while, and give us your opinion of our new instrument – you and Miss Smith. How do you do, Miss Smith? Very well, I thank you. And I begged Mrs Weston to come with me, that I might be sure of succeeding.'

'I hope Mrs Bates and Miss Fairfax are – '

'Very well, I am much obliged to you. My mother is delight-fully well; and Jane caught no cold last night. How is Mr Wood-house? I am so glad to hear such a good account. Mrs Weston told me you were here. "Oh, then," said I, "I must run across; I am sure Miss Woodhouse will allow me just to run across and entreat her to come in: my mother will be so very happy to see her; and now we are such a nice party, she cannot refuse." "Aye, pray do," said Mr Frank Churchill, "Miss Woodhouse's opinion of the instrument will be worth having." "But," said I "I shall be more sure of succeeding if one of you will go with me." "Oh," said he, "wait half a minute, till I have finished my job;" for, would you believe it, Miss Woodhouse, there he is, in the most obliging manner in the world, fastening in the rivet of my mother's specta-cles. The rivet came out, you know, this morning; so very obliging! For my mother had no use of her spectacles – could not put them on. And, by the by, everybody ought to have two pair of spectacles; they should indeed. Jane said so. I meant to take them over to John Saunders the first thing I did, but something or other hindered me all the morning; first one thing, then another, there is no saying what: you know. At one time Patty came to say she thought the kitchen chimney wanted sweeping. "Oh," said I, "Patty, do not come with your bad news to me. Here is the rivet of your mistress's spectacles out." Then the baked apples came home; Mrs Wallis sent them by her boy; they are extremely civil and obliging to us, the Wallises, always. I have heard some people say that Mrs Wallis can be uncivil and give a very rude answer; but we have never known anything but the greatest attention from them. And it cannot be for the value of our custom now, for what is our consumption of bread, you know? only three of us. Besides, dear Jane at present – and she really eats nothing – makes such a shocking breakfast, you would be quite frightened if you saw it. I dare not let my mother know how little she eats; so I say one thing, and then I say another, and it passes off. But about the middle of the day she gets hungry, and there is nothing she likes so well as these baked apples, and they are extremely wholesome; for I took the opportunity the other day of asking Mr Perry; I happened to meet him in the street. Not that I had any doubt before. I have so often heard Mr Woodhouse recommend a baked apple. I believe it is the only way that Mr Woodhouse thinks the fruit thoroughly wholesome. We have apples-dumplings, however, very often. Patty makes an excellent apple-dumpling. Well, Mrs Weston, you have prevailed, I hope, and these ladies will oblige us.'

Emma would be 'very happy to wait on Mrs Bates,' etc., and they did at last move out of the shop, with no further delay from Miss Bates than, 'How do you do, Mrs Ford? I beg your pardon; I did not see you before. I hear you have a charming collection of new ribbons from town. Jane came back delighted yesterday. Thank ye, the gloves do very well – only a little too large about the wrist; but Jane is taking them in.'

'What was I talking of?' said she, beginning again when they were all in the street.

Emma wondered on what, of all the medley, she would fix.

'I declare I cannot recollect what I was talking of. Oh, my mother's spectacles! So very obliging of Mr Frank Churchill! "Oh," said he, "I do think I can fasten the rivet; I like a job of this kind excessively." Which, you know, showed him to be so very – Indeed I must say that, much as I had heard of him before, and much as I had expected, he very far exceeds anything – I do congratulate you, Mrs Weston, most warmly. He seems everything the fondest parent could – "Oh!" said he, "I can fasten the rivet. I like a job of that sort excessively." I never shall forget his manner. And when I brought out the baked apples from the closet, and hoped our friends would be so very obliging as to take some, "Oh!" said he directly, "there is nothing in the way of fruit half so good, and these are the finest-looking home-baked apples I ever saw in my life." That, you know, was so very – And I am sure, by his manner, it was no compliment. Indeed they are very delightful apples, and Mrs Wallis does them full justice, only we do not have them baked more than twice, and Mr Woodhouse made us promise to have them done three times; but Miss Woodhouse will be so good as not to mention it. The apples themselves are the very finest sort for baking, beyond a doubt; all from Donwell – some of Mr Knightley's most liberal supply. He sends us a sack every year; and certainly there never was such a keeping apple anywhere as one of his trees – I believe there is two of them. My mother says the orchard was always famous in her younger days. But I was really quite shocked the other day; for Mr Knightley called one morning, and Jane was eating these apples, and we talked about them, and said how much she enjoyed them, and he asked whether we were not got to the end of our stock. "I am sure you must be," said he, "and I will send you another supply; for I have a great many more than I can ever use. William Larkins let me keep a larger quantity than usual this year. I will send you some more, before they get good for nothing." So I begged he would not – for really as to ours being gone, I could not absolutely say that we had a great many left – it was half a dozen indeed; but they should be all kept for Jane; and I could not at all bear that he should be sending us more, so liberal as he had been already; and Jane said the same. And when he was gone she almost quarrelled with me – no, I should not say quarrelled, for we never had quarrel in our lives – but she was quite distressed that I had owned the apples were so nearly gone; she wished I had made him believe we had a great many left. "Oh," said I, "my dear, I did say as much as I could." However, the very same evening, William Larkins came over with a large basket of apples, the same sort of apples, a bushel at least, and I was very much obliged, and went down and spoke to William Larkins, and said everything, as you may suppose. William Larkins is such an old acquaintance! I am always glad to see him. But, however, I found afterwards from Patty that William said it was all the apples of *that* sort his master had; he had brought them all – and now his master had not one left to bake or boil. William did not seem to mind it himself, he was so pleased to think his master had sold so many; for William, you know, thinks more of his master's profit than anything; but Mrs Hodges, he said, was quite displeased at their being all sent away. She could not bear that her master should not be able to have another apple-tart this spring. He told Patty this, but bid her not mind it, and be sure not to say anything to us about it, for Mrs Hodges *would* be cross sometimes and as long as so many sacks were sold it did not signify who ate the remainder. And so Patty told me, and I was excessively shocked indeed! I would not have Mr Knightley know anything about it for the world! He would be so very – I wanted to keep it from Jane's knowledge; but, unluckily, I had mentioned it before I was aware.'

Miss Bates had just done as Patty opened the door; and her visitors walked upstairs, without having any regular narration to attend to, pursued only by the sounds of her desultory goodwill.

'Pray, take care, Mrs Weston, there is a step at the turning. Pray, take care, Miss Woodhouse, ours is rather a dark staircase –

rather darker and narrower than one could wish. Miss Smith, pray take care. Miss Woodhouse, I am quite concerned, I am sure you hit your foot. Miss Smith, the step at the turning.'

Chapter 28

The appearance of the little sitting-room as they entered was tranquillity itself; Mrs Bates, deprived of her usual employment, slumbering on one side of the fire, Frank Churchill, at a table, near her, most deedily occupied about her spectacles, and Jane Fairfax, standing with her back to them, intent on her pianoforte.

Busy as he was, however, the young man was yet able to show a most happy countenance on seeing Emma again.

'This is a pleasure,' said he, in rather a low voice, 'coming at least ten minutes earlier than I had calculated. You find me trying to be useful; tell me if you think I shall succeed.'

'What!' said Mrs Weston, 'have you not finished it yet? You would not earn a very good livelihood as a working silversmith at this rate.'

'I have not been working uninterruptedly,' he replied, 'I have been assisting Miss Fairfax in trying to make her instrument stand steadily; it was not quite firm; an unevenness in the floor, I believe. You see we have been wedging one leg with paper. This was very kind of you to be persuaded to come. I was almost afraid you would be hurrying home.'

He contrived that she should be seated by him; and was sufficiently employed in looking out the best baked apple for her, and trying to make her help or advise him in his work, till Jane Fairfax was quite ready to sit down to the pianoforte again. That she was not immediately ready Emma did suspect to arise from the state of her nerves; she had not yet possessed the instrument long enough to touch it without emotion; she must reason herself into the power of performance; and Emma could not but pity such feelings, whatever their origin, and could not but resolve never to expose them to her neighbour again.

At last Jane began, and though the first bars were feebly given, the powers of the instrument were gradually done full justice to. Mrs Weston had been delighted before, and was delighted again; Emma joined her in all her praise; and the pianoforte, with every proper discrimination, was pronounced to be altogether of the highest promise.

'Whoever Colonel Campbell might emsploy,' said Frank Churchill, with a smile at Emma, 'the person has not chosen ill. I heard a good deal of Colonel Campbell's taste at Weymouth; and the softness of the upper notes I am sure is exactly what he and *all that party* would particularly prize. I dare say, Miss Fairfax, that he either gave his friend very minute directions, or wrote to Broadwood himself. Do not you think so?'

Jane did not look round. She was not obliged to hear. Mrs Weston had been speaking to her at the same moment.

'It is not fair,' said Emma, in a whisper; 'mine was a random guess. Do not distress her.'

He shook his head with a smile, and looked as if he had very little doubt and very little mercy. Soon afterwards he began again: 'How much your friends in Ireland must be enjoying your pleasure on this occasion, Miss Fairfax. I dare say they often think of you, and wonder which will be the day, the precise day, of the instrument's coming to hand. Do you imagine Colonel Campbell knows the business to be going forward just at this time? Do you imagine it to be the consequence of an immediate commission from him, or that he may have sent only a general direction, an order indefinite as to time, to depend upon contingencies and conveniences?'

He paused. She could not but hear; she could not avoid answering: 'Till I have a letter from Colonel Campbell,' said she, in a voice of forced calmness, 'I can imagine nothing with any confidence. It must be all conjecture.'

'Conjecture! aye, sometimes one conjectures right, and sometimes one conjectures wrong. I wish I could conjecture how soon I shall make this rivet quite firm. What nonsense one talks, Miss Woodhouse, when hard at work, if one talks at all; your real workmen, I suppose, hold their tongues; but we, gentlemen labourers, if we get hold of a word – Miss Fairfax said something about conjecturing. There, it is done. I have the pleasure, madam' (to Mrs Bates), 'of restoring your spectacles, healed for the present.'

He was very warmly thanked both by mother and daughter; to escape a little from the latter he went to the pianoforte, and begged Miss Fairfax, who was still sitting at it, to play something more.

'If you are very kind,' said he, 'it will be one of the waltzes we danced last night; let me live them over again. You did not enjoy them as I did: you appeared tired the whole time. I believe you were glad we danced no longer; but I would have given worlds – all the worlds one ever has to give – for another half-hour.'

She played.

'What felicity it is to hear a tune again which *has* made one happy! If I mistake not, that was danced at Weymouth.'

She looked up at him for a moment, coloured deeply, and played something else. He took some music from a chair near the pianoforte, and turning to Emma, said: 'Here is something quite new to me. Do you know it? Cramer. And here are a new set of Irish melodies. That, from such a quarter, one might expect. This was all sent with the instrument. Very thoughtful of Colonel Campbell, was not it? He knew Miss Fairfax could have no music here. I honour that part of the attention particularly; it shows it to have been so thoroughly from the heart. Nothing hastily done, nothing incomplete. True affection only could have prompted it.'

Emma wished he would be less pointed, yet could not help being amused, and, when, on glancing her eye towards Jane Fairfax, she caught the remains of a smile; when she saw that, with all the deep blush of consciousness, there had been a smile of secret delight, she had less scruple in the amusement, and much less compunction with respect to her. This amiable, upright, perfect Jane Fairfax, was apparently cherishing very reprehensible feelings.

He brought all the music to her, and they looked it over together. Emma took the opportunity of whispering: 'You speak too plain. She must understand you.'

'I hope she does. I would have her understand me. I am not in the least ashamed of my meaning.'

'But, really, I am half ashamed, and wish I had never taken up the idea.'

'I am very glad you did, and that you communicated it to me. I have now a key to all her odd looks and ways. Leave shame to her. If she does wrong, she ought to feel it.'

'She is not entirely without it, I think.'

'I do not see much sign of it. She is playing "Robin Adair" at this moment – *his* favourite.'

Shortly afterwards Miss Bates, passing near the window, descried Mr Knightley on horseback not far off.

'Mr Knightley, I declare! I must speak to him, if possible, just to thank him. I will not open the window here; it would give you all cold; but I can go into my mother's room, you know. I dare say he will come in when he knows who is here. Quite delightful to have you all meet so! Our little room so honoured!'

She was in the adjoining chamber while she still spoke, and, opening the casement there, immediately called Mr Knightley's attention, and every syllable of their conversation was as distinctly heard by the others as if it had passed within the same apartment.

'How d'ye do? How d'ye do? Very well, I thank you. So obliged to you for the carriage last night. We were just in time; my mother just ready for us. Pray come in; do come in. You will find some friends here.'

So began Miss Bates; and Mr Knightley seemed determined to be heard in his turn, for most resolutely and commandingly did he say: 'How is your niece, Miss Bates? I want to enquire after you all, but particularly your niece. How is Miss Fairfax? I hope she caught no cold last night? How is she today? Tell me how Miss Fairfax is.'

And Miss Bates was obliged to give a direct answer before he would hear her in anything else. The listeners were amused; and Mrs Weston gave Emma a look of particular meaning. But Emma still shook her head in steady scepticism.

'So obliged to you! so very much obliged to you for the carriage,' resumed Miss Bates.

He cut her short with, 'I am going to Kingston. Can I do anything for you?'

'Oh, dear! Kingston – are you? Mrs Cole was saying the other day she wanted something from Kingston.'

'Mrs Cole has servants to send; can I do anything for *you*?'

'No, I thank you. But do come in. Who do you think is here? Miss Woodhouse and Miss Smith; so kind as to call to hear the new pianoforte. Do put up your horse at the "Crown," and come in.'

'Well,' said he, in a deliberating manner, 'for five minutes, perhaps.'

'And here is Mrs Weston and Mr Frank Churchill too! Quite delightful! so many friends!'

'No, not now, I thank you. I could not stay two minutes. I must get on to Kingston as fast as I can.'

'Oh, do come in! They will be so very happy to see you.'

'No, no; your room is full enough! I will call another day and hear the pianoforte.'

'Well, I am so sorry! Oh, Mr Knightley, what a delightful party last night! how extremely pleasant! Did you ever see such dancing? Was not it delightful? Miss Woodhouse and Mr Frank Churchill; I never saw anything equal to it.'

'Oh, very delightful, indeed! I can say nothing less, for I suppose Miss Woodhouse and Mr Frank Churchill are hearing everything that passes. And' (raising his voice still more) 'I do not see why Miss Fairfax should not be mentioned too. I think Miss Fairfax dances very well; and Mrs Weston is the very best country-dance player, without exception, in England. Now, if your friends have my gratitude, they will say something pretty loud about you and me in return; but I cannot stay to hear it.'

'Oh, Mr Knightley, one moment more; something of consequence – so shocked! Jane and I are both so shocked about the apples!'

'What is the matter now?'

'To think of your sending us all your store apples! You said you had a great many, and now you have not one left. We really are so shocked! Mrs Hodges may well be angry. William Larkins mentioned it here. You should not have done it, indeed you should not. Ah, he is off! He never can bear to be thanked. But I thought he would have stayed now, and it would have been a pity not to have mentioned – well' (returning to the room), 'I have not been able to succeed. Mr Knightley cannot stop. He is going to Kingston. He asked me if he could do anything '

Yes,' said Jane, 'we heard his kind offers; we heard everything.'

'Oh, yes, my dear, I dare say you might; because, you know, the door was open, and the window was open, and Mr Knightley spoke loud. You must have heard everything, to be sure. "Can I do anything for you at Kingston?" said he; so I just mentioned – Oh, Miss Woodhouse, must you be going? You seem but just come; so very obliging of you.'

Emma found it really time to be at home; the visit had already lasted long; and, on examining watches, so much of the morning was perceived to be gone, that Mrs Weston and her companion, taking leave also, could allow themselves only to walk with the two young ladies to Hartfield gates before they set off for Randalls.

Chapter 29

It may be possible to do without dancing entirely. Instances have been known of young people passing many, many months successively without being at any ball of any description, and no material injury accrue either to body or mind; but when a beginning is made – when the felicities of rapid motion have once been, though slightly, felt – it must be a very heavy set that does not ask for more.

Frank Churchill had danced once at Highbury, and longed to dance again; and the last half-hour of an evening which Mr Woodhouse was persuaded to spend with his daughter at Randalls was passed by the two young people in schemes on the subject. Frank's was the first idea, and his the greatest zeal in pursuing it; for the lady was the best judge of the difficulties, and the most solicitous for accommodation and appearance. But still she had inclination enough for showing people again how delightfully Mr Frank Churchill and Miss Woodhouse danced – for doing that in which she need not blush to compare herself with Jane Fairfax – and even for simple dancing itself, without any of the wicked aids of vanity – to assist him first in pacing out the room they were in to see what it could be made to hold – and then in taking the dimensions of the other parlour, in the hope of discovering, in spite of all that Mr Weston could say of their exactly equal size, that it was a little the largest.

His first proposition and request, that the dance begun at Mr Cole's should be finished there – that the same party should be collected, and the same musician engaged – met with the readiest acquiescence. Mr Weston entered into the idea with thorough enjoyment, and Mrs Weston most willingly undertook to play as long as they could wish to dance; and the interesting employment had followed, of reckoning up exactly who there would be, and portioning out the indispensable division of space to every couple.

'You and Miss Smith and Miss Fairfax will be three, and the two Miss Coxes five,' had been repeated many times over. 'And there will be the two Gilberts, young Cox, my father, and myself, besides Mr Knightley. Yes, that will be quite enough for pleasure. You and Miss Smith and Miss Fairfax will be three, and the two Miss Coxes five, and for five couple there will be plenty of room.'

But soon it came to be on one side: 'But will there be good room for five couple? I really do not think there will.'

On another: 'And, after all, five couple are not enough to make it worth while to stand up. Five couple are nothing when one thinks seriously about it. It will not do to *invite* five couple. It can be allowable only as the thought of the moment.'

Somebody said that *Miss* Gilbert was expected at her brother's, and must be invited with the rest. Somebody else believed *Mrs* Gilbert would have danced the other evening if she had been asked. A word was put in for a second young Cox! and at last, Mr Weston naming one family of cousins who must be included, and another of very old acquaintance who could not be left out, it became a certainty that the five couple would be at least ten, and a very interesting speculation in what possible manner they could be disposed of.

The doors of the two rooms were just opposite each other. 'Might not they use both rooms, and dance across the passage?' It seemed the best scheme; and yet it was not so good but that many of them wanted a better. Emma said it would be awkward; Mrs Weston was in distress about the supper; and Mr Woodhouse opposed it earnestly on the score of health. It made him so very unhappy, indeed, that it could not be persevered in.

'Oh, no,' said he, 'it would be the extreme of imprudence. I could not bear it for Emma! Emma is not strong. She would catch a dreadful cold. So would poor little Harriet. So you would all. Mrs Weston, you would be quite laid up; do not let them talk of such a wild thing; pray do not let them talk of it. That young man' (speaking lower) 'is very thoughtless. Do not tell his father, but that young man is not quite the thing. He has been opening the doors very often this evening, and keeping them open very inconsiderately. He does not think of the draught. I do not mean to set you against him, but indeed he is not quite the thing.'

Mrs Weston was sorry for such a charge. She knew the importance of it, and said everything in her power to do it away. Every door was now closed, the passage plan given up, and the first scheme, of dancing only in the room they were in, resorted to again; and with such goodwill on Frank Churchill's part, that the space which a quarter of an hour before had been deemed barely sufficient for five couple was now endeavoured to be made out quite enough for ten.

'We were too magnificent,' said he. 'We allowed unnecessary room. Ten couple may stand here very well.'

Emma demurred. 'It would be a crowd – a sad crowd; and what could be worse than dancing without space to turn in?'

'Very true,' he gravely replied; 'it was very bad.' But still he went on measuring, and still he ended with: 'I think there will be very tolerable room for ten couple.'

'No, no,' said she, 'you are quite unreasonable. It would be dreadful to be standing so close. Nothing can be further from pleasure than to be dancing in a crowd – and a crowd in a little room.'

'There is no denying it,' he replied. 'I agree with you exactly. A crowd in a little room – Miss Woodhouse, you have the art of giving pictures in a few words. Exquisite, quite exquisite! Still, however, having proceeded so far, one is unwilling to give the matter up. It would be a disappointment to my father – and altogether – I do not know that – I am rather of opinion that ten couple might stand here very well.'

Emma perceived that the nature of his gallantry was a little self-willed, and that he would rather oppose than lose the pleasure of dancing with her; but she took the compliment, and forgave the rest. Had she intended ever to marry him, it might have been worth while to pause and consider, and try to understand the value of his preference, and the character of his temper; but for all the purposes of their acquaintance he was quite amiable enough.

Before the middle of the next day he was at Hartfield; and he entered the room with such an agreeable smile as certified the continuance of the scheme. It soon appeared that he came to announce an improvement.

'Well, Miss Woodhouse,' he almost immediately began, 'your inclination for dancing has not been quite frightened away, I hope, by the terrors of my father's little rooms. I bring a new proposal on the subject; a thought of my father's, which waits only your approbation to be acted upon. May I hope for the honour of your hand for the two first dances of this little projected ball, to be given, not at Randalls, but at the Crown Inn?'

'The Crown!'

'Yes; if you and Mr Woodhouse see no objection, and I trust you cannot, my father hopes his friends will be so kind as to visit him there. Better accommodations he can promise them, and not a less grateful welcome than at Randalls. It is his own idea. Mrs Weston sees no objection to it, provided you are satisfied. This is what we all feel. Oh, you were perfectly right! Ten couple, in either of the Randalls rooms, would have been insufferable – dreadful! I felt how right you were the whole time, but was too anxious for securing *anything* to like to yield. Is not it a good exchange? You consent – I hope you consent?'

'It appears to me a plan that nobody can object to, if Mr and Mrs Weston do not. I think it admirable; and, as far as I can answer for myself, shall be most happy – it seems the only improvement that could be. Papa, do you not think it an excellent improvement?'

She was obliged to repeat and explain it before it was fully comprehended; and then, being quite new, further representations were necessary to make it acceptable.

'No; he thought it very far from an improvement – a very bad plan – much worse than the other. A room at an inn was always damp and dangerous, never properly aired, or fit to be inhabited. If they must dance, they had better dance at Randalls. He had never been in the room at the Crown in his life – did not know the people who kept it by sight. Oh no – a very bad plan. They would catch worse colds at the Crown than anywhere.'

'I was going to observe, sir,' said Frank Churchill, 'that one of the great recommendations of this change would be the very little danger of anybody's catching cold – so much less danger at the Crown than at Randalls! Mr Perry might have reasons to regret the alteration, but nobody else could.'

'Sir,' said Mr Woodhouse, rather warmly, 'you are very much mistaken if you suppose Mr Perry to be that sort of character. Mr Perry is extremely concerned when any of us are ill. But I do not understand how the room at the Crown can be safer for you than your father's house.'

'From the very circumstance of its being larger, sir. We shall have no occasion to open the windows at all – not once the whole evening; and it is that dreadful habit of opening the windows, letting in cold air upon heated bodies, which (as you well know, sir) does the mischief.'

'Open the windows! but surely, Mr Churchill, nobody would think of opening the windows at Randalls. Nobody could be so imprudent! I never heard of such a thing. Dancing with open windows! I am sure neither your father nor Mrs Weston (poor Miss Taylor that was) would suffer it.'

'Ah! sir – but a thoughtless young person will sometimes step behind a window-curtain, and throw up a sash, without its being suspected. I have often known it done myself.'

'Have you, indeed, sir! Bless me! I never should have supposed it. But I live out of the world, and am often astonished at what I hear. However, this does make a difference; and perhaps, when we come to talk it over – but these sort of things require a good deal of consideration. One cannot resolve upon them in a hurry. If Mr and Mrs Weston will be so obliging as to call here one morning we may talk it over, and see what can be done.'

'But, unfortunately, sir, my time is so limited – '

'Oh,' interrupted Emma, 'there will be plenty of time for talking everything over. There is no hurry at all. If it can be contrived to be at the Crown, papa, it will be very convenient for the horses. They will be so near their own stable.'

'So they will, my dear. That is a great thing. Not that James ever complains; but it is right to spare our horses when we can. If I could be sure of the rooms being thoroughly aired – but is Mrs Stokes to be trusted? I doubt it. I do not know her, even by sight.'

'I can answer for everything of that nature, sir, because it will be under Mrs Weston's care. Mrs Weston undertakes to direct the whole.'

'There, papa! now you must be satisfied – our own dear Mrs Weston, who is carefulness itself. Do not you remember what Mr Perry said, so many years ago, when I had the measles? "If *Miss Taylor* undertakes to wrap Miss Emma up, you need not have any fears, sir." How often have I heard you speak of it as such a compliment to her!'

'Aye, very true, Mr Perry did say so. I shall never forget it. Poor little Emma! You were very bad with the measles; that is, you would have been very bad, but for Perry's great attentions. He came four times a day for a week. He said, from the first, it was a very good sort – which was our great comfort; but the measles are a dreadful complaint. I hope whenever poor Isabella's little ones have the measles she will send for Perry.'

'My father and Mrs Weston are at the Crown at this moment,' said Frank Churchill, 'examining the capabilities of the house. I left them there and came on to Hartfield, impatient for your opinion, and hoping you might be persuaded to join them and give your advice on the spot. I was desired to say so from both. It would be the greatest pleasure to them if you could allow me to attend you there. They can do nothing satisfactorily without you.'

Emma was most happy to be called to such a council: and, her father engaging to think it all over while she was gone, the two young people went off together without delay for the Crown. There were Mr and Mrs Weston; delighted to see her and receive her approbation, very busy and very happy in their different way: she, in some little distress; and he, finding everything perfect.

'Emma,' said she, 'this paper is worse than I expected. Look! in places you see it is dreadfully dirty: and the wainscot is more yellow and forlorn than anything I could have imagined.'

'My dear, you are too particular,' said her husband. 'What does all that signify? You will see nothing of it by candlelight. It will be as clean as Randalls by candlelight. We never see anything of it on our club-nights.'

The ladies here probably exchanged looks which meant, 'Men never know when things are dirty or not;' and the gentlemen perhaps thought each to himself, 'Women will have their little nonsenses and needless cares.'

One perplexity, however, arose, which the gentlemen did not disdain: it regarded a supper-room. At the time of the ballroom's being built suppers had not been in question; and a small card-room adjoining was the only addition. What was to be done? This card-room would be wanted as a card-room now; or, if cards were conveniently voted unnecessary by their four selves, still was it not too small for any comfortable supper? Another room of much better size might be secured for the purpose; but it was at the other end of the house, and a long awkward passage must be gone through to get at it. This made a difficulty. Mrs Weston was afraid of draughts for the young people in that passage; and neither Emma nor the gentlemen could tolerate the prospect of being miserably crowded at supper.

Mrs Weston proposed having no regular supper; merely sandwiches, etc., set out in the little room; but that was scouted as a wretched suggestion. A private dance, without sitting down to supper, was pronounced an infamous fraud upon the rights of men and women; and Mrs Weston must not speak of it again. She then took another line of expediency, and looking into the doubtful room, observed: 'I do not think it *is* so very small. We shall not be many, you know.'

And Mr Weston at the same time, walking briskly with long steps through the passage, was calling out: 'You talk a great deal of the length of this passage, my dear It is a mere nothing after all; and not the least draught from the stairs.'

'I wish,' said Mrs Weston, 'one could know which arrangement our guests in general would like best. To do what would be most generally pleasing must be our object – if one could but tell what that would be.'

'Yes, very true,' cried Frank, 'very true. You want your neighbours' opinions. I do not wonder at you. If one could ascertain what the chief of them – the Coles, for instance, they are not far off. Shall I call upon them? Or Miss Bates? She is still nearer. And I do not know whether Miss Bates is not as likely to understand the inclinations of the rest of the people as anybody. I think we do want a larger council. Suppose I go and invite Miss Bates to join us?'

'Well – if you please,' said Mrs Weston, rather hesitating. 'If you think she will be of any use.'

'You will get nothing to the purpose from Miss Bates,' said Emma; 'she will be all delight and gratitude, but she will tell you nothing. She will not even listen to your questions. I see no advantage in consulting Miss Bates.'

'But she is so amusing, so extremely amusing! I am very fond of hearing Miss Bates talk. And I need not bring the whole family, you know.'

Here Mr Weston joined them, and on hearing what was proposed gave it his decided approbation.

'Aye, do, Frank; go and fetch Miss Bates, and let us end the matter at once. She will enjoy the scheme, I am sure; and I do not know a properer person for showing us how to do away difficulties. Fetch Miss Bates. We are growing a little too nice. She is a standing lesson of how to be happy. But fetch them both. Invite them both.'

'Both, sir? Can the old lady – ?'

'The old lady! No, the young lady, to be sure! I shall think you a great blockhead, Frank, if you bring the aunt without the niece.'

'Oh! I beg your pardon, sir. I did not immediately recollect. Undoubtedly, if you wish it, I will endeavour to persuade them both.' And away he ran.

Long before he reappeared, attending the short, neat, brisk-moving aunt, and her elegant niece – Mrs Weston, like a sweet-tempered woman and a good wife, had examined the passage again, and found the evils of it much less than she had supposed before – indeed, very trifling; and here ended the difficulties of decision. All the rest, in speculation at least, was perfectly smooth. All the minor arrangements of table and chair, lights and music, tea and supper, made themselves; or were left as mere trifles, to be settled at any time between Mrs Weston and Mrs Stokes. Everybody invited was certainly to come; Frank had already written to Enscombe to propose staying a few days beyond his fortnight, which could not possibly be refused. And a delightful dance it was to be.

Most cordially, when Miss Bates arrived, did she agree that it must. As a counsellor she was not wanted; but as an approver (a much safer character) she was truly welcome. Her approbation, at once general and minute, warm and incessant, could not but please; and for another half-hour they were all walking to and fro between the different rooms, some suggesting, some attending, and all in happy enjoyment of the future. The party did not break up without Emma's being positively secured for the two first dances by the hero of the evening, nor without her overhearing

Mr Weston whisper to his wife, 'He has asked her, my dear. That's right. I knew he would!'

Chapter 30

One thing only was wanting to make the prospect of the ball completely satisfactory to Emma – its being fixed for a day within the granted term of Frank Churchill's stay in Surrey; for, in spite of Mr Weston's confidence, she could not think it so very impossible that the Churchills might not allow their nephew to remain a day beyond his fortnight. But this was not judged feasible. The preparations must take their time, nothing could be properly ready till the third week were entered on, and for a few days they must be planning, proceeding, and hoping in uncertainty, at the risk – in her opinion, the great risk – of its being all in vain.

Enscombe, however, was gracious – gracious in fact, if not in word. His wish of staying longer evidently did not please; but it was not opposed. All was safe and prosperous; and as the removal of one solicitude generally makes way for another, Emma being now certain of her ball, began to adopt as the next vexation Mr Knightley's provoking indifference about it. Either because he did not dance himself, or because the plan had been formed without his being consulted, he seemed resolved that it should not interest him, determined against its exciting any present curiosity, or affording him any future amusement. To her voluntary communications Emma could get no more approving reply than: 'Very well. If the Westons think it worth while to be at all this trouble for a few hours of noisy entertainment, I have nothing to say against it, but that they shall not choose pleasures for me. Oh, yes! I must be there; I could not refuse; and I will keep as much awake as I can; but I would rather be at home, looking over William Larkins's week's account; much rather, I confess. Pleasure in seeing dancing! not I, indeed – I never look at it – I do not know who does. Fine dancing, I believe, like virtue, must be its own reward. Those who are standing by are usually thinking of something very different.'

This Emma felt was aimed at her; and it made her quite angry. It was not in compliment to Jane Fairfax, however, that he was so indifferent, or so indignant; he was not guided by *her* feelings in reprobating the ball, for *she* enjoyed the thought of it to an extraordinary degree. It made her animated – open-hearted; she voluntarily said: 'Oh! Miss Woodhouse, I hope nothing may happen to prevent the ball! What a disappointment it would be! I do look forward to it, I own, with very great pleasure.'

It was not to oblige Jane Fairfax, therefore, that he would have preferred the society of William Larkins. No! – she was more and more convinced that Mrs Weston was quite mistaken in that surmise. There was a great deal of friendly and of compassionate attachment on his side – but no love.

Alas! there was soon no leisure for quarrelling with Mr Knightley. Two days of joyful security were immediately followed by the overthrow of everything. A letter arrived from Mr Churchill to urge his nephew's instant return. Mrs Churchill was unwell – far too unwell to do without him; she had been in a very suffering state (so said her husband) when writing to her nephew two days before, though from her usual unwillingness to give pain, and constant habit of never thinking of herself, she had not mentioned it; but now she was too ill to trifle, and must entreat him to set off for Enscombe without delay.

The substance of this letter was forwarded to Emma, in a note from Mrs Weston, instantly. As to his going, it was inevitable. He must be gone within a few hours, though without feeling any real alarm for his aunt, to lessen his repugnance. He knew her illnesses; they never occurred but for her own convenience.

Mrs Weston added, 'that he could only allow himself time to hurry to Highbury, after breakfast, and take leave of the few friends there whom he could suppose to feel any interest in him; and that he might be expected at Hartfield very soon.'

This wretched note was the finale of Emma's breakfast. When once it had been read there was no doing anything but lament and exclaim. The loss of the ball – the loss of the young man – and all that the young man might be feeling! It was too wretched! Such a delightful evening as it would have been! Everybody so happy! and she and her partner the happiest! 'I said it would be so,' was the only consolation.

Her father's feelings were quite distinct. He thought principally of Mrs Churchill's illness, and wanted to know how she was treated; and as for the ball, it was shocking to have dear Emma disappointed; but they would all be safer at home.

Emma was ready for her visitor some time before he appeared; but if this reflected at all upon his impatience, his sorrowful look and total want of spirits when he did come might redeem him. He felt the going away almost too much to speak of it. His dejection was most evident. He sat really lost in thought for the first few minutes; and when rousing himself it was only to say: 'Of all horrid things leave-taking is the worst.'

'But you will come again,' said Emma. 'This will not be your only visit to Randalls.'

'Ah!' – (shaking his head) – 'the uncertainty of when I may be able to return! I shall try for it with zeal! It will be the object of all my thoughts and cares! and if my uncle and aunt go to town this spring – but I am afraid – they did not stir last spring – I am afraid it is a custom gone for ever.'

'Our poor ball must be quite given up.'

'Ah! that ball! why did we wait for anything? – why not seize the pleasure at once? How often is happiness destroyed by preparation, foolish preparation! You told us it would be so. Oh! Miss Woodhouse, why are you always so right?'

'Indeed, I am very sorry to be right in this instance. I would much rather have been merry than wise.'

'If I can come again, we are still to have our ball. My father depends on it. Do not forget your engagement.'

Emma looked graciously.

'Such a fortnight as it has been!' he continued; 'every day more precious and more delightful than the day before! every day making me less fit to bear any other place. Happy those who can remain at Highbury!'

'As you do us ample justice now,' said Emma, laughing, 'I will venture to ask whether you did not come a little doubtfully at first? Do not we rather surpass your expectations? I am sure we do. I am sure you did not much expect to like us. You would not have been so long in coming if you had had a pleasant idea of Highbury.'

He laughed rather consciously; and though denying the sentiment, Emma was convinced that it had been so.

'And you must be off this very morning?'

'Yes; my father is to join me here: we shall walk back together, and I must be off immediately. I am almost afraid that every moment will bring him.'

'Not five minutes to spare even for your friends Miss Fairfax and Miss Bates? How unlucky! Miss Bates's powerful, argumentative mind might have strengthened yours.'

'Yes – I *have* called there; passing the door, I thought it better. It was a right thing to do. I went in for three minutes, and was detained by Miss Bates's being absent. She was out; and I felt it impossible not to wait till she came in. She is a woman that one may, that one *must* laugh at; but that one would not wish to slight. It was better to pay my visit, then – '

He hesitated, got up, walked to a window.

'In short,' said he, 'perhaps, Miss Woodhouse – I think you can hardly be quite without suspicion H ' e looked at her, as if wanting to read her thoughts. She hardly knew what to say. It seemed like the forerunner of something absolutely serious, which she did not wish. Forcing herself to speak, therefore, in the hope of putting it by, she calmly said: 'You are quite in the right; it was most natural to pay your visit, then – '

He was silent. She believed he was looking at her; probably reflecting on what she had said, and trying to understand the manner. She heard him sigh. It was natural for him to feel that he had *cause* to sigh. He could not believe her to be encouraging him. A few awkward moments passed, and he sat down again; and in a more determined manner said: 'It was something to feel that all the rest of my time might be given to Hartfield. My regard for Hartfield is most warm – '

He stopped again, rose again, and seemed quite embarrassed. He was more in love with her than Emma had supposed; and who can say how it might have ended, if his father had not made his appearance? Mr Woodhouse soon followed; and the necessity of exertion made him composed.

A very few minutes more, however, completed the present trial. Mr Weston, always alert when business was to be done, and as incapable of procrastinating any evil that was inevitable as of foreseeing any that was doubtful, said: 'It was time to go'; and the young man, though he might and did sigh, could not but agree, and rise to take leave.

'I shall hear about you all,' said he; 'that is my chief consolation. I shall hear of everything that is going on among you. I have engaged Mrs Weston to correspond with me. She has been so kind as to promise it. Oh! the blessing of a female correspondent, when one is really interested in the absent! she will tell me everything. In her letters I shall be at dear Highbury again.'

A very friendly shake of the hand, a very earnest 'Goodbye,' closed the speech, and the door had soon shut out Frank Churchill. Short had been the notice – short their meeting; he was gone; and Emma felt so sorry to part, and foresaw so great a loss to their little society from his absence as to begin to be afraid of being too sorry, and feeling it too much.

It was a sad change. They had been meeting almost every day since his arrival. Certainly his being at Randalls had given great spirit to the last two weeks – indescribable spirit; the idea, the expectation of seeing him which every morning had brought, the assurance of his attentions, his liveliness, his manners! It had been a very happy fortnight, and forlorn must be the sinking from it into the common course of Hartfield days. To complete every other recommendation, he had *almost* told her that he loved her. What strength or what constancy of affection he might be subject to was another point; but at present she could not doubt his having a decidedly warm admiration, a conscious preference of herself; and this persuasion, joined to all the rest, made her think that she *must* be a little in love with him, in spite of every previous determination against it.

'I certainly must,' said she. 'This sensation of listlessness, weariness, stupidity, this disinclination to sit down and employ myself, this feeling of everything's being dull and insipid about the house! I must be in love; I should be the oddest creature in the world if I were not – for a few weeks at least. Well, evil to some is always good to others. I shall have many fellow-mourners for the ball, if not for Frank Churchill; but Mr Knightley will be happy. He may spend the evening with his dear William Larkins now if he likes.'

Mr Knightley, however, showed no triumphant happiness. He could not say that he was sorry on his own account; his very cheerful look would have contradicted him if he had; but he said, and very steadily, that he was sorry for the disappointment of the others, and with considerable kindness added: 'You, Emma, who have so few opportunities of dancing, you are really out of luck; you are very much out of luck!'

It was some days before she saw Jane Fairfax, to judge of her honest regret in this woeful change; but when they did meet her composure was odious. She had been particularly unwell, however, suffering from headache to a degree which made her aunt declare that, had the ball taken place, she did not think Jane could have attended it; and it was charity to impute some of her unbecoming indifference to the languor of ill-health.

Chapter 31

Emma continued to entertain no doubt of her being in love. Her ideas only varied as to the how much. At first she thought it was a good deal; and afterwards but little. She had great pleasure in hearing Frank Churchill talked of; and for his sake, greater pleasure than ever in seeing Mr and Mrs Weston; she was very often thinking of him, and quite impatient for a letter, that she might know how he was, how were his spirits, how was his aunt, and what was the chance of his coming to Randalls again this spring. But, on the other hand, she could not admit herself to be unhappy, nor, after the first morning, to be less disposed for employment than usual; she was still busy and cheerful; and, pleasing as he was, she could yet imagine him to have faults; and further, though thinking of him so much, and, as she sat drawing or working, forming a thousand amusing schemes for the progress and close of their attachment, fancying interesting dialogues, and inventing elegant letters; the conclusion of every imaginary declaration on his side was that she *refused him*. Their affection was always to subside into friendship. Everything tender and charming was to mark their parting; but still they were to part. When she became sensible of this, it struck her that she could not be very much in love; for, in spite of her previous and fixed determination never to quit her father, never to marry, a strong attachment certainly must produce more of a struggle than she could foresee in her own feelings.

'I do not find myself making any use of the word *sacrifice*,' said she. 'In not one of all my clever replies, my delicate negatives, is there any allusion to making a sacrifice. I do suspect that he is not really necessary to my happiness. So much the better. I certainly will not persuade myself to feel more than I do. I am quite enough in love. I should be sorry to be more.'

Upon the whole, she was equally contented with her view of his feelings.

'*He* is undoubtedly very much in love – everything denotes it – very much in love indeed! – and when he comes again, if his affection continue, I must be on my guard not to encourage it. It would be most inexcusable to do otherwise, as my own mind is quite made up. Not that I imagine he can think I have been encouraging him hitherto. No; if he had believed me at all to share his feelings he would not have been so wretched. Could he have thought himself encouraged, his looks and language at parting would have been different. Still, however, I must be on my guard. This is in the supposition of his attachment continuing what it now is; but I do not know that I expect it will; I do not look upon him to be quite the sort of man – I do not altogether build upon his steadiness or constancy. His feelings are warm, but I can imagine them rather changeable. Every consideration of the subject, in short, makes me thankful that my happiness is not more deeply involved. I shall do very well again after a little while – and then, it will be a good thing over; for they say everybody is in love once in their lives, and I shall have been let off easily.'

When his letter to Mrs Weston arrived, Emma had the perusal of it; and she read it with a degree of pleasure and admiration which made her at first shake her head over her own sensations, and think she had undervalued their strength. It was a long, well-written letter, giving the particulars of his journey and of his feelings, expressing all the affection, gratitude, and respect which was natural and honourable, and describing everything exterior

and local that could be supposed attractive, with spirit and preci-
sion. No suspicious flourishes now of apology or concern; it was
the language of real feeling towards Mrs Weston; and the transition from Highbury to Enscombe, the contrast between the places
in some of the first blessings of social life, was just enough
touched on to show how keenly it was felt, and how much more
might have been said but for the restraints of propriety. The
charm of her own name was not wanting. *Miss Woodhouse*
appeared more than once, and never without a something of
pleasing connection, either a compliment to her taste, or a
remembrance of what she had said; and in the very last time of its
meeting her eye, unadorned as it was by any such broad wreath of
gallantry, she yet could discern the effect of her influence, and
acknowledge the greatest compliment perhaps of all conveyed.
Compressed into the very lowest vacant corner were these words –
'I had not a spare moment on Tuesday, as you know, for Miss
Woodhouse's beautiful little friend. Pray make my excuses and
adieus to her.' This, Emma could not doubt, was all for herself.
Harriet was remembered only from being *her* friend. His information and prospects, as to Enscombe, were neither worse nor
better than had been anticipated; Mrs Churchill was recovering,
and he dared not yet, even in his own imagination, fix a time for
coming to Randalls again.

Gratifying, however, and stimulative as was the letter in the
material part, its sentiments, she yet found, when it was folded
up and returned to Mrs Weston, that it had not added any
lasting warmth – that she could still do without the writer, and
that he must learn to do without her. Her intentions were
unchanged. Her resolution of refusal only grew more interesting by the addition of a scheme for his subsequent consolation and happiness. His recollection of Harriet, and the words
which clothed it – the 'beautiful little friend' – suggested to her
the idea of Harriet's succeeding her in his affections. Was it
impossible? No. Harriet undoubtedly was greatly his inferior
in understanding; but he had been very much struck with the

loveliness of her face and the warm simplicity of her manner; and all the probabilities of circumstance and connection were in her favour. For Harriet it would be advantageous and delightful indeed.

'I must not dwell upon it,' said she; 'I must not think of it. I know the danger of indulging such speculations. But stranger things have happened; and when we cease to care for each other as we do now, it will be the means of confirming us in that sort of true disinterested friendship which I can already look forward to with pleasure.'

It was well to have a comfort in store on Harriet's behalf, though it might be wise to let the fancy touch it seldom; for evil in that quarter was at hand. As Frank Churchill's arrival had succeeded Mr Elton's engagement in the conversation of Highbury, as the latest interest had entirely borne down the first, so now, upon Frank Churchill's disappearance, Mr Elton's concerns were assuming the most irresistible form. His wedding-day was named. He would soon be among them again – Mr Elton and his bride. There was hardly time to talk over the first letter from Enscombe before 'Mr Elton and his bride' was in everybody's mouth, and Frank Churchill was forgotten. Emma grew sick at the sound. She had had three weeks of happy exemption from Mr Elton; and Harriet's mind, she had been willing to hope, had been lately gaining strength. With Mr Weston's ball in view, at least, there had been a great deal of insensibility to other things; but it was now too evident that she had not attained such a state of composure as could stand against the actual approach – new carriage, bell-ringing, and all.

Poor Harriet was in a flutter of spirits which required all the reasonings, and soothings, and attentions of every kind that Emma could give. Emma felt that she could not do too much for her, that Harriet had a right to all her ingenuity and all her patience; but it was heavy work to be for ever convincing without producing any effect; for ever agreed to, without being able to make their opinions the same. Harriet listened submissively, and said: 'It was very true; it was just as Miss Woodhouse described – it was not worth while to think about them – and she would not think about them any longer.' But no change of subject could avail, and the next half-hour saw her as anxious and restless about the Eltons as before. At last Emma attacked her on another ground.

'Your allowing yourself to be so occupied and so unhappy about Mr Elton's marrying, Harriet, is the strongest reproach you can make me. You could not give me a greater reproof for the mistake I fell into. It was all my doing, I know. I have not forgotten it, I assure you. Deceived myself, I did very miserably deceive you; and it will be a painful reflection to me for ever. Do not imagine me in danger of forgetting it.'

Harriet felt this too much to utter more than a few words of eager exclamation. Emma continued: 'I have not said, exert yourself, Harriet, for my sake; think less, talk less of Mr Elton for my sake; because, for your own sake rather, I would wish it to be done, for the sake of what is more important than my comfort – a habit of self-command in you, a consideration of what is your duty, an attention to propriety, an endeavour to avoid the suspicions of others, to save your health and credit, and restore your tranquillity. These are the motives which I have been pressing on you. They are very important, and sorry I am that you cannot feel them sufficiently to act upon them. My being saved from pain is a very secondary consideration. I want you to save yourself from greater pain. Perhaps I may sometimes have felt that Harriet would not forget what was due – or rather, what would be kind by me.'

This appeal to her affections did more than all the rest. The idea of wanting gratitude and consideration for Miss Woodhouse, whom she really loved extremely, made her wretched for a while; and when the violence of grief was comforted away, still remained powerful enough to prompt to what was right, and support her in it very tolerably.

'You, who have been the best friend I ever had in my life! Want gratitude to you! Nobody is equal to you! I care for nobody as I do for you! Oh, Miss Woodhouse, how ungrateful I have been!'

Such expressions, assisted as they were by everything that look and manner could do, made Emma feel that she had never loved Harriet so well, nor valued her affection so highly before.

'There is no charm equal to tenderness of heart,' said she afterwards to herself. 'There is nothing to be compared to it. Warmth and tenderness of heart, with an affectionate, open manner, will beat all the clearness of head in the world, for attraction: I am sure it will. It is tenderness of heart which makes my dear father so generally beloved – which gives Isabella all her popularity. I have it not; but I know how to prize and respect it. Harriet is my superior in all the charm and all the felicity it gives. Dear Harriet! I would not change you for the clearest-headed, longest-sighted, best-judging female breathing. Oh, the coldness of a Jane Fairfax! Harriet is worth a hundred such; and for a wife – a sensible man's wife – it is invaluable. I mention no names; but happy the man who changes Emma for Harriet!'

Chapter 32

Mrs Elton was first seen at church: but though devotion might be interrupted, curiosity could not be satisfied by a bride in a pew, and it must be left for the visits in form which were then to be paid, to settle whether she were very pretty indeed, or only rather pretty, or not pretty at all.

Emma had feelings, less of curiosity than of pride or propriety, to make her resolve on not being the last to pay her respects: and she made a point of Harriet's going with her, that the worst of the business might be gone through as soon as possible.

She could not enter the house again, could not be in the same room to which she had with such vain artifice retreated three months ago, to lace up her boot, without *recollecting*. A thousand vexatious thoughts would recur. Compliments, charades, and horrible blunders; and it was not to be supposed that poor Harriet should not be recollecting too; but she behaved very well, and was only rather pale and silent. The visit was of course short! and there was so much embarrassment and occupation of mind to shorten it that Emma would not allow herself entirely to form an opinion of the lady, and on no account to give one, beyond the nothing-meaning terms of being 'elegantly dressed, and very pleasing.'

She did not really like her. She would not be in a hurry to find fault, but she suspected that there was no elegance; ease, but not elegance. She was almost sure that for a young woman, a stranger, a bride, there was too much ease. Her person was rather good; her face not unpretty; but neither feature nor air, nor voice, nor manner were elegant. Emma thought, at least, it would turn out so.

As for Mr Elton, his manners did not appear – but no, she would not permit a hasty or a witty word from herself about his manners. It was an awkward ceremony at any time to be receiving wedding visits; and a man had need be all grace to acquit himself well through it. The woman was better off; she might have the assistance of fine clothes, and the privilege of bashfulness; but the man had only his own good sense to depend on: and when she considered how peculiarly unlucky poor Mr Elton was in being in the same room at once with the woman he had just married, the woman he had wanted to marry, and the woman whom he had been expected to marry, she must allow him to have the right to look as little wise, and to be as much affectedly, and as little really, easy as could be.

'Well, Miss Woodhouse,' said Harriet, when they had quitted the house, and after waiting in vain for her friend to begin; 'well, Miss Woodhouse' (with a gentle sigh), 'what do you think of her? Is not she very charming?'

There was a little hesitation in Emma's answer.

'Oh! yes – very – a very pleasing young woman.'

'I think her beautiful, quite beautiful.'

'Very nicely dressed, indeed; a remarkably elegant gown.'

'I am not at all surprised that he should have fallen in love.'

'Oh! no; there is nothing to surprise one at all; a pretty fortune, and she came in his way.'

'I dare say,' returned Harriet, sighing again, 'I dare say she was very much attached to him.'

'Perhaps she might; but it is not every man's fate to marry the woman who loves him best. Miss Hawkins, perhaps, wanted a home, and thought this the best offer she was likely to have.'

'Yes,' said Harriet earnestly, 'and well she might; nobody could ever have a better. Well, I wish them happy with all my heart. And now, Miss Woodhouse, I do not think I shall mind seeing them again. He is just as superior as ever; but being married, you know, it is quite a different thing. No, indeed, Miss Woodhouse, you need not be afraid; I can sit and admire him now without any great misery. To know that he has not thrown himself away is such a comfort! She does seem a charming young woman, just what he deserves. Happy creature! He called her "Augusta". How delightful!'

When the visit was returned, Emma made up her mind. She could then see more and judge better. From Harriet's happening not to be at Hartfield, and her father's being present to engage Mr Elton, she had a quarter of an hour of the lady's conversation to herself, and could composedly attend to her; and the quarter of an hour quite convinced her that Mrs Elton was a vain woman, extremely well satisfied with herself, and thinking much of her own importance; that she meant to shine and be very superior, but with manners which had been formed in a bad school; pert and familiar; that all her notions were drawn from one set of people, and one style of living; that, if not foolish, she was ignorant, and that her society would certainly do Mr Elton no good.

Harriet would have been a better match. If not wise or refined herself, she would have connected him with those who were; but Miss Hawkins, it might be fairly supposed, from her easy conceit, had been the best of her own set. The rich brother-in-law, near Bristol, was the pride of the alliance, and his place and his carriages were the pride of him.

The very first subject, after being seated, was Maple Grove, 'My brother, Mr Suckling's seat'; a comparison of Hartfield to Maple Grove. The grounds of Hartfield were small, but neat and pretty; and the house was modern and well-built. Mrs Elton seemed most favourably impressed by the size of the room, the entrance, and all that she could see or imagine. 'Very like Maple Grove indeed! She was quite struck by the likeness! That room was the very shape and size of the morning-room at Maple Grove; her sister's favourite room.' Mr Elton was appealed to. 'Was not it astonishingly like? She could really almost fancy herself at Maple Grove.'

'And the staircase. You know, as I came in, I observed how very like the staircase was; placed exactly in the same part of the house. I really could not help exclaiming! I assure you, Miss Woodhouse, it is very delightful to me to be reminded of a place I am so extremely partial to as Maple Grove. I have spent so many happy months there!' (with a little sigh of sentiment.) 'A charming place, undoubtedly. Everybody who sees it is struck by its beauty; but to me it has been quite a home. Whenever you are transplanted, like me, Miss Woodhouse, you will understand how very delightful it is to meet with anything at all like what one has left behind. I always say this is quite one of the evils of matrimony.'

Emma made as slight a reply as she could; but it was fully sufficient for Mrs Elton, who only wanted to be talking herself.

'So extremely like Maple Grove! And it is not merely the house; the grounds, I assure you, as far as I could observe, are strikingly like. The laurels at Maple Grove are in the same profusion as here, and stand very much in the same way – just across the lawn; and I had a glimpse of a fine large tree, with a bench round it, which put me so exactly in mind! My brother and sister will be enchanted with this place. People who have extensive grounds themselves are always pleased with anything in the same style.'

Emma doubted the truth of this sentiment. She had a great idea that people who had extensive grounds themselves cared very little for the extensive grounds of anybody else; but it was not worth while to attack an error so double-dyed, and therefore only said in reply: 'When you have seen more of this country I am afraid you will think you have overrated Hartfield. Surrey is full of beauties.'

'Oh! yes, I am quite aware of that. It is the garden of England, you know. Surrey is the garden of England.'

'Yes; but we must not rest our claims on that distinction. Many counties, I believe, are called the garden of England, as well as Surrey.'

'No, I fancy not,' replied Mrs Elton, with a most satisfied smile. 'I never heard any county but Surrey called so.'

Emma was silenced.

'My brother and sister have promised us a visit in the spring, or summer at farthest,' continued Mrs Elton; 'and that will be our time for exploring. While they are with us we shall explore a great deal, I dare say. They will have their barouche-landau, of course, which holds four perfectly; and therefore, without saying anything of our carriage, we should be able to explore the different beauties extremely well. They would hardly come in their chaise, I think, at that season of the year. Indeed, when the time draws on, I shall decidedly recommend their bringing the barouche-landau; it will be so very much preferable. When people come into a beautiful country of this sort, you know, Miss Woodhouse, one naturally wishes them to see as much as possible; and Mr Suckling is extremely fond of exploring. We explored to King's-Weston twice last summer, in that way, most delightfully, just after their first having the barouche-landau. You have many parties of that kind here, I suppose, Miss Woodhouse, every summer?'

'No; not immediately here. We are rather out of distance of the very striking beauties which attract the sort of parties you speak of; and we are a very quiet set of people, I believe; more disposed to stay at home than engage in schemes of pleasure.'

'Ah! there is nothing like staying at home for real comfort. Nobody can be more devoted to home than I am. I was quite a proverb for it at Maple Grove. Many a time has Selina said, when she has been going to Bristol, "I really cannot get this girl to move from the house. I absolutely must go in by myself, though I hate being stuck up in the barouche-landau without a companion: but Augusta, I believe, with her own good will, would never stir beyond the park paling." Many a time has she said so; and yet I am no advocate for entire seclusion. I think, on the contrary, when people shut themselves up entirely from society, it is a very bad thing; and that it is much more advisable to mix in the world in a proper degree, without living in it either too much or too little. I perfectly understand your situation however, Miss Woodhouse' (looking towards Mr Woodhouse), 'your father's state of health must be a great drawback. Why does not he try Bath? Indeed he should. Let me recommend Bath to you. I assure you I have no doubt of its doing Mr Woodhouse good.'

'My father tried it more than once, formerly, but without receiving any benefit; and Mr Perry, whose name, I dare say, is not unknown to you, does not conceive it would be at all more likely to be useful now.'

'Ah! that's a great pity; for I assure you, Miss Woodhouse, where the waters do agree, it is quite wonderful the relief they give. In my Bath life I have seen such instances of it! And it is so cheerful a place that it could not fail of being of use to Mr Wood-house's spirits, which, I understand, are sometimes much depressed. And as to its recommendations to you, I fancy I need not take much pains to dwell on them. The advantages of Bath to the young are pretty generally understood. It would be a charming introduction for you, who have lived so secluded a life: and I could immediately secure you some of the best society in the place. A line from me would bring you a little host of acquaintance; and my particular friend Mrs Partridge, the lady I have always resided with when in Bath, would be most happy to show you any attentions, and would be the very person for you to go into public with.'

It was as much as Emma could bear, without being impolite! The idea of her being indebted to Mrs Elton for what was called an *introduction* – of her going into public under the auspices of a friend of Mrs Elton's – probably some vulgar dashing widow who, with the help of a boarder, just made a shift to live! The dignity of Miss Woodhouse, of Hartfield, was sunk indeed!

She restrained herself, however, from any of the reproofs she could have given, and only thanked Mrs Elton coolly; 'but their going to Bath was quite out of the question; and she was not perfectly convinced that the place might suit her better than her father.' And then, to prevent further outrage and indignation, changed the subject directly.

'I do not ask whether you are musical, Mrs Elton. Upon these occasions a lady's character generally precedes her; and Highbury has long known that you are a superior performer.'

'Oh! no, indeed; I must protest against any such idea. A superior performer! very far from it, I assure you: consider from how partial a quarter your information came. I am dotingly fond of music – passionately fond; and my friends say I am not entirely devoid of taste; but as to anything else, upon my honour my performance is *mediocre* to the last degree. You, Miss Woodhouse, I well know, play delightfully. I assure you it has been the greatest satisfaction, comfort, and delight to me to hear what a musical society I am got into. I absolutely cannot do without music: it is a necessary of life to me; and having always been used to a very musical society, both at Maple Grove and in Bath, it would have been a most serious sacrifice. I honestly said as much to Mr E. when he was speaking of my future home, and expressing his fears lest the retirement of it should be disagreeable; and the inferiority of the house too – knowing what I had been accustomed to – of course he was not wholly without apprehension. When he was speaking of it in that way, I honestly said that *the world* I could give up – parties, balls, plays – for I had no fear of retirement. Blessed with so many resources within myself the world was not necessary to me. I could do very well without it. To those who had no resources it was a different thing; but my resources made me quite independent. And as to smaller-sized rooms than I had been used to, I really could not give it a thought. I hoped I was perfectly equal to any sacrifice of that description. Certainly, I had been accustomed to every luxury at Maple Grove; but I did assure him that two carriages were not necessary to my happiness, nor were spacious apartments. "But," said I, "to be quite honest, I do not think I can live without something of a musical society. I condition for nothing else; but, without music, life would be a blank to me." '

'We cannot suppose,' said Emma, smiling, 'that Mr Elton would hesitate to assure you of there being a very musical society in Highbury; and I hope you will not find he has outstepped the truth more than may be pardoned, in consideration of the motive.'

'No, indeed, I have no doubts at all on that head. I am delighted to find myself in such a circle: I hope we shall have many sweet little concerts together. I think, Miss Woodhouse, you and I must establish a musical club, and have regular weekly meetings at your house, or ours. Will not it be a good plan? If *we* exert ourselves, I think we shall not be long in want of allies. Something of that nature would be particularly desirable for *me,* as an inducement to keep me in practice; for married women, you know – there is a sad story against them, in general. They are but too apt to give up music.'

'But you, who are so extremely fond of it – there can be no danger, surely?'

'I should hope not; but really when I look around among my acquaintance, I tremble. Selina has entirely given up music – never touches the instrument, though she played sweetly. And the same may be said of Mrs Jeffreys – Clara Partridge that was – and of the two Milmans, now Mrs Bird and Mrs James Cooper; and of more than I can enumerate. Upon my word, it is enough to put one in a fright. I used to be quite angry with Selina; but, really, I begin now to comprehend that a married woman has many things to call her attention. I believe I was half an hour this morning shut up with my housekeeper.'

'But everything of that kind,' said Emma, 'will soon be in so regular a train – '

'Well,' said Mrs Elton, laughing, 'we shall see.'

Emma, finding her so determined upon neglecting her music, had nothing more to say; and, after a moment's pause, Mrs Elton chose another subject.

'We have been calling at Randalls,' said she, 'and found them both at home; and very pleasant people they seem to be. I like them extremely. Mr Weston seems an excellent creature – quite a first-rate favourite with me already, I assure you. And *she* appears so truly good – there is something so motherly and kind-hearted about her, that it wins upon one directly. She was your governess, I think?'

Emma was almost too much astonished to answer; but Mrs Elton hardly waited for the affirmative before she went on: 'Having understood as much, I was rather astonished to find her so very ladylike. But she is really quite the gentlewoman.'

'Mrs Weston's manners,' said Emma, 'were always particularly good. Their propriety, simplicity, and elegance would make them the safest model for any young woman.'

'And who do you think came in while we were there?'

Emma was quite at a loss. The tone implied some old acquaintance, and how could she possibly guess?

'Knightley!' continued Mrs Elton; 'Knightley himself! Was not it lucky? For, not being within when he called the other day, I had never seen him before; and of course, as so particular a friend of Mr E.'s, I had a great curiosity. "My friend Knightley" had been so often mentioned, that I was really impatient to see him; and I must do my *caro sposo* the justice to say that he need not be ashamed of his friend. Knightley is quite the gentleman; I like him very much. Decidedly, I think, a very gentlemanlike man.'

Happily, it was now time to be gone. They were off, and Emma could breathe.

'Insufferable woman!' was her immediate exclamation. 'Worse than I had supposed. Absolutely insufferable! Knightley! I could not have believed it. Knightley! – never seen him in her life before, and call him Knightley! and discover that he is a gentleman. A little upstart, vulgar being, with her Mr E. and her *caro sposo,* and her resources, and all her airs of pert pretention and underbred finery. Actually to discover that Mr Knightley is a gentleman! I doubt whether he will return the compliment, and discover her to be a lady. I could not have believed it! And to propose that she and I should unite to form a musical club! One would fancy we were bosom friends! And Mrs Weston! Astonished that the person who had brought me up should be a gentlewoman! Worse and worse! I never met with her equal. Much beyond my hopes! Harriet is disgraced by any comparison. Oh! what would Frank Churchill say to her if he were here? How angry and how diverted he would be! Ah! there I am thinking of him directly. Always the first person to be thought of! How I catch myself out! Frank Churchill comes as regularly into my mind –!'

All this ran so glibly through her thoughts, that by the time her father had arranged himself, after the bustle of the Eltons' departure, and was ready to speak, she was very tolerably capable of attending.

'Well, my dear,' he deliberately began, 'considering we never saw her before, she seems a very pretty sort of young lady; and I dare say she was very much pleased with you. She speaks a little too quick. A little quickness of voice there iswhich rather hurts the ear. But I believe I am nice; I do not like strange voices; and nobody speaks like you and poor Miss Taylor. However, she seems a very obliging, pretty-behaved young lady, and no doubt will make him a very good wife. Though I think he had better not have married. I made the best excuses I could for not having been able to wait on him and Mrs Elton on this happy occasion: I said that I hoped I *should* in the course of the summer. But I ought to have gone before. Not to wait upon a bride is very remiss. Ah! it shows what a sad invalid I am! But I do not like the corner into Vicarage Lane.'

'I dare say your apologies were accepted, sir. Mr Elton knows you.'

'Yes; but a young lady – a bride – I ought to have paid my respects to her, if possible. It was being very deficient.'

'But, my dear papa, you are no friend to matrimony; and therefore why should you be so anxious to pay your respects to a *bride*? It ought to be no recommendation to *you*. It is encouraging people to marry if you make so much of them.'

'No, my dear, I never encouraged anybody to marry, but I would always wish to pay every proper attention to a lady – and a bride especially, is never to be neglected. More is avowedly due to *her*. A bride, you know, my dear, is always the first in company, let the others be who they may.'

'Well, papa, if this is not encouragement to marry, I do not know what is. And I should never have expected you to be lending your sanction to such vanity-baits for poor young ladies.'

'My dear, you do not understand me. This is a matter of mere common politeness and good-breeding, and has nothing to do with any encouragement to people to marry.'

Emma had done. Her father was growing nervous, and could not understand her. Her mind returned to Mrs Elton's offences, and long, very long, did they occupy her.

Chapter 33

Emma was not required, by any subsequent discovery, to retract her ill opinion of Mrs Elton. Her observation had been pretty correct. Such as Mrs Elton appeared to her on this second interview, such she appeared whenever they met again: self-important, presuming, familiar, ignorant, and ill-bred. She had a little beauty and a little accomplishment, but so little judgement that she thought herself coming with superior knowledge of the world, to enliven and improve a country neighbourhood; and conceived Miss Hawkins to have held such a place in society as Mrs Elton's consequence only could surpass.

There was no reason to suppose Mr Elton thought at all differently from his wife. He seemed not merely happy with her, but proud. He had the air of congratulating himself on having brought such a woman to Highbury, as not even Miss Woodhouse could equal; and the greater part of her new acquaintance, disposed to commend, or not in the habit of judging, following the lead of Miss Bates's goodwill, of taking it for granted that the bride must be as clever and as agreeable as she professed herself, were very well satisfied; so that Mrs Elton's praise passed from one mouth to another as it ought to do, unimpeded by Miss Woodhouse, who readily continued her first contribution, and talked with a good grace of her being 'very pleasant, and very elegantly dressed.'

In one respect Mrs Elton grew even worse than she had appeared at first. Her feelings altered towards Emma. Offended, probably, by the little encouragement which her proposals of intimacy met with, she drew back, in her turn, and gradually became much more cold and distant; and though the effect was agreeable, the ill-will which produced it was necessarily increasing Emma's dislike. Her manners, too – and Mr Elton's – were unpleasant towards Harriet. They were sneering and negligent. Emma hoped it must rapidly work Harriet's cure; but the sensations which could prompt such behaviour sunk them both very much. It was not to be doubted that poor Harriet's attachment had been an offering to conjugal unreserve, and her own share in the story, under a colouring the least favourable to her, and the most soothing to him, had in all likelihood been given also. She was, of course, the object of their joint dislike. When they had nothing else to say, it must be always easy to begin abusing Miss Woodhouse; and the enmity which they dared not show in open disrespect to her found a broader vent in contemptuous treatment of Harriet.

Mrs Elton took a great fancy to Jane Fairfax; and from the first. Not merely when a state of warfare with one young lady might be supposed to recommend the other, but from the very first; and she was not satisfied with expressing a natural and reasonable admiration, but without solicitation, or plea, or privilege, she must be wanting to assist and befriend her. Before Emma had forfeited her confidence, and about the third time of their meeting, she heard all Mrs Elton's knight-errantry on the subject.

'Jane Fairfax is absolutely charming, Miss Woodhouse. I quite rave about Jane Fairfax. A sweet, interesting creature. So mild and ladylike – and with such talents! I assure you think she has very extraordinary talents! I do not scruple to say that she plays extremely well. I know enough of music to speak decidedly on that point. Oh! she is absolutely charming! You will laugh at my warmth, but, upon my word, I talk of nothing but Jane Fairfax – and her situation is so calculated to affect one! Miss Woodhouse, we must exert ourselves and endeavour to do something for her. We must bring her forward. Such talents as hers must not be suffered to remain unknown. I dare say you have heard those charming lines of the poet:

Full many a flower is born to blush unseen
And waste its fragrance on the desert air.

We must not allow them to be verified in sweet Jane Fairfax.'

'I cannot think there is any danger of it,' was Emma's calm answer: 'and when you are better acquainted with Miss Fairfax's situation, and understand what her home has been, with Colonel and Mrs Campbell, I have no idea that you will suppose her talents can be unknown.'

'Oh! but, dear Miss Woodhouse, she is now in such retirement, such obscurity, so thrown away. Whatever advantages she may have enjoyed with the Campbells are so palpably at an end! And I think she feels it. I am sure she does. She is very timid and silent. One can see that she feels the want of encouragement. I like her the better for it. I must confess it is a recommendation to me. I am a great advocate for timidity – and I am sure one does not often meet with it. But in those who are not at all inferior, it is extremely prepossessing. Oh! I assure you, Jane Fairfax is a very delightful character, and interests me more than I can express.'

'You appear to feel a great deal; but I am not aware how you or any of Miss Fairfax's acquaintance here, any of those who have known her longer than yourself, can show her any other attention than – '

'My dear Miss Woodhouse, a vast deal may be done by those who dare to act. You and I need not be afraid. If we set the example, many will follow it as far as they can; though all have not our situations. *We* have carriages to fetch and convey her home; and *we* live in a style which could not make the addition of Jane Fairfax at any time the least inconvenient. I should be extremely displeased if Wright were to send up such a dinner as could make me regret having asked *more* than Jane Fairfax to partake of it. I have no idea of that sort of thing. It is not likely that I *should*, considering what I have been used to. My greatest danger, perhaps, in housekeeping, may be quite the other way, in doing too much, and being too careless of expense. Maple Grove will probably be my model more than it ought to be – for we do not at all affect to equal my brother, Mr Suckling, in income. However, my resolution is taken as to noticing Jane Fairfax. I shall certainly have her very often at my house, shall introduce her wherever I can, shall have musical parties to draw out her talents, and shall be constantly on the watch for an eligible situation. My acquaintance is so very extensive, that I have little doubt of hearing of something to suit her shortly. I shall introduce her, of course, very particularly to my brother and sister when they come to us. I am sure they will like her extremely; and when she gets a little acquainted with them, her fears will completely wear off, for there really is nothing in the manners of either but what is highly conciliating. I shall have her very often, indeed, while they are with me; and I dare say we shall sometimes find a seat for her in the barouche-landau in some of our exploring parties.'

'Poor Jane Fairfax,' thought Emma, 'you have not deserved this. You may have done wrong with regard to Mr Dixon; but this is a punishment beyond what you can have merited. The kindness and protection of Mrs Elton! – "Jane Fairfax and Jane Fairfax!" Heavens! let me not suppose that she dares go about Emma Woodhouseing me! But, upon my honour, there seems no limits to the licentiousness of that woman's tongue!'

Emma had not to listen to such paradings again – to any so exclusively addressed to herself – so disgustingly decorated with a 'dear Miss Woodhouse.' The change on Mrs Elton's side soon afterwards appeared, and she was left in peace – neither forced to be the very particular friend of Mrs Elton nor, under Mrs Elton's guidance, the very active patroness of Jane Fairfax, and only sharing with others in a general way, in knowing what was felt, what was meditated, what was done.

She looked on with some amusement. Miss Bates's gratitude for Mrs Elton's attentions to Jane was in the first style of guileless simplicity and warmth. She was quite one of her worthies – the most amiable, affable, delightful woman – just as accomplished and condescending as Mrs Elton meant to be considered. Emma's only surprise was that Jane Fairfax should accept those attentions, and tolerate Mrs Elton as she seemed to do. She heard of her walking with the Eltons, sitting with the Eltons, spending a day with the Eltons! This was astonishing! She could not have believed it possible that the taste or the pride of Miss Fairfax could endure such society and friendship as the Vicarage had to offer.

'She is a riddle, quite a riddle,' said she. 'To choose to remain here month after month, under privations of every sort. And now to choose the mortification of Mrs Elton's notice, and the penury of her conversation, rather than return to the superior companions who have always loved her with such real, generous affection.'

Jane had come to Highbury professedly for three months; the Campbells were gone to Ireland for three months; but now the Campbells had promised their daughter to stay at least till Midsummer, and fresh invitations had arrived for her to join them there. According to Miss Bates – it all came from her – Mrs Dixon had written most pressingly. Would Jane but go, means were to be found, servants sent, friends contrived – no travelling difficulty allowed to exist; but still she had declined it.

'She must have some motive, more powerful than appears, forrefusing this invitation,' was Emma's conclusion. 'She must be under some sort of penance, inflicted either by the Campbells or herself. There is great fear, great caution, great resolution somewhere. She is *not* to be with the *Dixons*. The decree is issued by somebody. But why must she consent to be with the Eltons? Here is quite a separate puzzle.'

Upon her speaking her wonder aloud on that part of the subject, before the few who knew her opinion of Mrs Elton, Mrs Weston ventured this apology for Jane.

'We cannot suppose that she has any great enjoyment at the Vicarage, my dear Emma – but it is better than being always at home. Her aunt is a good creature; but, as a constant companion, must be very tiresome. We must consider what Miss Fairfax quits, before we condemn her taste for what she goes to.'

'You are right, Mrs Weston,' said Mr Knightley warmly; 'Miss Fairfax is as capable as any of us of forming a just opinion of Mrs Elton. Could she have chosen with whom to associate, she would not have chosen her. But' (with reproachful smile at Emma) 'she receives attentions from Mrs Elton, which nobody else pays her.'

Emma felt that Mrs Weston was giving her a momentary glance, and she was herself struck by his warmth. With a faint blush, she presently replied: 'Such attentions as Mrs Elton's, I should have imagined, would rather disgust than gratify Miss Fairfax. Mrs Elton's invitations I should have imagined anything but inviting.'

'I should not wonder,' said Mrs Weston, 'if Miss Fairfax were to have been drawn on beyond her own inclination, by her aunt's eagerness in accepting Mrs Elton's civilities for her. Poor Miss Bates may very likely have committed her niece, and hurried her into a greater appearance of intimacy than her own good sense would have dictated, in spite of the very natural wish of a little change.'

Both felt rather anxious to hear him speak again; and, after afew minutes' silence, he said: 'Another thing must be taken into consideration too – Mrs Elton does not talk to Miss Fairfax as she speaks *of* her. We all know the difference between the pronouns he or she and thou, the plainest spoken amongst us; we all feel the influence of a something beyond common civility in our personal intercourse with each other – a something more early implanted. We cannot give anybody the disagreeable hints that we may have been very full of the hour before. We feel things differently. And besides the operation of this, as a general principle, you may be sure that Miss Fairfax awes Mrs Elton by her superiority both of mind and manner; and that, face to face, Mrs Elton treats her with all the respect which she has a claim to. Such a woman as Jane Fairfax probably never fell in Mrs Elton's way before – and no degree of vanity can prevent her acknowledging her own comparative littleness in action, if not in consciousness.'

'I know how highly you think of Jane Fairfax,' said Emma. Little Henry was in her thoughts, and a mixture of alarm and delicacy made her irresolute what else to say.

'Yes,' he replied, 'anybody may know how highly I think of her.'

'And yet,' said Emma, beginning hastily, and with an arch look, but soon stopping – it was better, however, to know the worst at once – she hurried on, 'and yet, perhaps, you may hardly be aware yourself how highly it is. The extent of your admiration may take you by surprise some day or other.'

Mr Knightley was hard at work upon the lower buttons of his thick leather gaiters, and either the exertion of getting them together, or some other cause, brought the colour into his face, as he answered: 'Oh! are you there? But you are miserably behind-hand. Mr Cole gave me a hint of it six weeks ago.'

He stopped. Emma felt her foot pressed by Mrs Weston, and did not herself know what to think. In a moment he went on: 'That will never be, however, I can assure you. Miss Fairfax, I dare say, would not have me if I were to ask her; and I am very sure I shall never ask her.'

Emma returned her friend's pressure with interest; and was pleased enough to exclaim: 'You are not vain, Mr Knightley. I will say that for you.'

He seemed hardly to hear her; he was thoughtful, and, in a manner which showed him not pleased, soon afterwards said: 'So you have been settling that I should marry Jane Fairfax?'

'No, indeed, I have not. You have scolded me too much for match-making for me to presume to take such a liberty with you. What I said just now meant nothing. One says those sort of things, of course, without any idea of a serious meaning. Oh! no; upon my word I have not the smallest wish for your marrying Jane Fairfax, or Jane anybody. You would not come in and sit with us in this comfortable way if you were married.'

Mr Knightley was thoughtful again. The result of his reverie was – 'No, Emma, I do not think the extent of my admiration for her will ever take me by surprise. I never had a thought of her in that way, I assure you.'

And soon afterwards, 'Jane Fairfax is a very charming young woman – but not even Jane Fairfax is perfect. She has a fault. She has not the open temper which a man would wish for in a wife.'

Emma could not but rejoice to hear that she had a fault.

'Well,' said she, 'and you soon silenced Mr Cole, I suppose?'

'Yes, very soon. He gave me a quiet hint; I told him he was mistaken; he asked my pardon, and said no more. Cole does not want to be wiser or wittier than his neighbours.'

'In that respect how unlike dear Mrs Elton, who wants to be wiser and wittier than all the world! I wonder how she speaks of the Coles – what she calls them. How can she find any appellation for them, deep enough in familiar vulgarity? She calls you Knightley; what can she do for Mr Cole? And so I am not to be surprised that Jane Fairfax accepts her civilities, and consents to be with her. Mrs Weston, your argument weighs most with me. I can much more readily enter into the temptation of getting away from Miss Bates, than I can believe in the triumph of Miss Fairfax's mind over Mrs Elton. I have no faith in Mrs Elton's acknowledging herself the inferior in thought, word, or deed; or in her being under any restraint beyond her own scanty rule of good breeding. I cannot imagine that she will not be continually insulting her visitor with praise, encouragement, and offers of service; that she will not be continually detailing her magnificent intentions, from the procuring her a permanent situation to the including her in those delightful exploring parties, which are to take place in the barouche-landau.'

'Jane Fairfax has feeling,' said Mr Knightley; 'I do not accuse her of want of feeling. Her sensibilities, I suspect, are strong, and her temper excellent in its power of forbearance, patience, self-control; but it wants openness. She is reserved; more reserved, I think, than she used to be: and I love an open temper. No; till Cole alluded to my supposed attachment, it had never entered my head. I saw Jane Fairfax, and conversed with her, with admiration and pleasure always; but with no thought beyond.'

'Well, Mrs Weston,' said Emma triumphantly, when he left them, 'what do you say now to Mr Knightley's marrying Jane Fairfax?'

'Why, really, dear Emma, I say that he is so very much occupied by the idea of not being in love with her, that I should not wonder if it were to end in his being so at last. Do not beat me.'

Chapter 34

🌿 🌿 🌿

Everybody in and about Highbury, who had ever visited Mr Elton, was disposed to pay him attention on his marriage. Dinner parties and evening parties were made for him and his lady; and invitations flowed in so fast that she had soon the pleasure of apprehending they were never to have a disengaged day.

'I see how it is,' said she; 'I see what a life I am to lead among you. Upon my word we shall be absolutely dissipated. We really seem quite the fashion. If this is living in the country, it is nothing very formidable. From Monday next to Saturday I assure you we have not a disengaged day! A woman with fewer resources than I have need not have been at a loss.'

No invitation came amiss to her. Her Bath habits made evening parties perfectly natural to her, and Maple Grove had given her a taste for dinners. She was a little shocked at the want of two drawing-rooms, at the poor attempt at rout-cakes, and there being no ice in the Highbury card-parties. Mrs Bates, Mrs Perry, Mrs Goddard, and others, were a good deal behindhand in knowledge of the world, but *she* would soon show them how everything ought to be arranged. In the course of the spring she must return their civilities by one very superior party; in which hercard-tables should be set out with their separate candles and unbroken packs in the true style, and more waiters engaged for the evening than their own establishment could furnish, to carry round the refreshments at exactly the proper hour, and in the proper order.

Emma, in the meanwhile, could not be satisfied without a dinner at Hartfield for the Eltons. They must not do less than others, or she should be exposed to odious suspicion, and imagined capable of pitiful resentment. A dinner there must be. After Emma had talked about it for ten minutes, Mr Woodhouse felt no unwillingness, and only made the usual stipulation of not sitting at the bottom of the table himself, with the usual regular difficulty of deciding who should do it for him.

The persons to be invited required little thought. Besides the Eltons, it must be the Westons and Mr Knightley; so far it was all of course: and it was hardly less inevitable that poor little Harriet must be asked to make the eighth; but this invitation was not given with equal satisfaction, and, on many accounts, Emma was particularly pleased by Harriet's begging to be allowed to decline it. 'She would rather not be in *his* company more than she could help. She was not yet quite able to see him and his charming happy wife together, without feeling uncomfortable. If Miss Woodhouse would not be displeased, she would rather stay at home.' It was precisely what Emma would have wished, had she deemed it possible enough for wishing. She was delighted with the fortitude of her little friend – for fortitude she knew it was in her to give up being in company, and stay at home; and she could now invite the very person whom she really wanted to make the eighth, Jane Fairfax. Since her last conversation with Mrs Weston and Mr Knightley, she was more conscience-stricken about Jane Fairfax than she had often been. Mr Knightley's words dwelt with her. He had said that Jane Fairfax received attentions from Mrs Elton which nobody else paid her.

'This is very true,' said she, 'at least as far as related to me, which was all that was meant, and it is very shameful. Of the same age, and always knowing her, I ought to have been more her friend. She will never like me now. I have neglected her too long. But I will show her greater attention than I have done.'

Every invitation was successful. They were all disengaged and all happy. The preparatory interest of this dinner, however, was not yet over. A circumstance rather unlucky occurred. The two eldest little Knightleys were engaged to pay their grandpapa and aunt a visit of some weeks in the spring and their papa now proposed bringing them, and staying one whole day at Hartfield – which one day would be the very day of this party. His professional engagements did not allow of his being put off, but both father and daughter were disturbed by its happening so. Mr Woodhouse considered eight persons at dinner together as the utmost that his nerves could bear – and here would be a ninth – and Emma apprehended that it would be a ninth very much out of humour, at not being able to come even to Hartfield for forty-eight hours, without falling in with a dinner party.

She comforted her father better than she could comfort herself, by representing that though he certainly would make them nine, yet he always said so little, that the increase of noise would be very immaterial. She thought it in reality a sad exchange for herself, to have him, with his grave looks and recluctant conversation, opposed to her instead of his brother.

The event was more favourable to Mr Woodhouse than to Emma. John Knightley came; but Mr Weston was unexpectedly summoned to town, and must be absent on the very day. He might be able to join them in the evening, but certainly not to dinner. Mr Woodhouse was quite at ease; and the seeing him so, with the arrival of the little boys, and the philosophic composure of her brother on hearing his fate, removed the chief of even Emma's vexation.

The day came, the party were punctually assembled, and Mr John Knightley seemed early to devote himself to the business of being agreeable. Instead of drawing his brother off to a window while they waited for dinner, he was talking to Miss Fairfax. Mrs Elton, as elegant as lace and pearls could make her, he looked at in silence – wanting only to observe enough for Isabella's information – but Miss Fairfax was an old acquaintance and a quiet girl, and he could talk to her. He had met her before breakfast as he was returning from a walk with his little boys, when it had been just beginning to rain. It was natural to have some civil hopes on the subject, and he said: 'I hope you did not venture far, Miss Fairfax, this morning, or I am sure you must have been wet. We scarcely got home in time. I hope you turned directly.'

'I went only to the post office,' said she, 'and reached home before the rain was much. It is my daily errand. I always fetch the letters when I am here. It saves trouble, and is a something to get me out. A walk before breakfast does me good.'

'Not a walk in the rain, I should imagine.'

'No; but it did not absolutely rain when I set out.'

Mr John Knightley smiled, and replied: 'That is to say, you chose to have your walk, for you were not six yards from your own door when I had the pleasure of meeting you; and Henry and John had seen more drops than they could count long before. The post office has a great charm at one period of our lives. When you have lived to my age, you will begin to think letters are never worth going through the rain for.'

There was a little blush, and then this answer: 'I must not hope to be ever situated as you are, in the midst of every dearest connection, and therefore I cannot expect that simply growing older should make me indifferent about letters.'

'Indifferent! Oh, no – I never conceived you could become indifferent. Letters are no matter of indifference; they are generally a very positive curse.'

'You are speaking of letters of business; mine are letters of friendship.'

'I have often thought them the worst of the two,' replied he coolly. 'Business you know, may bring money, but friendship hardly ever does.'

'Ah! you are not serious now. I know Mr John Knightley too well – I am very sure he understands the value of friendship as well as anybody. I can easily believe that letters are very little to you, much less than to me; but it is not your being ten years older than myself which makes the difference; it is not age, but situation. You have everybody dearest to you always at hand, I, probably, never shall again; and therefore, till I have outlived all my affections, a post office, I think, must always have power to draw me out, in worse weather than today.'

'When I talked of your being altered by time, by the progress of years,' said John Knightley, 'I meant to imply the change of situation which time usually brings. I consider one as including the other. Time will generally lessen the interest of every attachment not within the daily circle – but that is not the change I had in view for you. As an old friend, you will allow me to hope, Miss Fairfax, that ten years hence, you may have as many concentrated objects as I have.'

It was kindly said, and very far from giving offence. A pleasant 'thank you' seemed meant to laugh it off; but a blush, a quivering lip, a tear in the eye, showed that it was felt beyond a laugh. Her attention was now claimed by Mr Woodhouse, who being, according to his custom on such occasions, making the circle of his guests, and paying his particular compliments to the ladies, was ending with her – and with all his mildest urbanity, said: 'I am very sorry to hear, Miss Fairfax, of your being out this morning in the rain. Young ladies should take care of themselves. Young ladies are delicate plants. They should take care of their health and their complexion. My dear, did you change your stockings?'

'Yes, sir, I did indeed; and I am very much obliged by your kind solicitude about me.'

'My dear Miss Fairfax, young ladies are very sure to be cared for. I hope your good grandmamma and aunt are well. They are some of my very old friends. I wish my health allowed me to be a better neighbour. You do us a great deal of honour today, I am sure. My daughter and I are both highly sensible of your goodness, and have the greatest satisfaction in seeing you at Hartfield.'

The kind-hearted, polite old man might then sit down and feel that he had done his duty, and made every fair lady welcome and easy.

By this time the walk in the rain had reached Mrs Elton, and her remonstrances now opened upon Jane.

'My dear Jane, what is this I hear? Going to the post office in the rain! This must not be, I assure you. You sad girl, how could you do such a thing? It is a sign I was not there to take care of you.'

Jane very patiently assured her that she had not caught any cold.

'Oh! do not tell *me*. You really are a very sad girl, and do not know how to take care of yourself. To the post office indeed! Mrs Weston, did you ever hear the like? You and I must positively exert our authority.'

'My advice,' said Mrs Weston, kindly and persuasively, 'I certainly do feel tempted to give. Miss Fairfax, you must not run such risks. Liable as you have been to severe colds, indeed you ought to be particularly careful, especially at this time of year. The spring I always think requires more than common care. Better wait an hour or two, or even half a day for your letters, than run the risk of bringing on your cough again. Now do not you feel that you had? Yes, I am sure you are much too reasonable. You look as if you would not do such a thing again.'

'Oh! she *shall not* do such a thing again,' eagerly rejoined Mrs Elton. 'We will not allow her to do such a thing again' – and nodding significantly – 'there must be some arrangement made, there must indeed. I shall speak to Mr E. The man who fetches our letters every morning (one of our men, I forget his name) shall enquire for yours too and bring them to you. That will obviate all difficulties, you know; and from us I really think, my dear Jane, you can have no scruple to accept such an accommodation.'

'You are extremely kind,' said Jane; 'but I cannot give up my early walk. I am advised to be out-of-doors as much as I can; I must walk somewhere, and the post office is an object; and, upon my word, I have scarcely ever had a bad morning before.'

'My dear Jane, say no more about it. The thing is determined, that is' (laughing affectedly) 'as far as I can presume to determine anything without the concurrence of my lord and master. You know, Mrs Weston, you and I must be cautious how we express ourselves. But I do flatter myself, my dear Jane, that my influence is not entirely worn out. If I meet with no insuperable difficulties, therefore, consider that point as settled.'

'Excuse me,' said Jane earnestly, 'I cannot by any means consent to such an arrangement, so needlessly troublesome to your servant. If the errand were not a pleasure to me, it could be done, as it always is when I am not here, by my grandmamma's – '

'Oh! my dear; but so much as Patty has to do! And it is a kindness to employ our men.'

Jane looked as if she did not mean to be conquered; but, instead of answering, she began speaking again to Mr John Knightley.

'The post office is a wonderful establishment!' said she. 'The regularity and despatch of it! If one thinks of all that it has to do, and all that it does so well, it is really astonishing!'

'It is certainly very well regulated.'

'So seldom that any negligence or blunder appears! So seldom that a letter, among the thousands that are constantly passing about the kingdom, is ever carried wrong – and not one in a million, I suppose, actually lost! And when one considers the variety of hands, and of bad hands too, that are to be deciphered, it increases the wonder.'

'The clerks grow expert from habit. They must begin with some quickness of sight and hand, and exercise improves them. If you want any further explanation,' continued he, smiling, 'they are paid for it. That is the key to a great deal of capacity. The public pays and must be served well.'

The varieties of handwriting were further talked of, and the usual observations made.

'I have heard it asserted,' said John Knightley, 'that the same sort of handwriting often prevails in a family; and where the same master teaches, it is natural enough. But for that reason, I should imagine the likeness must be chiefly confined to the females, for boys have very little teaching after an early age, and scramble into any hand they can get. Isabella and Emma, I think, do write very much alike. I have not always known their writing apart.'

'Yes,' said his brother hesitatingly; 'there is a likeness. I know what you mean – but Emma's hand is the strongest.'

'Isabella and Emma both write beautifully,' said Mr Woodhouse; 'and always did. And so does poor Mrs Weston' – with half a sigh and half a smile at her.

'I never saw any gentleman's handwriting' – Emma began, looking also at Mrs Weston; but stopped, on perceiving that Mrs Weston was attending to some one else – and the pause gave her time to reflect. 'Now, how am I going to introduce him? Am I unequal to speaking his name at once before all these people? Is it necessary for me to use any roundabout phrase? Your Yorkshire friend – your correspondent in Yorkshire – that would be the way, I suppose, if I were very bad. No, I can pronounce his name without the smallest distress. I certainly get better and better. Now for it.'

Mrs Weston was disengaged, and Emma began again – 'Mr Frank Churchill writes one of the best gentleman's hands I ever saw.'

'I do not admire it,' said Mr Knightley. 'It is too small – wants strength. It is like a woman's writing.'

This was not submitted to by either lady. They vindicated him against the base aspersion. 'No, it by no means wanted strength – it was not a large hand, but very clear, and certainly strong. Had not Mrs Weston any letter about her to produce?' No, she had heard from him very lately, but having answered the letter, had put it away.

'If we were in the other room,' said Emma – 'If I had my writing-desk, I am sure I could produce a specimen. I have a note of his. Do not you remember, Mrs Weston, employing him to write for you one day?'

'He chose to say he was employed.'

'Well, well, I have that note; and can show it after dinner to convince Mr Knightley.'

'Oh! when a gallant young man, like Mr Frank Churchill,' said Mr Knightley dryly, 'writes to a fair lady like Miss Woodhouse, he will, of course, put forth his best.'

Dinner was on table. Mrs Elton, before she could be spoken to, was ready; and before Mr Woodhouse had reached her, with his request to be allowed to hand her into the dining-parlour, was saying: 'Must I go first? I really am ashamed of always leading the way.'

Jane's solicitude about fetching her own letters had not escaped Emma. She had heard and seen it all; and felt some curiosity to know whether the wet walk of this morning had produced any. She suspected that it *had;* that it would not have been so resolutely encountered but in full expectation of hearing from some one very dear, and that it had not been in vain. She thought there was an air of greater happiness than usual – a glow both of complexion and spirits.

She could have made an enquiry or two, as to the expedition and the expense of the Irish mails – it was at her tongue's end – but she abstained. She was quite determined not to utter a word that should hurt Jane Fairfax's feelings: and they followed the other ladies out of the room, arm in arm, with an appearance of goodwill highly becoming to the beauty and grace of each.

Chapter 35

When the ladies returned to the drawing-room after dinner, Emma found it hardly possible to prevent their making two distinct parties; with so much perseverance in judging and behaving ill did Mrs Elton engross Jane Fairfax and slight herself. She and Mrs Weston were obliged to be almost always either talking together or silent together. Mrs Elton left them no choice. If Jane repressed her for a little time she soon began again; and though much that passed between them was in a half-whisper, especially on Mrs Elton's side, there was no avoiding a knowledge of their principal subjects: the post office – catching cold – fetching letters – and friendship, were long under discussion; and to them succeeded one which must be at least equally unpleasant to Jane – enquiries whether she had yet heard of any situation likely to suit her, and professions of Mrs Elton's meditated activity.

'Here is April come,' said she; 'I get quite anxious about you. June will soon be here.'

'But I have never fixed on June or any other month – merely looked forward to the summer in general.'

'But have you really heard of nothing?'

'I have not even made any enquiry; I do not wish to make any yet.'

'Oh! my dear, we cannot begin too early; you are not aware of the difficulty of procuring exactly the desirable thing.'

'I not aware!' said Jane, shaking her head; 'dear Mrs Elton, who can have thought of it as I have done?'

'But you have not seen so much of the world as I have. You do not know how many candidates there always are for the first situations. I saw a vast deal of that in the neighbourhood round Maple

Grove. A cousin of Mr Suckling, Mrs Bragge, had such an infinity of applications; everybody was anxious to be in her family, for she moves in the first circle. Wax-candles in the schoolroom! You may imagine how desirable! Of all houses in the kingdom, Mrs Bragge's is the one I would most wish to see you in.'

'Colonel and Mrs Campbell are to be in town again by midsummer,' said Jane, 'and I must spend some time with them; I am sure they will want it – afterwards I may probably be glad to dispose of myself. But I would not wish you to take the trouble of making any enquiries at present.'

'Trouble! ay, I know your scruples. You are afraid of giving me trouble; but I assure you, my dear Jane, the Campbells can hardly be more interested about you than I am. I shall write to Mrs Partridge in a day or two, and shall give her a strict charge to be on the look-out for anything eligible.'

'Thank you, but I would rather you did not mention the subject to her; till the time draws nearer, I do not wish to be giving anybody trouble.'

'But, my dear child, the time *is* drawing near; here is April, and June, or say even July, is very near, with such business to accomplish before us. Your inexperience really amuses me! A situation such as you deserve, and your friends would require for you, is no everyday occurrence, is not obtained at a moment's notice; indeed, indeed, we must begin enquiring directly.'

'Excuse me, ma'am, but this is by no means my intention; I make no enquiry myself, and should be sorry to have any made by my friends. When I am quite determined as to the time, I am not at all afraid of being long unemployed. There are places in town, offices, where enquiry would soon produce something – offices for the sale, not quite of human flesh, but of human intellect!'

'Oh! my dear, human flesh! You quite shock me; if you mean a fling at the slave trade, I assure you Mr Suckling was always rather a friend to the abolition.'

'I did not mean – I was not thinking of the slave-trade,' replied Jane; 'governess-trade, I assure you, was all that I had in view;

widely different, certainly, as to the guilt of those who carry it on; but as to the greater misery of the victims, I do not know where it lies. But I only mean to say that there are advertising offices, and that by applying to them I should have no doubt of very soon meeting with something that would do.'

'Something that would do!' repeated Mrs Elton. 'Ay, *that* may suit your humble ideas of yourself; I know what a modest creature you are; but it will not satisfy your friends to have you taking up with anything that may offer, any inferior commonplace situation, in a family not moving in a certain circle, or able to command the elegancies of life.'

'You are very obliging; but as to all that I am very indifferent; it would be no object to me to be with the rich; my mortifications, I think, would only be the greater; I should suffer more from comparison. A gentleman's family is all that I should condition for.'

'I know you, I know you; you would take up with anything; but I shall be a little more nice, and I am sure the good Campbells will be quite on my side; with your superior talents, you have a right to move in the first circle. Your musical knowledge alone would entitle you to name your own terms, have as many rooms as you like, and mix in the family as much as you chose – that is – I do not know – if you knew the harp, you might do all that, I am very sure; but you sing as well as play; yes, I really believe you might, even without the harp, stipulate for what you chose; and you must and shall be delightfully, honourably, and comfortably settled before the Campbells or I have any rest.'

'You may well class the delight, the honour, and the comfort of such a situation together,' said Jane, 'they are pretty sure to be equal; however, I am very serious in not wishing anything to be attempted at present for me. I am exceedingly obliged to you, Mrs Elton; I am obliged to anybody who feels for me, but I am quite serious in wishing nothing to be done till the summer. For two or three months longer I shall remain where I am, and as I am.'

'And I am quite serious too, I assure you,' replied Mrs Elton gaily, 'in resolving to be always on the watch, and employing my friends to watch also, that nothing really unexceptionable may pass us.'

In this style she ran on; never thoroughly stopped by anything till Mr Woodhouse came into the room; her vanity had then a change of object, and Emma heard her saying in the same half-whisper to Jane: 'Here comes this dear old beau of mine, I protest! Only think of his gallantry in coming away before the other men! what a dear creature he is! I assure you I like him excessively. I admire all that quaint, old-fashioned politeness; it is much more to my taste than modern ease; modern ease often disgusts me. But this good old Mr Woodhouse, I wish you had heard his gallant speeches to me at dinner. Oh! I assure you I began to think my *caro sposo* would be absolutely jealous. I fancy I am rather a favourite; he took notice of my gown. How do you like it? Selina's choice – handsome, I think, but I do not know whether it is not over-trimmed; I have the greatest dislike to the idea of being over-trimmed; quite a horror of finery. I must put on a few ornaments *now*, because it is expected of me. A bride, you know, must appear like a bride, but my natural taste is all for simplicity; a simple style of dress is so infinitely preferable to finery. But I am quite in the minority, I believe; few people seem to value simplicity of dress – show and finery are everything. I have some notion of putting such a trimming as this to my white and silver poplin. Do you think it will look well?'

The whole party were but just re-assembled in the drawing-room, when Mr Weston made his appearance among them. He had returned to a late dinner, and walked to Hartfield as soon as it was over. He had been too much expected by the best judges, for surprise – but there was great joy. Mr Woodhouse was almost as glad to see him now, as he would have been sorry to see him before. John Knightley only was in mute astonishment. That a man who might have spent his evening quietly at home after a day of business in London should set off again, and walk half a mile to another man's house for the sake of being in mixed company till bedtime, of finishing his day in the efforts of civility and the noise of numbers, was a circumstance to strike him deeply. A man who had been in motion since eight o'clock in the morning, and might now have been still – who had been long talking, and might have been silent – who had been in more than one crowd, and might have been alone! Such a man to quit the tranquillity and inde-pendence of his own fireside, and on the evening of a cold sleety April day rush out again into the world! Could he, by a touch of his finger, have instantly taken back his wife, there would have been a motive; but his coming would probably prolong rather than break up the party. John Knightley looked at him with amazement, then shrugged his shoulders, and said, 'I could not have believed it even of him.'

Mr Weston, meanwhile, perfectly unsuspicious of the indig-nation he was exciting, happy and cheerful as usual, and with all the right of being principal talker, which a day spent anywhere from home confers, was making himself agreeable among the rest; and having satisfied the enquiries of his wife as to his dinner, convincing her that none of all her careful directions to the servants had been forgotten, and spread abroad what public news he had heard, was proceeding to a family communication, which, though principally addressed to Mrs Weston, he had not the smallest doubt of being highly interesting to everybody in the room. He gave her a letter – it was from Frank, and to herself; he had met with it in his way, and had taken the liberty of opening it.

'Read it, read it,' said he – 'it will give you pleasure; only a few lines – will not take you long; read it to Emma.'

The two ladies looked over it together; and he sat smiling and talking to them the whole time, in a voice a little subdued, but very audible to everybody.

'Well, he is coming, you see; good news, I think. Well, what do you say to it? I always told you he would be here again soon, did not I? Anne, my dear, did not I always tell you so, and you would not believe me? In town next week, you see – at the latest, I dare say; for *she* is as impatient as the black gentleman when anything is to be done; most likely they will be there tomorrow or Saturday. As to her illness, all nothing, of course. But it is an excellent thing to have Frank among us again, so near the town. They will stay a good while when they do come, and he will be half his time with us. This is precisely what I wanted. Well, pretty good news, is not it? Have you finished it? Has Emma read it all? Put it up, put it up; we will have a good talk about it some other time, but it will not do now. I shall only just mention the circumstance to the others in a common way.'

Mrs Weston was most comfortably pleased on the occasion. Her looks and words had nothing to restrain them. She was happy, she knew she was happy, and knew she ought to be happy. Her congratulations were warm and open; but Emma could not speak so fluently. *She* was a little occupied in weighing her own feelings, and trying to understand the degree of her agitation, which she rather thought was considerable.

Mr Weston, however, too eager to be very observant, too communicative to want others to talk, was very well satisfied with what she did say, and soon moved away to make the rest of hisfriends happy, by a partial communication of what the whole room must have overheard already.

It was well that he took everybody's joy for granted, or he might not have thought either Mr Woodhouse or Mr Knightley particularly delighted. They were the first entitled, after Mrs Weston and Emma, to be made happy. From them he would have proceeded to Miss Fairfax; but she was so deep in conversation with John Knightley, that it would have been too positive an interruption; and, finding himself close to Mrs Elton, and her attention disengaged, he necessarily began on the subject with her.

Chapter 36

'I hope I shall soon have the pleasure of introducing my son to you,' said Mr Weston.

Mrs Elton, very willing to suppose a particular compliment intended her by such a hope, smiled most graciously.

'You have heard of a certain Frank Churchill, I presume,' he continued, 'and know him to be my son, though he does not bear my name.'

'Oh, yes, and I shall be very happy in his acquaintance. I am sure Mr Elton will lose no time in calling on him; and we shall both have great pleasure in seeing him at the Vicarage.'

'You are very obliging. Frank will be extremely happy, I am sure. He is to be in town next week, if not sooner. We have notice of it in a letter today. I met the letters in my way this morning, and seeing my son's hand, presumed to open it, though it was not directed to me – it was to Mrs Weston. She is his principal correspondent, I assure you. I hardly ever get a letter.'

'And so you absolutely opened what was directed to her! Oh, Mr Weston' (laughing affectedly), 'I must protest against that. A most dangerous precedent indeed! I beg you will not let your neighbours follow your example. Upon my word, if this is what I am to expect, we married women must begin to exert ourselves. Oh, Mr Weston, I could not have believed it of you!'

'Ay, we men are sad fellows. You must take care of yourself, Mrs Elton. This letter tells us – it is a short letter, written in a hurry, merely to give us notice – it tells us that they are all coming up to town directly, on Mrs Churchill's account! she has not been well the whole winter, and thinks Enscombe too cold for her; so they are all to move southward without loss of time.'

'Indeed! from Yorkshire, I think. Enscombe is in Yorkshire?'

'Yes, they are about 190 miles from London: a considerable journey.'

'Yes, upon my word, very considerable. Sixty-five miles farther than from Maple Grove to London. But what is distance Mr Weston, to people of large fortune? You would be amazed to hear how my brother, Mr Suckling, sometimes flies about. You will hardly believe me, but twice in one week he and Mr Bragge went to London and back again with four horses.'

'The evil of the distance from Enscombe,' said Mr Weston, 'is that Mrs Churchill, *as we understand,* has not been able to leave the sofa for a week together. In Frank's last letter she complained, he said, of being too weak to get into her conservatory without having both his arm and his uncle's. This, you know, speaks a great degree of weakness; but now she is so impatient to be in town, that she means to sleep only two nights on the road – so Frank writes word. Certainly, delicate ladies have very extraordinary constitutions, Mrs Elton; you must grant me that.'

'No, indeed, I shall grant you nothing. I always take the part of my own sex; I do, indeed. I give you notice, you will find me a formidable antagonist on that point. I always stand up for women; and I assure you, if you knew how Selina feels with respect to sleeping at an inn, you would not wonder at Mrs Churchill's making incredible exertions to avoid it. Selina says it is quite horror to her; and I believe I have caught a little of her nicety. She always travels with her own sheets; an excellent precaution. Does Mrs Churchill do the same?'

'Depend upon it, Mrs Churchill does everything that any other fine lady ever did. Mrs Churchill will not be second to any lady in the land for – '

Mrs Elton eagerly interposed with: 'Oh, Mr Weston, do not mistake me. Selina is no fine lady, I assure you. Do not run away with such an idea.'

'Is not she? Then she is no rule for Mrs Churchill, who is as thorough a fine lady as anybody ever beheld.'

Mrs Elton began to think she had been wrong in disclaiming so warmly. It was by no means her object to have it believed that her sister was not a fine lady; perhaps there was want of spirit in the pretence of it; and she was considering in what way she had best retract, when Mr Weston went on: 'Mrs Churchill is not much in my good graces, as you may suspect; but this is quite between ourselves. She is very fond of Frank, and therefore I would not speak ill of her. Besides, she is out of health now; but *that* indeed, by her own account, she has always been. I would not say so to everybody, Mrs Elton; but I have not much faith in Mrs Churchill's illness.'

'If she is really ill, why not go to Bath, Mr Weston? To Bath, or to Clifton?'

'She has taken it into her head that Enscombe is too cold for her. The fact is, I suppose, that she is tired of Enscombe. She has now been a longer time stationary there than she ever was before, and she begins to want change. It is a retired place. A fine place, but very retired.'

'Ay, like Maple Grove, I dare say. Nothing can stand more retired from the road than Maple Grove. Such an immense plantation all round it! You seem shut out from everything – in the most complete retirement. And Mrs Churchill probably has not health or spirits like Selina to enjoy that sort of seclusion. Or, perhaps, she may not have resources enough in herself to be qualified for a country life. I always say a woman cannot have too many resources, and I feel very thankful that I have so many myself as to be quite independent of society.'

'Frank was here in February for a fortnight.'

'So I remember to have heard. He will find an *addition* to the society of Highbury when he comes again; that is, if I may presume to call myself an addition. But perhaps he may never have heard of there being such a creature in the world.'

This was too loud a call for a compliment to be passed by, and Mr Weston, with a very good grace, immediately exclaimed: 'My dear madam! Nobody but yourself could imagine such a thing possible. Not heard of you! I believe Mrs Weston's letters lately have been full of very little else than Mrs Elton.'

He had done his duty, and could return to his son.

'When Frank left us,' continued he, 'it was quite uncertain when we might see him again, which makes this day's news doubly welcome. It has been completely unexpected. That is, I always had a strong persuasion he would be here again soon; I was sure something favourable would turn up – but nobody believed me. He and Mrs Weston were both dreadfully desponding. "How could he contrive to come? And how could it be supposed that his uncle and aunt would spare him again?" and so forth. I always felt that something would happen in our favour, and so it has, you see. I have observed, Mrs Elton, in the course of my life, that if things are going untowardly one month, they are sure to mend the next.'

'Very true, Mr Weston, perfectly true. It is just what I used to say to a certain gentleman in company in the days of courtship, when, because things did not go quite right – did not proceed with all the rapidity, which suited his feelings – he was apt to be in despair, and exclaim that he was sure at this rate it would be *May* before Hymen's saffron robe would be put on for us! Oh! the pains I have been at to dispel those gloomy ideas, and give him cheerfuller views! The carriage – we had disappointments about the carriage – one morning, I remember, he came to me quite in despair.'

She was stopped by a slight fit of coughing, and Mr Weston instantly seized the opportunity of going on: 'You were mentioning May. May is the very month which Mrs Churchill is ordered, or has ordered herself to spend in some warmer place than Enscombe – in short, to spend in London; so that we have the agreeable prospect of frequent visits from Frank, the whole spring – precisely the season of the year which one should have chosen for it: days almost at the longest: weather genial and pleasant, always inviting one out, and never too hot for exercise. When he was here before, we made the best of it: but there was a good deal of wet, damp, cheerless weather; there always is in February, you know; and we could not do half that we intended. Now will be the time. This will be complete enjoyment; and I do not know, Mrs Elton, whether the uncertainty of our meetings, the sort of constant expectation there will be of his coming in today or tomorrow, and at any hour, may not be more friendly to happiness than having him actually in the house. I think it is so. I think it is the state of mind which gives most spirit and delight. I hope you will be pleased with my son; but you must not expect a prodigy. He is generally thought a fine young man, but do not expect a prodigy. Mrs Weston's partiality for him is very great, and, as you may suppose, most gratifying to me. She thinks nobody equal to him.'

'And I assure you, Mr Weston, I have very little doubt that my opinion will be decidedly in his favour. I have heard so much in praise of Mr Frank Churchill. At the same time, it is fair to observe, that I am one of those who always judge for themselves, and are by no means implicitly guided by others. I give you notice, that as I find your son, so I shall judge of him. I am no flatterer.'

Mr Weston was musing.

'I hope,' said he presently, 'I have not been severe upon poor Mrs Churchill. If she is ill, I should be sorry to do her injustice; but there are some traits in her character which make it difficult for me to speak of her with the forbearance I could wish. You cannot be ignorant, Mrs Elton, of my connection with the family, nor of the treatment I have met with; and, between ourselves, the whole blame of it is to be laid to her. She was the instigator. Frank's mother would never have been slighted as she was but for her. Mr Churchill has pride; but his pride is nothing to his wife's; his is a quiet, indolent, gentleman-like sort of pride, that would harm nobody, and only make himself a little helpless and tiresome; but her pride is arrogance and insolence. And what inclines one less to bear, she has no fair pretence of family or blood. She was nobody when he married her, barely the daughter of a gentleman; but ever since her being turned into a Churchill, she has out-Churchill'd them all in high and mighty claims; but in herself, I assure you, she is an upstart.'

'Only think! well, that must be infinitely provoking! I have quite a horror of upstarts. Maple Grove has given me a thorough disgust to people of that sort; for there is a family in that neighbourhood who are such an annoyance to my brother and sister from the airs they give themselves! Your description of Mrs Churchill made me think of them directly. People of the name of Tupman, very lately settled there, and encumbered with many low connections, but giving themselves immense airs, and expecting to be on a footing with the old-established families. A year and a half is the very utmost that they can have lived at West Hall; and how they got their fortune nobody knows. They came from Birmingham, which is not a place to promise much, you know, Mr Weston. One has not great hopes from Birmingham. I always say there is something direful in the sound; but nothing more is positively known of the Tupmans, though a good many things, I assure you, are suspected; and yet by their manners they evidently think themselves equal even to my brother, Mr Suckling, who happens to be one of their nearest neighbours. It is infinitely too bad. Mr Suckling, who has been eleven years a resident at Maple Grove, and whose father had it before him – I believe, at least – I am almost sure that old Mr Suckling had completed the purchase before his death.'

They were interrupted. Tea was carrying round, and Mr Weston, having said all that he wanted, soon took the opportunity of walking away.

After tea, Mr and Mrs Weston, and Mr Elton, sat down with Mr Woodhouse to cards. The remaining five were left to their own powers, and Emma doubted their getting on very well; for Mr Knightley seemed little disposed for conservation; Mrs Elton was wanting notice, which nobody had inclination to pay, and she was herself in a worry of spirits which would have made her prefer being silent.

Mr John Knightley proved more talkative than his brother. He was to leave them early the next day; and he soon began with: 'Well, Emma, I do not believe I have anything more to say about the boys; but you have your sister's letter, and everything is down at full length there, we may be sure. My charge would be much more concise than hers, and probably not much in the same spirit; all that I have to recommend being comprised in – Do not spoil them, and do not physic them.'

'I rather hope to satisfy you both,' said Emma; 'for I shall do all in my power to make them happy, which will be enough for Isabella; and happiness must preclude false indulgence and physic.'

'And if you find them troublesome, you must send them home again.'

'That is very likely. You think so, do not you?'

'I hope I am aware that they may be too noisy for your father; or even may be some encumbrance to you, if your visiting engagements continue to increase as much as they have done lately.'

'Increase!'

'Certainly; you must be sensible that the last half-year has made a great difference in your way of life.'

'Difference! No, indeed, I am not.'

'There can be no doubt of your being much more engaged with company than you used to be. Witness this very time. Here am I come down for only one day, and you are engaged with a dinner-party! When did it happen before, or anything like it? Your neighbourhood is increasing, and you mix more with it. A little while ago, every letter to Isabella brought an account of fresh gaieties; dinners at Mr Cole's, or balls at the Crown. The difference which Randalls, Randalls alone, makes in your goings on is very great.'

'Yes,' said his brother quickly, 'it is Randalls that does it all.'

'Very well; and as Randalls, I suppose, is not likely to have less influence than heretofore, it strikes me as a possible thing,

Emma, that Henry and John may be sometimes in the way. And if they are, I only beg you to send them home.'

'No,' cried Mr Knightley; 'that need not be the consequence. Let them be sent to Donwell. I shall certainly be at leisure.'

'Upon my word,' exclaimed Emma, 'you amuse me! I should like to know how many of all my numerous engagements take place without your being of the party; and why I am to be supposed in danger of wanting leisure to attend to the little boys. These amazing engagements of mine – what have they been? Dining once with the Coles, and having a ball talked of, which never took place. I can understand you' – (nodding at Mr John Knightley) – 'your good fortune in meeting with so many of your friends at once here delights you too much to pass unnoticed. But you' (turning to Mr Knightley), 'who know how very, very seldom I am ever two hours from Hartfield – why you should foresee such a series of dissipation for me, I cannot imagine. And as to my dear little boys, I must say, that if Aunt Emma has not time for them, I do not think they would fare much better with Uncle Knightley, who is absent from home about five hours where she is absent one; and who, when he is at home, is either reading to himself or settling his accounts.'

Mr Knightley seemed to be trying not to smile; and succeeded without difficulty, upon Mrs Elton's beginning to talk to him.

Chapter 37

A very little quiet reflection was enough to satisfy Emma as to the nature of her agitation on hearing this news of Frank Churchill. She was soon convinced that it was not for herself she was feeling at all apprehensive or embarrassed – it was for him. Her own attachment had really subsided into a mere nothing – it was not worth thinking of; but if he, who had undoubtedly been always so much the most in love of the two, were to be returning with the same warmth of sentiment which he had taken away, it would be very distressing. If a separation of two months should not have cooled him, there were dangers and evils before her: caution for him and for herself would be necessary. She did not mean to have her own affections entangled again, and it would be incumbent on her to avoid any encouragement of his.

She wished she might be able to keep him from an absolute declaration. That would be so very painful a conclusion of their present acquaintance; and yet she could not help rather anticipating something decisive. She felt as if the spring would not pass without bringing a crisis, an event, a something to alter her present composed and tranquil state.

It was not very long, though rather longer than Mr Weston had foreseen, before she had the power of forming some opinion of Frank Churchill's feelings. The Enscombe family were not in town quite so soon as had been imagined, but he was at Highbury very soon afterwards. He rode down for a couple of hours; he could not yet do more; but as he came from Randalls immediately to Hartfield, she could then exercise all her quick observation, and speedily determine how he was influenced, and how she must act. They met with the utmost friendliness. There could be no doubt of his great pleasure in seeing her. But she had an almost instant doubt of his caring for her as he had done, of his feeling the same tenderness in the same degree. She watched him well. It was a clear thing he was less in love than he had been. Absence, with the conviction probably of her indifference, had produced this very natural and very desirable effect.

He was in high spirits; as ready to talk and laugh as ever; and seemed delighted to speak of his former visit, and recur to old stories; and he was not without agitation. It was not in his calmness that she read his comparative difference. He was not calm; his spirits were evidently fluttered; there was restlessness about him. Lively as he was, it seemed a liveliness that did not satisfy himself; but what decided her belief on the subject, was his staying only a quarter of an hour, and hurrying away to make other calls in Highbury. 'He had seen a group of old acquaintance in the street as he passed – he had not stopped, he would not stop for more than a word – but he had the vanity to think they would be disappointed if he did not call; and, much as he wished to stay longer at Hartfield, he must hurry off.'

She had no doubt as to his being less in love, but neither his agitated spirits nor his hurrying away seemed like a perfect cure; and she was rather inclined to think it implied a dread of her returning power, and a discreet resolution of not trusting himself with her long.

This was the only visit from Frank Churchill in the course of ten days. He was often hoping, intending to come; but was always prevented. His aunt could not bear to have him leave her. Such was his own account at Randalls. If he were quite sincere, if he really tried to come, it was to be inferred that Mrs Churchill's removal to London had been of no service to the wilful or nervous part of her disorder. That she was really ill was very certain; he had declared himself convinced of it, at Randalls. Though much might he fancy, he could not doubt, when he looked back, that she was in a weaker state of health than she had been half a year ago. He did not believe it to proceed from anything that care and medicine might not remove, or at least that she might not have many years of existence before her; but he could not be prevailed on, by all his father's doubts, to say that her complaints were merely imaginary, or that she was as strong as ever.

It soon appeared that London was not the place for her. She could not endure its noise. Her nerves were under continual irritation and suffering; and by the ten days' end, her nephew's letter to Randalls communicated a change of plan. They were going to remove immediately to Richmond. Mrs Churchill had been recommended to the medical skill of an eminent person there, and had otherwise a fancy for the place. A ready-furnished house in a favourite spot was engaged, and much benefit expected from the change.

Emma heard that Frank wrote in the highest spirits of this arrangement, and seemed most fully to appreciate the blessing of having two months before him of such near neighbourhood to many dear friends; for the house was taken for May and June. She was told that now he wrote with the greatest confidence of being often with them, almost as often as he could even wish.

Emma saw how Mr Weston understood these joyous prospects. He was considering her as the source of all the happiness they offered. She hoped it was not so. Two months must bring it to the proof.

Mr Weston's own happiness was indisputable. He was quite delighted. It was the very circumstance he could have wished for. Now, it would be really having Frank in their neighbourhood. What were nine miles to a young man? An hour's ride. He would be always coming over. The difference in that respect of Richmond and London was enough to make the whole difference of seeing him always and seeing him never. Sixteen miles – nay, eighteen – it must be full eighteen to Manchester Street – was a serious obstacle. Were he ever able to get away, the day would be spent in coming and returning. There was no comfort in having him in London; he might as well be at Enscombe; but Richmond was the very distance for easy intercourse. Better than nearer!

One good thing was immediately brought to a certainty by this removal – the ball at the Crown. It had not been forgotten before; but it had been soon acknowledged vain to attempt to fix a day. Now, however, it was absolutely to be; every preparation was resumed; and very soon after the Churchills had removed to Richmond, a few lines from Frank, to say that his aunt felt already much better for the change, and that he had no doubt of being able to join them for twenty-four hours at any given time, induced them to name as early a day as possible.

Mr Weston's ball was to be a real thing. A very few tomorrows stood between the young people of Highbury and happiness.

Mr Woodhouse was resigned. The time of year lightened the evil to him. May was better for everything than February. Mrs Bates was engaged to spend the evening at Hartfield; James had due notice, and he sanguinely hoped that neither dear little Henry nor dear little John would have anything the matter with them while dear Emma were gone.

Chapter 38

No misfortune occurred again to prevent the ball. The day approached, the day arrived; and, after a morning of some anxious watching, Frank Churchill, in all the certainty of his own self, reached Randalls before dinner; and everything was safe.

No second meeting had there yet been between him and Emma. The room at the Crown was to witness it; but it would be better than a common meeting in a crowd. Mr Weston had been so very earnest in his entreaties for her early attendance, for her arriving there as soon as possible after themselves, for the purpose of taking her opinion as to the propriety and comfort of the rooms before any other persons came, that she could not refuse him, and therefore must spend some quiet interval in the young man's company. She was to convey Harriet, and they drove to the Crown in good time, the Randalls' party just sufficiently before them.

Frank Churchill seemed to have been on the watch; and though he did not say much, his eyes declared that he meant to have a delightful evening. They all walked about together, to see that everything was as it should be; and within a few minutes were joined by the contents of another carriage, which Emma could not hear the sound of at first without great surprise. 'So unreasonably early!' she was going to exclaim; but she presently found that it was a family of old friends, who were coming, like herself, by particular desire, to help Mr Weston's judgement; and they were so very closely followed by another carriage of cousins, who had been entreated to come early with the same distinguishing earnestness, on the same errand, that it seemed as if half the company might soon be collected together for the purpose of preparatory inspection.

Emma perceived that her taste was not the only taste on which Mr Weston depended, and felt that to be the favourite and intimate of a man who had so many intimates and confidantes, was not the very first distinction in the scale of vanity. She liked his open manners, but a little less of open-heartedness would have made him a higher character. General benevolence, but not general friendship, made a man what he ought to be. She could fancy such a man.

The whole party walked about, and looked, and praised again; and then, having nothing else to do, formed a sort of half-circle round the fire, to observe in their various modes, till other subjects were started, that, though *May*, a fire in the evening was still very pleasant.

Emma found that it was not Mr Weston's fault that the number of privy counsellors was not yet larger. They had stopped at Mrs Bates's door to offer the use of their carriage, but the aunt and niece were to be brought by the Eltons.

Frank was standing by her, but not steadily; there was a restlessness, which showed a mind not at ease. He was looking about, he was going to the door, he was watching for the sound of other carriages – impatient to begin, or afraid of being always near her.

Mrs Elton was spoken of. 'I think she must be here soon,' said he. 'I have a great curiosity to see Mrs Elton, I have heard so much of her. It cannot be long, I think, before she comes.'

A carriage was heard. He was on the move immediately; but coming back, said: 'I am forgetting that I am not acquainted with her. I have never seen either Mr or Mrs Elton. I have no business to put myself forward.'

Mr and Mrs Elton appeared; and all the smiles and the proprieties passed.

'But Miss Bates and Miss Fairfax!' said Mr Weston, looking about. 'We thought you were to bring them.'

The mistake had been slight. The carriage was sent for them now. Emma longed to know what Frank's first opinion of Mrs Elton might be; how he was affected by the studied elegance of her dress, and her smiles of graciousness. He was immediately qualifying himself to form an opinion, by giving her very proper attention, after the introduction had passed.

In a few minutes the carriage returned. Somebody talked of rain. 'I will see that there are umbrellas, sir,' said Frank to his father: 'Miss Bates must not be forgotten;' and away he went. Mr Weston was following but Mrs Elton detained him, to gratify him by her opinion of his son; and so briskly did she begin, that the young man himself, though by no means moving slowly, could hardly be out of hearing.

'A very fine young man, indeed, Mr Weston. You know I candidly told you I should form my own opinion; and I am happy to say that I am extremely pleased with him. You may believe me. I never compliment. I think him a very handsome young man, and his manners are precisely what I like and approve – so truly the gentleman, without the least conceit or puppyism. You must know I have a vast dislike to puppies – quite a horror of them. They were never tolerated at Maple Grove. Neither Mr Suckling nor me had ever any patience with them; and we used sometimes to say very cutting things. Selina, who is mild almost to a fault, bore with them much better.'

While she talked of his son, Mr Weston's attention was chained; but when she got to Maple Grove, he could recollect that there were ladies just arriving to be attended to, and with happy smiles must hurry away.

Mrs Elton turned to Mrs Weston. 'I have no doubt of its being our carriage with Miss Bates and Jane. Our coachman and horses are so extremely expeditious! I believe we drive faster than anybody. What a pleasure it is to send one's carriage for a friend! I understand you were so kind as to offer, but another time it will be quite unnecessary. You may be very sure I shall always take care of *them.*'

Miss Bates and Miss Fairfax, escorted by the two gentlemen, walked into the room; and Mrs Elton seemed to think it as much her duty as Mrs Weston's to receive them. Her gestures and movements might be understood by any one who looked on like Emma; but her words, everybody's words, were soon lost under the incessant flow of Miss Bates, who came in talking, and had not finished her speech under many minutes after her being admitted into the circle at the fire. As the door opened she was heard: 'So very obliging of you! No rain at all. Nothing to signify. I do not care for myself. Quite thick shoes. And Jane declares – Well!' (as soon as she was within the door), 'Well! This is brilliant indeed! This is admirable! Excellently contrived, upon my word. Nothing wanting. Could not have imagined it. So well lighted up! Jane, Jane, look! did you ever see anything – ? Oh! Mr Weston, you must really have had Aladdin's lamp. Good Mrs Stokes would not know her own room again. I saw her as I came in; she was standing in the entrance. "Oh! Mrs Stokes," said I – but I had not time for more.' She was now met by Mrs Weston. 'Very well, I thank you, ma'am. I hope you are quite well. Very happy to hear it. So afraid you might have a headache! seeing you pass by so often, and knowing how much trouble you must have. Delighted to hear it indeed! Ah! dear Mrs Elton, so obliged to you for the carriage; excellent time; Jane and I quite ready. Did not keep the horses a moment. Most comfortable carriage. Oh! and I am sure our thanks are due to you, Mrs Weston, on that score. Mrs Elton had most kindly sent Jane a note, or we should have been. But two such offers in one day! Never were such neighbours. I said to my mother, "Upon my word, ma'am –" Thank you, my mother is remarkably well. Gone to Mr Woodhouse's. I made her take her shawl – for the evenings are not warm – her large new shawl, Mrs Dixon's wedding present. So kind of her to think of my mother! Bought at Weymouth, you know; Mr Dixon's choice. There were three others, Jane says, which they hesitated about some time. Colonel Campbell rather preferred an olive. My dear Jane, are you sure you did not wet your feet! It was but a drop or two, but I am so afraid; but Mr Frank Churchill was so extremely – and there was a mat to step upon. I shall never forget his extreme politeness. Oh! Mr Frank Churchill, I must tell you my mother's spectacles have never been in fault since; the rivet never came out again. My mother often talks of your good nature; does not she, Jane? Do not we often talk of Mr Frank Churchill? Ah! here's Miss Woodhouse. Dear Miss Woodhouse, how do you do? Very well, I thank you, quite well. This is meeting quite in fairy land. Such a transformation! Must not compliment, I know' (eyeing Emma most complacently) – 'that would be rude; but upon my word, Miss Woodhouse, you do look – how do you like Jane's hair? You are a judge. She did it all herself. Quite wonderful how she does her hair! No hairdresser from London, I think, could – Ah! Dr Hughes, I declare – and Mrs Hughes. Must go and speak to Dr and Mrs Hughes for a moment. How do you do? How do you do? Very well, I thank you. This is delightful, is not it? Where's dear Mr Richard? Oh! there he is. Don't disturb him. Much better employed talking to the young ladies. How do you do, Mr Richard? I saw you the other day as you rode through the town. Mrs Otway, I protest, and good Mr Otway, and Miss Otway, and Miss Caroline. Such a host of friends! and Mr George and Mr Arthur! How do you do? How do you all do? Quite well, I am much obliged to you. Never better. Don't I hear another carriage? Who can this be? very likely the worthy Coles. Upon my word, this is charming, to be standing about among such friends! and such a noble fire! I am quite roasted. No coffee, I thank you, for me; never take coffee. A little tea, if you please, sir, by and by; no hurry. Oh! here it comes. Everything is so good!'

Frank Churchill returned to his station by Emma; and as soon as Miss Bates was quiet, she found herself necessarily over-hearing the discourse of Mrs Elton and Miss Fairfax, who were standing a little way behind her. He was thoughtful. Whether he were overhearing too she could not determine. After a good many compliments to Jane on her dress and look – compliments very quietly and properly taken – Mrs Elton was evidently wanting to be complimented herself – and it was, 'How do you like my gown? How do you like my trimming? How has Wright done my hair?' with many other relative questions, all answered with patient politeness. Mrs Elton then said: 'Nobody can think less of dress in general than I do: but upon such an occasion as this, when every-body's eyes are so much upon me, and in compliment to the Westons, who I have no doubt are giving this ball chiefly to do me honour. I would not wish to be inferior to others; and I see very few pearls in the room except mine. So Frank Churchill is a capital dancer, I understand. We shall see if our styles suit. A fine young man certainly is Frank Churchill. I like him very well.'

At this moment Frank began talking so vigorously, that Emma could not but imagine he had overheard his own praises, and did not want to hear more; and the voices of the ladies were drowned for a while, till another suspension brought Mrs Elton's tones again distinctly forward. Mr Elton had just joined them, and his wife was exclaiming: 'Oh! you have found us out at last, have you, in our seclusion? I was this moment telling Jane, I thought you would begin to be impatient for tidings of us.'

'Jane!' repeated Frank Churchill, with a look of surprise and displeasure. 'That is easy; but Miss Fairfax does not disapprove it, I suppose.'

'How do you like Mrs Elton?' said Emma, in a whisper.

'Not at all.'

'You are ungrateful.'

'Ungrateful! What do you mean?' Then changing from a frown to a smile: 'No, do not tell me – I do not want to know what you mean. Where is my father? When are we to begin dancing?'

Emma could hardly understand him; he seemed in an odd humour. He walked off to find his father, but was quickly back again with both Mr and Mrs Weston. He had met with them in a little perplexity, which must be laid before Emma. It had just occurred to Mrs Weston that Mrs Elton must be asked to begin the ball; that she would expect it; which interfered with all their wishes of giving Emma that distinction. Emma heard the sad truth with fortitude.

'And what are we to do for a proper partner for her?' said Mr Weston. 'She will think Frank ought to ask her.'

Frank turned instantly to Emma, to claim her former promise; and boasted himself an engaged man, which his father looked his most perfect approbation of – and it then appeared that Mrs Weston was wanting *him* to dance with Mrs Elton himself, and that their business was to help to persuade him into it, which was done pretty soon. Mr Weston and Mrs Elton led the way; Mr Frank Churchill and Miss Woodhouse followed. Emma must submit to stand second to Mrs Elton though she had always considered the ball as peculiarly for her. It was almost enough to make her think of marrying.

Mrs Elton had undoubtedly the advantage, at this time, in vanity completely gratified; for though she had intended to begin with Frank Churchill, she could not lose by the change. Mr Weston might be his son's superior. In spite of this little rub, however, Emma was smiling with enjoyment, delighted to see the respectable length of the set as it was forming, and to feel that she had so many hours of unusual festivity before her. She was more disturbed by Mr Knightley's not dancing than by anything else. There he was, among the standers-by, where he ought not to be; he ought to be dancing, not classing himself with the husbands, and fathers, and whist-players, who were pretending to feel an interest in the dance till their rubbers were made up, – so young as he looked! He could not have appeared to greater advantage perhaps anywhere, than where he had placed himself. His tall, firm, upright figure, among the bulky forms and stooping shoulders of the elderly men, was such as Emma felt must draw everybody's eyes; and, excepting her own partner, there was not one among the whole row of young men who could be compared with him. He moved a few steps nearer, and those few steps were enough to prove in how gentlemanlike a manner, with what natural grace, he must have danced, would he but take the trouble. Whenever she caught his eye, she forced him to smile; but in general he was looking grave. She wished he could love a ballroom better, and could like Frank Churchill better. He seemed often observing her. She must not flatter herself that he thought of her dancing; but if he were criticising her behaviour, she did not feel afraid. There was nothing like flirtation between her and her partner. They seemed more like cheerful easy friends than lovers. That Frank Churchill thought less of her than he had done was indubitable.

The ball proceeded pleasantly. The anxious cares, the incessant attentions of Mrs Weston were not thrown away. Everybody seemed happy; and the praise of being a delightful ball, which is seldom bestowed till after a ball has ceased to be, was repeatedly given in the very beginning of the existence of this. Of very important, very recordable events, it was not more productive than such meetings usually are. There was one, however, which Emma thought something of. The two last dances before supper were begun, and Harriet had no partner – the only young lady sitting down; and so equal had been hitherto the number of dancers, that how there could be anyone disengaged was the wonder. But Emma's wonder lessened soon afterwards, on seeing Mr Elton sauntering about. He would not ask Harriet to dance, if it were possible to be avoided; she was sure he would not – and she was expecting him every moment to escape into the card-room.

Escape, however, was not his plan. He came to the part of the room where the sitters-by were collected, spoke to some, and walked about in front of them, as if to show his liberty, and his resolution of maintaining it. He did not omit being sometimes directly before Miss Smith, or speaking to those who were close to her. Emma saw it. She was not yet dancing; she was working her way up from the bottom, and had therefore leisure to look round, and by only turning her head a little she saw it all. When she was half way up the set, the whole group were exactly behind her, and she would no longer allow her eyes to watch; but Mr Elton was so near, that she heard every syllable of a dialogue which just then took place between him and Mrs Weston; and she perceived that his wife, who was standing immediately above her, was not only listening also, but even encouraging him by significant glances. The kind-hearted, gentle Mrs Weston had left her seat to join him and say, 'Do not you dance, Mr Elton?' to which his prompt reply was, 'Most readily, Mrs Weston, if you will dance with me.'

'Me! oh! no – I would get you a better partner than myself. I am no dancer.'

'If Mrs Gilbert wishes to dance,' said he, 'I shall have great pleasure, I am sure; for, though beginning to feel myself rather an old married man, and that my dancing days are over, it would give me very great pleasure at any time to stand up with an old friend like Mrs Gilbert.'

'Mrs Gilbert does not mean to dance, but there is a young lady disengaged whom I should be very glad to see dancing – Miss Smith.'

'Miss Smith – oh! – I had not observed. You are extremely obliging – and if I were not an old married – but my dancing days are over, Mrs Weston. You will excuse me. Anything else I should be most happy to do, at your command – but my dancing days are over.'

Mrs Weston said no more; and Emma could imagine with what surprise and mortification she must be returning to her seat. This was Mr Elton! the amiable, obliging, gentle Mr Elton. She looked round for a moment; he had joined Mr Knightley at a little distance, and was arranging himself for settled conversation, while smiles of high glee passed between him and his wife. She would not look again. Her heart was in a glow, and she feared her face might be as hot.

In another moment a happier sight caught her – Mr Knightley leading Harriet to the set! Never had she been more surprised, seldom more delighted, than at that instant. She was all pleasure and gratitude, both for Harriet and herself, and longed to be thanking him; and though too distant for speech, her countenance said much, as soon as she could catch his eye again.

His dancing proved to be just what she had believed it, extremely good; and Harriet would have seemed almost too lucky, if it had not been for the cruel state of things before, and for the very complete enjoyment and very high sense of the distinction which her happy features announced. It was not thrown away on her; she bounded higher than ever, flew farther down the middle, and was in a continual course of smiles.

Mr Elton had retreated into the card-room, looking (Emma trusted) very foolish. She did not think he was quite so hardened as his wife, though growing very like her; *she* spoke some of her feelings, by observing audibly to her partner: 'Knightley has taken pity on poor little Miss Smith! Very good-natured, I declare.'

Supper was announced. The move began; and Miss Bates might be heard from that moment without interruption, till her being seated at table and taking up her spoon.

'Jane, Jane, my dear Jane, where are you? Here is your tippet. Mrs Weston begs you to put on your tippet. She says she is afraid there will be draughts in the passage, though everything has been done – one door nailed up – quantities of matting – my dear Jane, indeed you must. Mr Churchill, oh! you are too obliging. How well you put it on – so gratified! Excellent dancing indeed. Yes, my dear, I ran home, as I said I should, to help grandmamma to bed, and got back again, and nobody missed me. I set off without saying a word, just as I told you. Grandmamma was quite well, had a charming evening with Mr Woodhouse, a vast deal of chat, and backgammon. Tea was made downstairs, biscuits and baked apples, and wine before she came away: amazing luck in some of her throws: and she enquired a great deal about you, how you were amused, and who were your partners. "Oh!" said I, "I shall not forestall Jane; I left her dancing with Mr George Otway; she will love to tell you all about it herself tomorrow: her first partner was Mr Elton; I do not know who will ask her next, perhaps Mr William Cox." My dear sir, you are too obliging. Is there nobody you would not rather? I am not helpless. Sir, you are most kind. Upon my word, Jane on one arm, and me on the other. Stop, stop, let us stand a little back, Mrs Elton is going; dear Mrs Elton, how elegant she looks – beautiful lace. Now we all follow in her train. Quite the queen of the evening! Well, here we are at the passage. Two steps, Jane, take care of the two steps. Oh, no, there is but one. Well, I was persuaded there were two. How very odd! I was convinced there were two, and there is but one. I never saw anything equal to the comfort and style candles everywhere. I was telling you of your grandmamma, Jane – there was a little disappointment. The baked apples and biscuits, excellent in their way, you know; but there was a delicate fricassee of sweetbread and some asparagus brought in at first, and good Mr Woodhouse, not thinking the asparagus quite boiled enough, sent it all out again. Now there is nothing grandmamma loves better than sweetbread and asparagus – so she was rather disappointed; but we agreed we would not speak of it to anybody, for fear of its getting round to dear Miss Woodhouse, who would be so very much concerned. Well, this is brilliant! I am all amazement! – could not have supposed anything – such elegance and profusion! I have seen nothing like it since – Well, where shall we sit? Where shall we sit? Anywhere, so that Jane is not in a draught. Where *I* sit is of no consequence. Oh! do you recommend this side? Well, I am sure, Mr Churchill – only it seems too good – but just as you please. What you direct in this house cannot be wrong. Dear Jane, how shall we ever recollect half the dishes for grandmamma? Soup too! Bless me! I should not be helped so soon, but it smells most excellent, and I cannot help beginning.'

Emma had no opportunity of speaking to Mr Knightley till after supper; but, when they were all in the ballroom again, her eyes invited him irresistibly to come to her and be thanked. He was warm in his reprobation of Mr Elton's conduct; it had been unpardonable rudeness; and Mrs Elton's looks also received the due share of censure.

'They aimed at wounding more than Harriet,' said he. 'Emma, why is it that they are your enemies?'

He looked with smiling penetration; and, on receiving no answer, added, '*She* ought not to be angry with you, I suspect, whatever he may be. To that surmise, you say nothing, of course: but confess, Emma, that you did want him to marry Harriet.'

'I did,' replied Emma, 'and they cannot forgive me.'

He shook his head; but there was a smile of indulgence with it, and he only said: 'I shall not scold you. I leave you to your own reflections.'

'Can you trust me with such flatterers? Does my vain spirit ever tell me I am wrong?'

'Not your vain spirit, but your serious spirit. If one leads you wrong, I am sure the other tells you of it.'

'I do own myself to have been completely mistaken in Mr Elton. There is a littleness about him which you discovered, and which I did not: and I was fully convinced of his being in love with Harriet. It was through a series of strange blunders!'

'And, in return for your acknowledging so much, I will do you the justice to say, that you would have chosen for him better than he has chosen for himself. Harriet Smith has some first-rate qualities, which Mrs Elton is totally without. An unpretending, single-minded, artless girl – infinitely to be preferred by any man of sense and taste to such a woman as Mrs Elton. I found Harriet more conversable than I expected.'

Emma was extremely gratified. They were interrupted by the bustle of Mr Weston calling on everybody to begin dancing again.

'Come, Miss Woodhouse, Miss Otway, Miss Fairfax, what are you all doing? Come, Emma, set your companions the example. Everybody is lazy! Everybody is asleep!'

'I am ready,' said Emma, 'whenever I am wanted.'

'Whom are you going to dance with?' asked Mr Knightley.

She hesitated a moment, and then replied, 'With you, if you will ask me.'

'Will you?' said he, offering his hand.

'Indeed, I will. You have shown that you can dance, and you know we are not really so much brother and sister as to make it at all improper.'

'Brother and sister! – no, indeed.'

Chapter 39

This little explanation with Mr Knightley gave Emma considerable pleasure. It was one of the agreeable recollections of the ball, which she walked about the lawn the next morning to enjoy. She was extremely glad that they had come to so good an understanding respecting the Eltons, and that their opinions of both husband and wife were so much alike; and his praise of Harriet, his concession in her favour, was peculiarly gratifying. The impertinence of the Eltons, which for a few moments had threatened to ruin the rest of her evening, had been the occasion of some of its highest satisfactions; and she looked forward to another happy result – the cure of Harriet's infatuation. From Harriet's manner of speaking of the circumstance before they quitted the ballroom she had strong hopes. It seemed as if her eyes were suddenly opened, and she were enabled to see that Mr

Elton was not the superior creature she had believed him. The fever was over, and Emma could harbour little fear of the pulse being quickened again by injurious courtesy. She depended on the evil feelings of the Eltons for supplying all the discipline of pointed neglect that could be further requisite. Harriet rational, Frank Churchill not too much in love, and Mr Knightley not wanting to quarrel with her, how very happy a summer must be before her.

She was not to see Frank Churchill this morning. He had told her that he could not allow himself the pleasure of stopping at Hartfield, as he was to be home by the middle of the day. She did not regret it.

Having arranged all these matters, looked them through, and put them all to rights, she was just turning to the house, with spirits freshened up for the demands of the two little boys, as well as of their grandpapa, when the great iron sweep-gate opened, and two persons entered whom she had never less expected to see together – Frank Churchill, with Harriet leaning on his arm – actually Harriet! A moment sufficed to convince her that something extraordinary had happened. Harriet looked white and frightened, and he was trying to cheer her. The iron gates and the front-door were not twenty yards asunder – they were all three soon in the hall; and Harriet immediately sinking into a chair, fainted away.

A young lady who faints must be recovered; questions must be answered, and surprises be explained. Such events are very interesting; but the suspense of them cannot last long. A few minutes made Emma acquainted with the whole.

Miss Smith, and Miss Bickerton, another parlour boarder at Mrs Goddard's, who had been also at the ball, had walked out together, and taken a road – the Richmond Road, which, though apparently public enough for safety, had led them into alarm. About half a mile beyond Highbury, making a sudden turn, and deeply shaded by elms on each side, it became for a considerable stretch very retired; and when the young ladies had advanced some way into it, they had suddenly perceived, at a small distance before them, on a broader patch of greensward by the side, a party of gypsies. A child on the watch came towards them to beg; and Miss Bickerton, excessively frightened, gave a great scream, and calling on Harriet to follow her, ran up a steep bank, cleared a slight hedge at the top, and made the best of her way by a short cut back to Highbury. But poor Harriet could not follow. She had suffered very much from cramp after dancing, and her first attempt to mount the bank brought on such a return of it as made her absolutely powerless; and in this state, and exceedingly terrified, she had been obliged to remain.

How the trampers might have behaved, had the young ladies been more courageous, must be doubtful; but such an invitation for attack could not be resisted; and Harriet was soon assailed by half a dozen children, headed by a stout woman, and a great boy, all clamorous, and impertinent in look, though not absolutely in word. More and more frightened, she immediately promised them money, and taking out her purse gave them a shilling, and begged them not to want more, or to use her ill. She was then able to walk, though but slowly, and was moving away – but her terror and her purse were too tempting; and she was followed, or rather surrounded, by the whole gang, demanding more.

In this state Frank Churchill had found her, she trembling and conditioning, they loud and insolent. By a most fortunate chance, his leaving Highbury had been delayed so as to bring him to her assistance at this critical moment. The pleasantness of the morning had induced him to walk forward, and leave his horses to meet him by another road, a mile or two beyond Highbury; and happening to have borrowed a pair of scissors the night before of Miss Bates, and to have forgotten to restore them, he had been obliged to stop at her door, and go in for a few minutes; he was therefore later than he had intended; and being on foot, was unseen by the whole party till almost close to them. The terror which the woman and boy had been creating in Harriet was then their own portion. He had left them completely frightened; and

Harriet eagerly clinging to him, and hardly able to speak, had just strength enough to reach Hartfield, before her spirits were quite overcome. It was his idea to bring her to Hartfield; he had thought of no other place.

This was the amount of the whole story – of his communication and of Harriet's, as soon as she had recovered her senses and speech. He dared not stay longer than to see her well; these several delays left him not another minute to lose; and Emma engaging to give assurance of her safety to Mrs Goddard, and notice of there being such a set of people in the neighbourhood to Mr Knightley, he set off, with all the grateful blessings that he could utter for her friend and herself.

Such an adventure as this – a fine young man and a lovely young woman thrown together in such a way – could hardly fail of suggesting certain ideas to the coldest heart and the steadiest brain. So Emma thought, at least. Could a linguist, could a grammarian, could even a mathematician have seen what she did, have witnessed their appearance together, and heard their history of it, without feeling that circumstances had been at work to make them peculiarly interesting to each other? How much more must an imaginist, like herself, be on fire with speculation and foresight? especially with such a groundwork of anticipation as her mind had already made.

It was a very extraordinary thing! Nothing of the sort had ever occurred before to any young ladies in the place, within her memory; no rencontre, no alarm of the kind; and now it had happened to the very person, and at the very hour, when the other very person was chancing to pass by to rescue her! It certainly was very extraordinary! And knowing, as she did, the favourable state of mind of each at this period, it struck her the more. He was wishing to get the better of his attachment to herself, she just recovering from her mania for Mr Elton. It seemed as if everything united to promise the most interesting consequences. It was not possible that the occurrence should not be strongly recommending each to the other.

In the few minutes' conversation which she had yet had with him, while Harriet had been partially insensible, he had spoken of her terror, her *naïveté*, her fervour as she seized and clung to his arm, with a sensibility amused and delighted; and just at last, after Harriet's own account had been given, he had expressed his indignation at the abominable folly of Miss Bickerton in the warmest terms. Everything was to take its natural course, however, neither impelled nor assisted. She would not stir a step nor drop a hint. No, she had had enough of interference. There could be no harm in a scheme, a mere passive scheme. It was no more than a wish. Beyond it she would on no account proceed.

Emma's first resolution was to keep her father from the knowledge of what had passed, aware of the anxiety and alarm it would occasion; but she soon felt that concealment must be impossible. Within half an hour it was known all over Highbury. It was the very event to engage those who talk most – the young and the low; and all the youth and servants in the place were soon in the happiness of frightful news. The last night's ball seemed lost in the gypsies. Poor Mr Woodhouse trembled as he sat, and, as Emma had foreseen, would scarcely be satisfied without their promising never to go beyond the shrubbery again. It was some comfort to him that many enquiries after himself and Miss Wood- house (for his neighbours knew that he loved to be enquired after), as well as Miss Smith, were coming in during the rest of the day; and he had the pleasure of returning for answer, that they were all very indifferent; which, though not exactly true, for she was perfectly well, and Harriet not much otherwise, Emma would not interfere with. She had an unhappy state of health in general for the child of such a man, for she hardly knew what indisposi- tion was; and if he did not invent illnesses for her, she would make no figure in a message.

The gypsies did not wait for the operations of justice; they took themselves off in a hurry. The young ladies of Highbury might have walked again in safety before their panic began, and the whole history dwindled soon into a matter of little importance but to Emma and her nephews: in her imagination it maintained its ground; and Henry and John were still asking every day for the story of Harriet and the gypsies, and still tenaciously setting her right if she varied in the slightest particular from the original recital.

Chapter 40

A very few days had passed after this adventure, when Harriet came one morning to Emma with a small parcel in her hand, and after sitting down and hesitating, thus began: 'Miss Woodhouse – if you are at leisure, I have something that I should like to tell you: a sort of confession to make – and then, you know, it will be over.'

Emma was a good deal surprised; but begged her to speak. There was a seriousness in Harriet's manner which prepared her, quite as much as her words, for something more than ordinary.

'It is my duty, and I am sure it is my wish,' she continued, 'to have no reserves with you on this subject. As I am, happily, quite an altered creature, in *one respect,* it is very fit that you should have the satisfaction of knowing it. I do not want to say more than is necessary; I am too much ashamed of having given way as I have done, and I dare say you understand me.'

'Yes,' said Emma, 'I hope I do.'

'How I could so long a time be fancying myself ... ' cried Harriet warmly. 'It seems like madness! I can see nothing at all extraordinary in him now. I do not care whether I meet him or not, except that, of the two, I had rather not see him; and, indeed, I would go any distance round to avoid him; but I do not envy his wife in the least: I neither admire her nor envy her, as I have done. She is very charming, I dare say, and all that; but I think her very ill-tempered and disagreeable: I shall never forget her look the other night. However, I assure you, Miss Woodhouse, I wish her no evil. No; let them be ever so happy together, it will not give me another moment's pang; and, to convince you that I have been speaking truth, I am now going to destroy – what I ought to have destroyed long ago – what I ought never to have kept: I know that very well' (blushing as she spoke). 'However, now I will destroy it all; and it is my particular wish to do it in your presence, that you may see how rational I am grown. Cannot you guess what this parcel holds?' said she, with a conscious look.

'Not the least in the world. Did he ever give you anything?'

'No – I cannot call them gifts; but they are things that I have valued very much.'

She held the parcel towards her, and Emma read the words *Most precious treasures* on the top. Her curiosity was greatly excited. Harriet unfolded the parcel, and she looked on with impatience. Within abundance of silver paper was a pretty little Tunbridgeware box, which Harriet opened: it was well lined with the softest cotton; but, excepting the cotton, Emma saw only a small piece of court-plaster.

'Now,' said Harriet, 'you *must* recollect.'

'No, indeed, I do not.'

'Dear me! I should not have thought it possible you could forget what passed in this very room about court-plaster, one of the very last times we ever met in it. It was but a very few days before I had my sore throat – just before Mr and Mrs John Knightley came; I think the very evening. Do not you remember his cutting his finger with your new penknife, and your recommending court-plaster? But, as you had none about you, and knew I had, you desired me to supply him; and so I took mine out and cut him a piece: but it was a great deal too large, and he cut it smaller, and kept playing some time with what was left, before he gave it back to me. And so then, in my nonsense, I could not help making a treasure of it; so I put it by, never to be used, and looked at it now and then as a great treat.'

'My dearest Harriet!' cried Emma, putting her hand before her face, and jumping up, 'you make me more ashamed of myself than I can bear. Remember it? Aye, I remember it all now; all, except your saving this relic: I knew nothing of that till this moment – but the cutting the finger, and my recommending court-plaster, and saying I had none about me. Oh! my sins! my sins! – And I had plenty all the while in my pocket! One of my senseless tricks. I deserve to be under a continual blush all the rest of my life. Well' (sitting down again), 'go on: what else?'

'And had you really some at hand yourself? I am sure I never suspected it, you did it so naturally.'

'And so you actually put this piece of court-plaster by for his sake!' said Emma, recovering from her state of shame and feeling divided between wonder and amusement; and secretly she added to herself, 'Lord bless me! when should I ever have thought of putting by in cotton a piece of court-plaster that Frank Churchill had been pulling about! I never was equal to this.'

'Here,' resumed Harriet, turning to her box again, 'here is something still more valuable – I mean that *has been* more valuable – because this is what did really once belong to him, which the court-plaster never did.'

Emma was quite eager to see this superior treasure. It was the end of an old pencil, the part without any lead.

'This was really his,' said Harriet. 'Do not you remember one morning? – no, I dare say you do not. But one morning – I forget exactly the day – but perhaps it was the Tuesday or Wednesday before *that evening,* he wanted to make a memorandum in his pocket-book; it was about spruce-beer. Mr Knightley had been telling him something about brewing spruce-beer, and he wanted to put it down; but when he took out his pencil, there was so little lead that he soon cut it all away, and it would not do, so you lent him another, and this was left upon the table as good for nothing.

But I kept my eye on it; and, as soon as I dared, caught it up, and never parted with it again from that moment.'

'I do remember it,' cried Emma; 'I perfectly remember it. Talking about spruce-beer. Oh! yes. Mr Knightley and I both saying we liked it, and Mr Elton's seeming resolved to learn to like it too. I perfectly remember it. Stop – Mr Knightley was standing just here, was not he? I have an idea he was standing just here.'

'Ah! I do not know. I cannot recollect. It is very odd, but I cannot recollect. Mr Elton was sitting here, I remember, much about where I am now.'

'Well, go on.'

'Oh! that's all. I have nothing more to show you, or to say, except that I am now going to throw them both behind the fire, and I wish you to see me do it.'

'My poor dear Harriet! and have you actually found happiness in treasuring up these things?'

'Yes, simpleton as I was! but I am quite ashamed of it now, and wish I could forget as easily as I can burn them. It was very wrong of me, you know, to keep any remembrances after he was married. I knew it was – but had not resolution enough to part with them.'

'But, Harriet, is it necessary to burn the court-plaster? I have not a word to say for the bit of old pencil, but the court-plaster might be useful.'

'I shall be happier to burn it,' replied Harriet. 'It has a disagreeable look to me. I must get rid of everything. There it goes, and there is an end, thank Heaven! of Mr Elton.'

'And when,' thought Emma, 'will there be a beginning of Mr Churchill?'

She had soon afterwards reason to believe that the beginning was already made, and could not but hope that the gypsy, though she had *told* no fortune, might be proved to have made Harriet's. About a fortnight after the alarm they came to a sufficient explanation, and quite undesignedly. Emma was not thinking of it at the moment, which made the information she received more valuable. She merely said in the course of some trivial chat, 'Well, Harriet, whenever you marry, I would advise you to do so and so' – and thought no more of it, till after a minute's silence she heard Harriet say, in a very serious tone, 'I shall never marry.'

Emma then looked up, and immediately saw how it was; and after a moment's debate, as to whether it should pass unnoticed or not, replied: 'Never marry! This is a new resolution.'

'It is one that I shall never change, however.'

After another short hesitation, 'I hope it does not proceed from – I hope it is not in compliment to Mr Elton?'

'Mr Elton, indeed!' cried Harriet indignantly. 'Oh! no' – and Emma could just catch the words, 'so superior to Mr Elton!'

She then took a longer time for consideration. Should she proceed no further? should she let it pass, and seem to suspect nothing? Perhaps Harriet might think her cold or angry if she did; or, perhaps, if she were totally silent, it might only drive Harriet into asking her to hear too much; and against anything like such an unreserve as had been, such an open and frequent discussion of hopes and chances, she was perfectly resolved. She believed it would be wiser for her to say and know at once all that she meant to say and know. Plain dealing was always best. She had previously determined how far she would proceed, on any application of the sort; and it would be safer for both to have the judicious law of her own brain laid down with speed. She was decided, and thus spoke: 'Harriet, I will not affect to be in doubt of your meaning. Your resolution, or rather your expectation of never marrying, results from an idea that the person whom you might prefer would be too greatly your superior in situation to think of you. Is not it so?'

'Oh, Miss Woodhouse, believe me, I have not the presumption to suppose – indeed I am not so mad. But it is a pleasure to me to admire him at a distance, and to think of his infinite superiority to all the rest of the world, with the gratitude, wonder, and veneration which are so proper, in me especially.'

'I am not at all surprised at you, Harriet. The service he rendered you was enough to warm your heart.'

'Service! oh, it was such an inexpressible obligation! The very recollection of it, and all that I felt at the time, when I saw him coming – his noble look, and my wretchedness before. Such a change! In one moment such a change! From perfect misery to perfect happiness!'

'It is very natural. It is natural, and it is honourable. Yes, honourable, I think, to choose so well and so gratefully. But that it will be a fortunate preference is more than I can promise. I do not advise you to give way to it, Harriet. I do not by any means engage for its being returned. Consider what you are about. Perhaps it will be wisest in you to check your feelings while you can: at any rate do not let them carry you far, unless you are persuaded of his liking you. Be observant of him. Let his behaviour be the guide of your sensations. I give you this caution now, because I shall never speak to you again on the subject. I am determined against all interference. Henceforward I know nothing of the matter. Let no name ever pass our lips. We were very wrong before; we will be cautious now. He is your superior, no doubt, and there do seem objections and obstacles of a very serious nature; but yet, Harriet, more wonderful things have taken place: there have been matches of greater disparity. But take care of yourself; I would not have you too sanguine; though, however it may end, be assured that your raising your thoughts to *him* is a mark of good taste which I shall always know how to value.'

Harriet kissed her hand in silent and submissive gratitude. Emma was very decided in thinking such an attachment no bad thing for her friend. Its tendency would be to raise and refine her mind – and it must be saving her from the danger of degradation.

Chapter 41

In this state of schemes and hopes, and connivance, June opened upon Hartfield. To Highbury, in general, it brought no material change. The Eltons were still talking of a visit from the Sucklings, and of the use to be made of their barouche-landau, and Jane Fairfax was still at her grandmother's; and as the return of the Campbells from Ireland was again delayed, and August, instead of Midsummer, fixed for it, she was likely to remain there full two months longer, provided at least she were able to defeat Mrs Elton's activity in her service, and save herself from being hurried into a delightful situation against her will.

Mr Knightley, who, for some reason best known to himself, had certainly taken an early dislike to Frank Churchill, was only growing to dislike him more. He began to suspect him of some double dealing in his pursuit of Emma. That Emma was his object appeared indisputable. Everything declared it; his own attentions, his father's hints, his mother-in-law's guarded silence; it was all in unison; words, conduct, discretion and indiscretion, told the same story. But while so many were devoting him to Emma, and Emma herself making him over to Harriet, Mr Knightley began to suspect him of some inclination to trifle with Jane Fairfax. He could not understand it; but there were symptoms of intelligence between them – he thought so at least – symptoms of admiration on his side, which, having once observed, he could not persuade himself to think entirely void of meaning, however he might wish to escape any of Emma's errors of imagination. *She* was not present when the suspicion first arose. He was dining with the Randalls family and Jane at the Eltons'; and he had seen a look, more than a single look, at Miss Fairfax, which, from the admirer of Miss Woodhouse, seemed somewhat out of place. When he was again in their company, he could not help remembering what he had seen; nor could he avoid observations which, unless it were like Cowper and his fire at twilight, 'Myself creating what I saw,' brought him yet stronger suspicion of there being a something of private liking, of private understanding even, between Frank Churchill and Jane.

He had walked up one day after dinner, as he very often did, to spend his evening at Hartfield. Emma and Harriet were going to walk; he joined them; and, on returning, they fell in with a larger party, who, like themselves, judged it wisest to take their exercise early, as the weather threatened rain; Mr and Mrs Weston and their son, Miss Bates and her niece, who had accidentally met. They all united; and, on reaching Hartfield gates, Emma, who knew it was exactly the sort of visiting that would be welcome to her father, pressed them all to go in and drink tea with him. The Randalls party agreed to it immediately; and after a pretty long speech from Miss Bates, which few persons listened to, she also found it possible to accept dear Miss Woodhouse's most obliging invitation.

As they were turning into the grounds, Mr Perry passed by on horseback. The gentlemen spoke of his horse.

'By the by,' said Frank Churchill to Mrs Weston presently, 'what became of Mr Perry's plan of setting up his carriage?'

Mrs Weston looked surprised, and said, 'I did not know that he ever had any such plan.'

'Nay, I had it from you. You wrote me word of it three months ago.'

'Me! impossible!'

'Indeed you did. I remember it perfectly. You mentioned it as what was certainly to be very soon. Mrs Perry had told somebody and was extremely happy about it. It was owing to *her* persuasion, as she thought his being out in bad weather did him a great deal of harm. You must remember it now?'

'Upon my word, I never heard of it till this moment.'

'Never! really never! Bless me! how could it be? Then I must have dreamt it – but I was completely persuaded – Miss Smith, you walk as if you were tired. You will not be sorry to find yourself at home.'

'What is this? What is this?' cried Mr Weston, 'about Perry and a carriage? Is Perry going to set up his carriage, Frank? I am glad he can afford it. You had it from himself, had you?'

'No, sir,' replied his son, laughing. 'I seem to have had it from nobody. Very odd! I really was persuaded of Mrs Weston's having mentioned it in one of her letters to Enscombe, many weeks ago, with all these particulars; but as she declares she never heard a syllable of it before, of course it must have been a dream. I am a great dreamer. I dream of everybody at Highbury, when I am away; and when I have gone through my particular friends, then I begin dreaming of Mr and Mrs Perry.'

'It is odd, though,' observed his father, 'that you should have had such a regular connected dream about people whom it was not very likely you should be thinking of at Enscombe. Perry's setting up his carriage! and his wife's persuading him to it, out of care for his health – just what will happen, I have no doubt, some time or other; only a little premature. What an air of probability sometimes runs through a dream! And at others, what a heap of absurdities it is! Well, Frank, your dream certainly shows that Highbury is in your thoughts when you are absent. Emma, you are a great dreamer, I think?'

Emma was out of hearing. She had hurried on before her guests to prepare her father for their appearance, and was beyond the reach of Mr Weston's hint.

'Why, to own the truth,' cried Miss Bates, who had been trying in vain to be heard the last two minutes, 'if I must speak on this subject, there is no denying that Mr Frank Churchill might have – I do not mean to say that he did not dream it – I am sure I have sometimes the oddest dreams in the world – but if I am questioned about it, I must acknowledge that there was such an idea last spring; for Mrs Perry herself mentioned it to my mother, and the Coles knew of it as well as ourselves – but it was quite a secret, known to nobody else, and only thought of about three days. Mrs Perry was very anxious that he should have a carriage, and came to my mother in great spirits one morning because she thought she had prevailed. Jane, don't you remember grandmamma's telling us of it when we got home? I forget where we had been walking to – very likely to Randalls; yes, I think it was to Randalls. Mrs Perry was always particularly fond of my mother – indeed I do not know who is not – and she had mentioned it to her in confidence; she had no objection to her telling us, of course, but it was not to go beyond; and from that day to this I never mentioned it to a soul that I know of. At the same time, I will not positively answer for my having never dropt a hint, because I know I do sometimes pop out a thing before I am aware. I am a talker, you know; I am rather a talker; and now and then I have let a thing escape me which I should not. I am not like Jane; I wish I were. I will answer for it *she* never betrayed the least thing in the world. Where is she? Oh! just behind. Perfectly remember Mrs Perry's coming. Extraordinary dreams, indeed!'

They were entering the hall. Mr Knightley's eyes had preceded Miss Bates's in a glance at Jane. From Frank Churchill's face, where he thought he saw confusion suppressed or laughed away, he had involuntarily turned to hers; but she was indeed behind, and too busy with her shawl. Mr Weston had walked in. The two other gentlemen waited at the door to let her pass. Mr Knightley suspected in Frank Churchill the determination of catching her eye – he seemed watching her intently – in vain, however, if it were so. Jane passed between them into the hall, and looked at neither.

There was no time for further remark or explanation. The dream must be borne with, and Mr Knightley must take his seat with the rest round the large modern circular table which Emma had introduced at Hartfield, and which none but Emma could have had power to place there and persuade her father to use, instead of the small-sized Pembroke, on which two of his daily meals had for forty years been crowded. Tea passed pleasantly, and nobody seemed in a hurry to move.

'Miss Woodhouse,' said Frank Churchill, after examining a table behind him, which he could reach as he sat, 'have your nephews taken away their alphabets – their box of letters? It used to stand here. Where is it? This is a sort of dull-looking evening, that ought to be treated rather as winter than summer. We had great amusement with those letters one morning. I want to puzzle you again.'

Emma was pleased with the thought; and producing the box, the table was quickly scattered over with alphabets, which no one seemed so much disposed to employ as their two selves. They were rapidly forming words for each other, or for anybody else who would be puzzled. The quietness of the game made it particularly eligible for Mr Woodhouse, who had often been distressed by the more animated sort, which Mr Weston had occasionally introduced, and who now sat happily occupied in lamenting, with tender melancholy, over the departure of the 'poor little boys,' or in fondly pointing out, as he took up any stray letter near him, how beautifully Emma had written it.

Frank Churchill placed a word before Miss Fairfax. She gave a slight glance round the table, and applied herself to it. Frank was next to Emma, Jane opposite to them; and Mr Knightley so placed as to see them all; and it was his object to see as much as he could, with as little apparent observation. The word was discovered, and with a faint smile pushed away. If meant to be immediately mixed with the others, and buried from sight, she should have looked on the table instead of looking just across, for it was not mixed; and Harriet, eager after every fresh word, and finding out none, directly took it up, and fell to work. She was sitting by Mr Knightley, and turned to him for help. The word was *blunder* and as Harriet exultingly proclaimed it, there was a blush on Jane's cheek which gave it a meaning not otherwise ostensible. Mr Knightley connected it with the dream; but how it could all be, was beyond his comprehension. How the delicacy, the discretion of his favourite could have been so lain asleep! He feared there must be some decided involvement. Disingenuousness and double dealing seemed to meet him at every turn. These letters were but the vehicle for gallantry and trick. It was a child's play, chosen to conceal a deeper game on Frank Churchill's part.

With great indignation did he continue to observe him; with great alarm and distrust, to observe also his two blinded companions. He saw a short word prepared for Emma, and given to her with a look sly and demure. He saw that Emma had soon made it out, and found it highly entertaining, though it was something which she judged it proper to appear to censure; for she said, 'Nonsense! for shame!' He heard Frank Churchill next say, with a glance towards Jane, 'I will give it to her – shall I?' and as clearly heard Emma opposing it with eager laughing warmth, 'No, no, you must not, you shall not, indeed.'

It was done, however. This gallant young man, who seemed to love without feeling, and to recommend himself without complaisance, directly handed over the word to Miss Fairfax, and with a particular degree of sedate civility entreated her to study it. Mr Knightley's excessive curiosity to know what this word might be, made him seize every possible moment for darting his eye towards it, and it was not long before he saw it to be *Dixon*. Jane Fairfax's perception seemed to accompany his; her comprehension was certainly more equal to the covert meaning, the superior intelligence, of those five letters so arranged. She was evidently displeased; looked up, and, seeing herself watched, blushed more deeply than he had ever perceived her, and saying only, 'I did not know that proper names were allowed,' pushed away the letters with even an angry spirit, and looked resolved to be engaged by no other word that could be offered. Her face was averted from those who had made the attack, and turned towards her aunt.

'Aye, very true, my dear,' cried the latter, though Jane had not spoken a word: 'I was just going to say the same thing. It is time for us to be going, indeed. The evening is closing in, and grandmamma will be looking for us. My dear sir, you are too obliging. We really must wish you good night.'

Jane's alertness in moving proved her as ready as her aunt had preconceived. She was immediately up, and wanting to quit the table; but so many were also moving that she could not get away; and Mr Knightley thought he saw another collection of letters anxiously pushed towards her, and resolutely swept away by her unexamined. She was afterwards looking for her shawl – Frank Churchill was looking also: it was growing dusk, and the room was in confusion; and how they parted Mr Knightley could not tell.

He remained at Hartfield after all the rest, his thoughts full of what he had seen; so full, that when the candles came to assist his observations, he must – yes, he certainly must, as a friend – an anxious friend – give Emma some hint, ask her some question. He could not see her in a situation of such danger without trying to preserve her. It was his duty.

'Pray, Emma,' said he, 'may I ask in what lay the great amusement, the poignant sting of the last word given to you and Miss Fairfax? I saw the word, and am curious to know how it could be so very entertaining to the one, and so very distressing to the other.'

Emma was extremely confused. She could not endure to give him the true explanation; for, though her suspicions were by no means removed, she was really ashamed of having ever imparted them.

'Oh!' she cried, in evident embarrassment, 'it all meant nothing, a mere joke among ourselves.'

'The joke,' he replied gravely, 'seemed confined to you and Mr Churchill.'

He had hoped she would speak again, but she did not. She would rather busy herself about anything than speak. He sat a little while in doubt. A variety of evils crossed his mind. Interference – fruitless interference. Emma's confusion, and the acknowledged intimacy, seemed to declare her affection engaged.

Yet he would speak. He owed it to her, to risk anything that might be involved in an unwelcome interference, rather than her welfare; to encounter anything, rather than the remembrance of neglect in such a cause.

'My dear Emma,' said he at last, with earnest kindness, 'do you think you perfectly understand the degree of acquaintance between the gentleman and lady we have been speaking of?'

'Between Mr Frank Churchill and Miss Fairfax? Oh! yes, perfectly. Why do you make a doubt of it?'

'Have you never at any time had reason to think that he admired her, or that she admired him?'

'Never, never!' she cried with a most open eagerness. 'Never, for the twentieth part of a moment, did such an idea occur to me. And how could it possibly come into your head?'

'I have lately imagined that I saw symptoms of attachment between them; certain expressive looks, which I did not believe meant to be public.'

'Oh! you amuse me excessively. I am delighted to find that you can vouchsafe to let your imagination wander; but it will not do – very sorry to check you in your first essay, but indeed it will not do. There is no admiration between them, I do assure you: and the appearances which have caught you, have arisen from some peculiar circumstances; feelings rather of a totally different nature; it is impossible exactly to explain – there is a good deal of nonsense in it – but the part which is capable of being communicated, which is sense, is, that they are as far from any attachment or admiration for one another as any two beings in the world can be. That is, I *presume* it to be so on her side, and I can *answer* for its being so on his. I will answer for the gentleman's indifference.'

She spoke with a confidence which staggered, with a satisfaction which silenced Mr Knightley. She was in gay spirits, and would have prolonged the conversation, wanting to hear the particulars of his suspicions, every look described, and all the wheres and hows of a circumstance which highly entertained her; but his gaiety did not meet hers. He found he could not be useful, and his feelings were too much irritated for talking. That he might not be irritated into an absolute fever by the fire which Mr Woodhouse's tender habits required almost every evening throughout the year, he soon afterwards took a hasty leave, and walked home to the coolness and solitude of Donwell Abbey.

Chapter 42

After being long fed with hopes of a speedy visit from Mr and Mrs Suckling, the Highbury world were obliged to endure the mortification of hearing that they could not possibly come till the autumn. No such importation of novelties could enrich their intellectual stores at present. In the daily interchange of news, they must be again restricted to the other topics, with which for a while the Sucklings' coming had been united, such as the last accounts of Mrs Churchill, whose health seemed every day to supply a different report, and the situation of Mrs Weston, whose happiness, it was to be hoped, might eventually be as much increased by the arrival of a child, as that of all her neighbours was by the approach of it.

Mrs Elton was very much disappointed. It was the delay of a great deal of pleasure and parade. Her introductions and recommendations must all wait, and every projected party be still only talked of. So she thought at first; but a little consideration convinced her that everything need not be put off. Why should not they explore to Box Hill though the Sucklings did not come? They could go there again with them in the autumn. It was settled that they should go to Box Hill. That there was to be such a party had been long generally known; it had even given the idea of another.

Emma had never been to Box Hill; she wished to see what every-body found so well worth seeing, and she and Mr Weston had agreed to choose some fine morning and drive thither. Two or three more of the chosen only were to be admitted to join them, and it was to be done in a quiet, unpretending, elegant way, infi-nitely superior to the bustle and preparation, the regular eating and drinking, and picnic parade of the Eltons and the Sucklings.

This was so very well understood between them that Emma could not but feel some surprise, and a little displeasure, on hearing from Mr Weston that he had been proposing to Mrs Elton, as her brother and sister had failed her, that the two parties should unite, and go together; and that as Mrs Elton had very readily acceded to it, so it was to be, if she had no objection. Now, as her objection was nothing, but her very great dislike of Mrs Elton, of which Mr Weston must already be perfectly aware, it was not worth bringing forward again: it could not be done without a reproof to him, which would be giving pain to his wife; and she found herself, therefore, obliged to consent to an arrangement which she would have done a great deal to avoid; an arrangement which would, probably, expose her even to the degradation of being said to be of Mrs Elton's party! Every feeling was offended; and the forbearance of her outward submission left a heavy arrear due of secret severity in her reflections, on the unmanageable goodwill of Mr Weston's temper.

'I am glad you approve of what I have done,' said he, very comfortably. 'But I thought you would. Such schemes as these are nothing without numbers. One cannot have too large a party. A large party secures its own amusement. And she is a good-natured woman after all. One could not leave her out.'

Emma denied none of it aloud, and agreed to none of it in private.

It was now the middle of June and the weather fine; and Mrs Elton was growing impatient to name the day, and settle with Mr Weston as to pigeon-pies and cold lamb, when a lame carriage-horse threw everything into sad uncertainty. It might be weeks, it might be only a few days, before the horse were usable; but no preparations could be ventured on, and it was all melancholy stagnation. Mrs Elton's resources were inadequate to such an attack.

'Is not this most vexatious, Knightley?' she cried; 'and such weather for exploring! these delays and disappointments are quite odious. What are we to do? The year will wear away at this rate, and nothing done. Before this time last year, I assure you, we had had a delightful exploring party from Maple Grove to Kings Weston.'

'You had better explore to Donwell,' replied Mr Knightley. 'That may be done without horses. Come and eat my strawberries; they are ripening fast.'

If Mr Knightley did not begin seriously, he was obliged to proceed so; for his proposal was caught at with delight; and the 'Oh! I should like it of all things,' was not plainer in words than manner. Donwell was famous for its strawberry-beds, which seemed a plea for the invitation; but no plea was necessary; cabbage-beds would have been enough to tempt the lady, who only wanted to be going somewhere. She promised him again and again to come – much oftener than he doubted – and was extremely gratified by such a proof of intimacy, such a distinguishing compliment as she chose to consider it.

'You may depend upon me,' said she; 'I certainly will come. Name your day, and I will come. You will allow me to bring Jane Fairfax?'

'I cannot name a day,' said he, 'till I have spoken to some others, whom I would wish to meet you.'

'Oh, leave all that to me; only give me a *carte blanche*. I am Lady Patroness, you know. It is my party. I will bring a friend with me.'

'I hope you will bring Elton,' said he; 'but I will not trouble you to give any other invitations.'

'Oh, now you are looking very sly; but consider – you need not be afraid of delegating power to *me*. I am no young lady on her preferment. Married women, you know, may be safely authorised. It is my party. Leave it all to me. I will invite your guests.'

'No,' he calmly replied, 'there is but one married woman in the world whom I can ever allow to invite what guests she pleases to Donwell, and that one is – '

'Mrs Weston, I suppose,' interrupted Mrs Elton, rather mortified.

'No – Mrs Knightley; and till she is in being, I will manage such matters myself.'

'Ah, you are an odd creature!' she cried, satisfied to have no one preferred to herself. 'You are a humorist, and may say what you like. Quite a humorist. Well, I shall bring Jane with me – Jane and her aunt. The rest I leave to you. I have no objections at all to meeting the Hartfield family. Don't scruple, I know you are attached to them.'

'You certainly will meet them, if I can prevail; and I shall call on Miss Bates in my way home.'

'That's quite unnecessary; I see Jane every day; but as you like. It is to be a morning scheme, you know, Knightley; quite a simple thing. I shall wear a large bonnet, and bring one of my little baskets hanging on my arm. Here – probably this basket with pink ribbon. Nothing can be more simple, you see. And Jane will have such another. There is to be no form or parade – a sort of gypsy party. We are to walk about your gardens, and gather the strawberries ourselves, and sit under trees; and whatever else you may like to provide, it is to be all out of doors; a table spread in the shade, you know. Everything as natural and simple as possible. Is not that your idea?'

'Not quite. My idea of the simple and the natural will be to have the table spread in the dining-room. The nature and the simplicity of gentlemen and ladies, with their servants and furniture, I think is best observed by meals within doors. When you are tired of eating strawberries in the garden, there shall be cold meat in the house.'

'Well, as you please; only don't have a great set-out. And, by the by, can I or my housekeeper be of any use to you with our opinion? Pray be sincere, Knightley. If you wish me to talk to Mrs Hodges, or to inspect anything – '

'I have not the least wish for it, I thank you.'

'Well – but if any difficulties should arise, my housekeeper is extremely clever.'

'I will answer for it that mine thinks herself full as clever and would spurn anybody's assistance.'

'I wish we had a donkey. The thing would be for us all to come on donkeys, Jane, Miss Bates, and me, and my *caro sposo* walking by. I really must talk to him about purchasing a donkey. In a country life I conceive it to be a sort of necessity; for, let a woman have ever so many resources, it is not possible for her to be always shut up at home; and very long walks, you know – in summer there is dust, and in winter there is dirt.'

'You will not find either between Donwell and Highbury. Donwell Lane is never dusty, and now it is perfectly dry. Come on a donkey, however, if you prefer it. You can borrow Mrs Cole's. I would wish everything to be as much to your taste as possible.'

'That I am sure you would. Indeed, I do you justice, my good friend. Under that peculiar sort of dry, blunt manner, I know you have the warmest heart. As I tell Mr E., you are a thorough humorist. Yes, believe me, Knightley, I am fully sensible of your attention to me in the whole of this scheme. You have hit upon the very thing to please me.'

Mr Knightley had another reason for avoiding a table in the shade. He wished to persuade Mr Woodhouse, as well as Emma, to join the party; and he knew that to have any of them sitting down out of doors to eat would inevitably make him ill. Mr Woodhouse must not, under the specious pretence of a morning drive, and an hour or two spent at Donwell, be tempted away to his misery.

He was invited on good faith. No lurking horrors were to upbraid him for his easy credulity. He did consent. He had not been at Donwell for two years. 'Some very fine morning, he, and Emma, and Harriet could go very well; and he could sit still with Mrs Weston while the dear girls walked about the gardens. He did not suppose they could be damp now, in the middle of the day. He should like to see the old house again exceedingly, and should be very happy to meet Mr and Mrs Elton, and any other of his neighbours. He could not see any objection at all to his, and Emma's, and Harriet's going there some very fine morning. He thought it very well done of Mr Knightley to invite them; very kind and sensible; much cleverer than dining out. He was not fond of dining out.'

Mr Knightley was fortunate in everybody's most ready concurrence. The invitation was everywhere so well received, that it seemed as if, like Mrs Elton, they were all taking the scheme as a particular compliment to themselves. Emma and Harriet professed very high expectations of pleasure from it; and Mr Weston, unasked, promised to get Frank over to join them, if possible; a proof of approbation and gratitude which could have been dispensed with. Mr Knightley was then obliged to say that he should be glad to see him; and Mr Weston engaged to lose no time in writing, and spare no arguments to induce him to come.

In the meanwhile the lame horse recovered so fast that the party to Box Hill was again under happy consideration; and at last Donwell was settled for one day; and Box Hill for the next, the weather appearing exactly right.

Under a bright midday sun, at almost Midsummer, Mr Woodhouse was safely conveyed in his carriage with one window down, to partake of this al fresco party; and in one of the most comfortable rooms in the Abbey, especially prepared for him by a fire all the morning, he was happily placed, quite at his ease, ready to talk with pleasure of what had been achieved, and advise everybody to come and sit down, and not to heat themselves. Mrs Weston, who seemed to have walked there on purpose to be tired, and sit all the time with him, remained, when all the others were invited or persuaded out, his patient listener and sympathiser.

It was so long since Emma had been at the Abbey, that as soon as she was satisfied of her father's comfort, she was glad to leave him and look around her; eager to refresh and correct her memory with more particular observation, more exact understanding of a house and grounds which must ever be so interesting to her and all her family.

She felt all the honest pride and complacency which her alliance with the present and future proprietor could fairly warrant, as she viewed the respectable size and style of the building, its suitable, becoming, characteristic situation, low and sheltered; its ample gardens stretching down to meadows washed by a stream, of which the Abbey, with all the old neglect of prospect, had scarcely a sight – and its abundance of timber in rows and avenues, which neither fashion nor extravagance had rooted up. The house was larger than Hartfield, and totally unlike it, covering a good deal of ground, rambling and irregular, with many comfortable, and one or two handsome rooms. It was just what it ought to be, and it looked what it was; and Emma felt an increasing respect for it, as the residence of a family of such true gentility, untainted in blood and understanding. Some faults of temper John Knightley had; but Isabella had connected herself unexceptionably. She had given them neither men, nor names, nor places, that could raise a blush. These were pleasant feelings, and she walked about and indulged them till it was necessary to do as the others did, and collect round the strawberry-beds. The whole party were assembled, excepting Frank Churchill, who was expected every moment from Richmond; and Mrs Elton, in all her apparatus of happiness, her large bonnet and her basket, was very ready to lead the way in gathering, accepting, or talking. Strawberries, and only strawberries, could now be thought or spoken of. 'The best fruit in England – everybody's favourite – always wholesome. These the finest beds and finest sorts. Delightful to gather for oneself – the only way of really enjoying them. Morning decidedly the best time – never tired – every sort good – hautboy infinitely superior – no comparison – the others hardly eatable –

hautboys very scarce – Chili preferred – white wood finest flavour of all – price of strawberries in London – abundance about Bristol – Maple Grove – cultivation – beds when to be renewed – gardeners thinking exactly different – no general rule – gardeners never to be put out of their way – delicious fruit – only too rich to be eaten much of – inferior to cherries – currants more refreshing – only objection to gathering strawberries the stooping – glaring sun – tired to death – could bear it no longer – must go and sit in the shade.'

Such, for half an hour, was the conversation; interrupted only once by Mrs Weston, who came out, in her solicitude after her son-in-law, to enquire if he were come; and she was a little uneasy. She had some fears of his horse.

Seats tolerably in the shade were found; and now Emma was obliged to overhear what Mrs Elton and Jane Fairfax were talking of. A situation, a most desirable situation, was in question. Mrs Elton had received notice of it that morning, and was in raptures. It was not with Mrs Suckling, it was not with Mrs Bragge, but in felicity and splendour it fell short only of them: it was with a cousin of Mrs Bragge, an acquaintance of Mrs Suckling, a lady known at Maple Grove. Delightful, charming, superior, first circles, spheres, lines, ranks, everything: and Mrs Elton was wild to have the offer closed with immediately. On her side, all was warmth, energy, and triumph; and she positively refused to take her friend's negative, though Miss Fairfax continued to assure her that she would not at present engage in anything – repeating the same motives which she had been heard to urge before. Still Mrs Elton insisted on being authorised to write an acquiescence by the morrow's post. How Jane could bear it at all, was astonishing to Emma. She did look vexed, she did speak pointedly – and at last, with a decision of action unusual to her, proposed a removal. 'Should not they walk? Would not Mr Knightley show them the gardens – all the gardens? She wished to see the whole extent.' The pertinacity of her friend seemed more than she could bear.

It was hot; and after walking some time over the gardens in a scattered, dispersed way, scarcely any three together, they insensibly followed one another to the delicious shade of a broad short avenue of limes, which, stretching beyond the garden at an equal distance from the river, seemed the finish of the pleasure grounds. It led to nothing; nothing but a view at the end over a low stone wall with high pillars, which seemed intended, in their erection, to give the appearance of an approach to the house, which never had been there. Disputable, however, as might be the taste of such a termination, it was in itself a charming walk and the view which closed it extremely pretty. The considerable slope, at nearly the foot of which the Abbey stood, gradually acquired a steeper form beyond its grounds; and at half a mile distant was a bank of considerable abruptness and grandeur, well clothed with wood; and at the bottom of this bank, favourably placed and sheltered, rose the Abbey Mill Farm, with meadows in front, and the river making a close and handsome curve around it.

It was a sweet view – sweet to the eye and the mind. English verdure, English culture, English comfort, seen under a sun bright, without being oppressive.

In this walk Emma and Mr Weston found all the others assembled; and towards this view she immediately perceived Mr Knightley and Harriet distinct from the rest, quietly leading the way. Mr Knightley and Harriet! It was an odd tête-à-tête; but she was glad to see it. There had been a time when he would have scorned her as a companion, and turned from her with little ceremony. Now they seemed in pleasant conversation. There had been a time also when Emma would have been sorry to see Harriet in a spot so favourable for the Abbey Mill Farm; but now she feared it not. It might be safely viewed, with all its appendages of prosperity and beauty, its rich pastures, spreading flocks, orchard in blossom, and light column of smoke ascending. She joined them at the wall, and found them more engaged in talking than in looking around. He was giving Harriet information as to modes of agriculture, etc.; and Emma received a smile which seemed to say: 'These are my own concerns. I have a right to talk on such subjects, without being suspected of introducing Robert Martin.' She did not suspect him. It was too old a story. Robert Martin had probably ceased to think of Harriet. They took a few turns together along the walk. The shade was most refreshing, and Emma found it the pleasantest part of the day.

The next remove was to the house; they must all go in and eat; and they were all seated and busy, and still Frank Churchill did not come. Mrs Weston looked, and looked in vain. His father would not own himself uneasy, and laughed at her fears; but she could not be cured of wishing that he would part with his black mare. He had expressed himself as to coming with more than common certainty. 'His aunt was so much better, that he had not a doubt of getting over to them.' Mrs Churchill's state, however, as many were ready to remind her, was liable to such sudden variation as might disappoint her nephew in the most reasonable dependence; and Mrs Weston was at last persuaded to believe, or to say, that it must be by some attack of Mrs Churchill that he was prevented coming. Emma looked at Harriet while the point was under consideration; she behaved very well, and betrayed no emotion.

The cold repast was over, and the party were to go out once more to see what had not yet been seen, the old Abbey fish-ponds; perhaps get as far as the clover, which was to be begun cutting on the morrow, or, at any rate, have the pleasure of being hot, and growing cool again. Mr Woodhouse, who had already taken his little round in the highest part of the gardens, where no damps from the river were imagined even by him, stirred no more; and his daughter resolved to remain with him, that Mrs Weston might be persuaded away by her husband to the exercise and variety which her spirits seemed to need.

Mr Knightley had done all in his power for Mr Woodhouse's entertainment. Books of engravings, drawers of medals, cameos, corals, shells, and every other family collection within his cabinets, had been prepared for his old friend, to while away the morning; and the kindness had perfectly answered. Mr Wood-house had been exceedingly well amused. Mrs Weston had been showing them all to him, and now he would show them all to Emma; fortunate in having no other resemblance to a child, than in a total want of taste for what he saw, for he was slow, constant, and methodical. Before this second looking over was begun, however, Emma walked into the hall for the sake of a few moments' free observation of the entrance and ground-plot of the house, and was hardly there when Jane Fairfax appeared, coming quickly in from the garden, and with a look of escape. Little expecting to meet Miss Woodhouse so soon, there was a start at first; but Miss Woodhouse was the very person she was in quest of.

'Will you be so kind,' said she, 'when I am missed, as to say that I am gone home? I am going this moment. My aunt is not aware how late it is, nor how long we have been absent; but I am sure we shall be wanted, and I am determined to go directly. I have said nothing about it to anybody. It would only be giving trouble and distress. Some are gone to the ponds, and some to the lime-walk. Till they all come in I shall not be missed; and when they do, will you have the goodness to say that I am gone?'

'Certainly, if you wish it; but you are not going to walk to Highbury alone?'

'Yes; what should hurt me? I walk fast. I shall be at home in twenty minutes.'

'But it is too far, indeed it is, to be walking quite alone. Let my father's servant go with you. Let me order the carriage. It can be round in five minutes.'

'Thank you, thank you – but on no account – I would rather walk. And for *me* to be afraid of walking alone! I, who may so soon have to guard others!'

She spoke with great agitation; and Emma very feelingly replied: 'That can be no reason for your being exposed to danger now. I must order the carriage. The heat even would be danger. You are fatigued already.'

'I am,' she answered, 'I am fatigued; but it is not the sort of fatigue – quick walking will refresh me. Miss Woodhouse, we all know at times what it is to be wearied in spirits. Mine, I confess, are exhausted. The greatest kindness you can show me will be to let me have my own way, and only say that I am gone when it is necessary.'

Emma had not another word to oppose. She saw it all; and entering into her feelings, promoted her quitting the house immediately, and watched her safely off with the zeal of a friend. Her parting look was grateful; and her parting words, 'Oh! Miss Woodhouse, the comfort of being sometimes alone!' seemed to burst from an overcharged heart, and to describe somewhat of the continual endurance to be practised by her, even towards some of those who loved her best.

'Such a home, indeed! such an aunt!' said Emma, as she turned back into the hall again. 'I do pity you. And the more sensibility you betray of their just horrors, the more I shall like you.'

Jane had not been gone a quarter of an hour, and they had only accomplished some views of St Mark's Place, Venice, when Frank Churchill entered the room. Emma had not been thinking of him; she had forgotten to think of him, but she was very glad to see him. Mrs Weston would be at ease. The black mare was blameless; *they* were right who had named Mrs Churchill as the cause. He had been detained by a temporary increase of illness in her – a nervous seizure which had lasted some hours; and he had quite given up every thought of coming till very late; and had he known how hot a ride he should have, and how late, with all his hurry, he must be, he believed he should not have come at all. The heat was excessive; he had never suffered anything like it – almost wished he had stayed at home – nothing killed him like heat – he could bear any degree of cold, etc., but heat was intolerable; and he sat down, at the greatest possible distance from the slight remains of Mr Woodhouse's fire, looking very deplorable.

'You will soon be cooler, if you sit still,' said Emma.

'As soon as I am cooler I shall go back again. I could very ill be spared; but such a point had been made of my coming! You will all be going soon, I suppose; the whole party breaking up. I met *one* as I came – madness in such weather! – absolute madness!'

Emma listened, and looked, and soon perceived that Frank Churchill's state might best be defined by the expressive phrase of being out of humour. Some people were always cross when they were hot. Such might be his constitution; and as she knew that eating and drinking were often the cure of such incidental complaints, she recommended his taking some refreshment; he would find abundance of everything in the dining-room; and she humanely pointed out the door.

'No; he should not eat. He was not hungry; it would only make him hotter.' In two minutes, however, he relented in his own favour; and muttering something about spruce-beer, walked off. Emma returned all her attention to her father, saying in secret, 'I am glad I have done being in love with him. I should not like a man who is so soon discomposed by a hot morning. Harriet's sweet easy temper will not mind it.'

He was gone long enough to have had a very comfortable meal, and came back all the better – grown quite cool, and with good manners, like himself, able to draw a chair close to them, take an interest in their employment, and regret, in a reasonable way, that he should be so late. He was not in his best spirits, but seemed trying to improve them; and, at last, made himself talk nonsense very agreeably. They were looking over views in Switzerland.

'As soon as my aunt gets well I shall go abroad,' said he. 'I shall never be easy till I have seen some of these places. You will have my sketches, some time or other, to look at – or my tour to read – or my poem. I shall do something to expose myself.'

'That may be – but not by sketches in Switzerland. You will never go to Switzerland. Your uncle and aunt will never allow you to leave England.'

'They may be induced to go too. A warm climate may be prescribed for her. I have more than half an expectation of our all going abroad. I assure you, I have. I feel a strong persuasion, this morning, that I shall soon be abroad. I ought to travel. I am tired of doing nothing. I want a change. I am serious, Miss Woodhouse, whatever your penetrating eyes may fancy – I am sick of England, and would leave it tomorrow if I could.'

'You are sick of prosperity and indulgence! Cannot you invent a few hardships for yourself, and be contented to stay?'

'*I* sick of prosperity and indulgence! You are quite mistaken. I do not look upon myself as either prosperous or indulged. I am thwarted in everything material. I do not consider myself at all a fortunate person.'

'You are not quite so miserable, though, as when you first came. Go and eat and drink a little more, and you will do very well. Another slice of cold meat, another draught of Madeira and water, will make you nearly on a par with the rest of us.'

'No – I shall not stir. I shall sit by you. You are my best cure.'

'We are going to Box Hill tomorrow: you will join us. It is not Switzerland, but it will be something for a young man so much in want of a change. You will stay and go with us?'

'No, certainly not; I shall go home in the cool of the evening.'

'But you may come again in the cool of tomorrow morning.'

'No – it will not be worth while. If I come, I shall be cross.'

'Then pray stay at Richmond.'

'But if I do, I shall be crosser still. I can never bear to think of you all there without me.'

'These are difficulties which you must settle for yourself. Choose your own degree of crossness. I shall press you no more.'

The rest of the party were now returning, and all were soon collected. With some there was great joy at the sight of Frank Churchill; others took it very composedly; but there was a very general distress and disturbance on Miss Fairfax's disappearance being explained. That it was time for everybody to go concluded the subject; and with a short final arrangement for the next day's scheme, they parted. Frank Churchill's little inclination to exclude himself increased so much, that his last words to Emma were, 'Well; if you wish me to stay and join the party, I will.'

She smiled her acceptance; and nothing less than a summons from Richmond was to take him back before the following evening.

Chapter 43

They had a very fine day for Box Hill; and all the other outward circumstances of arrangement, accommodation, and punctuality, were in favour of a pleasant party. Mr Weston directed the whole, officiating safely between Hartfield and the Vicarage, and everybody was in good time. Emma and Harriet went together; Miss Bates and her niece with the Eltons; the gentlemen on horseback. Mrs Weston remained with Mr Woodhouse. Nothing was wanting but to be happy when they got there. Seven miles were travelled in expectation of enjoyment, and everybody had a burst of admiration on first arriving; but in the general amount of the day there was deficiency. There was a languor, a want of spirits, a want of union, which could not be got over. They separated too much into parties. The Eltons walked together; Mr Knightley took charge of Miss Bates and Jane; and Emma and Harriet belonged to Frank Churchill. And Mr Weston tried, in vain, to make them harmonise better. It seemed at first an accidental division, but it never materially varied. Mr and Mrs Elton, indeed, showed no unwillingness to mix, and to be as agreeable as they could; but during the two whole hours that were spent on the hill, there seemed a principle of separation between the other parties, too strong for any fine prospects, or any cold collation, or any cheerful Mr Weston, to remove.

At first it was downright dullness to Emma. She had never seen Frank Churchill so silent and stupid. He said nothing worth hearing – looked without seeing – admired without intelligence – listened without knowing what she said. While he was so dull, it was no wonder that Harriet should be dull likewise; and they were both insufferable.

When they all sat down it was better – to her taste a great deal better – for Mr Frank Churchill grew talkative and gay, making her his first object. Every distinguishing attention that could be paid, was paid to her. To amuse her, and be agreeable in her eyes, seemed all that he cared for – and Emma, glad to be enlivened, not sorry to be flattered, was gay and easy too, and gave him all the friendly encouragement, the admission to be gallant, which she had ever given in the first and most animating period of their acquaintance: but which now, in her own estimation, meant nothing, though in the judgement of most people looking on, it must have had such an appearance as no English word but flirtation could very well describe. 'Mr Frank Churchill and Miss Woodhouse flirted together excessively.' They were laying themselves open to that very phrase – and to having it sent off in a letter to Maple Grove by one lady, to Ireland by another. Not that Emma was gay and thoughtless from any real felicity; it was rather because she felt less happy than she had expected. She laughed because she was disappointed; and though she liked him for his attentions, and thought them all, whether in friendship, admiration, or playfulness, extremely judicious, they were not winning back her heart. She still intended him for her friend.

'How much I am obliged to you,' said he, 'for telling me to come today! If it had not been for you, I should certainly have lost all the happiness of this party. I had quite determined to go away again.'

'Yes, you were very cross; and I do not know what about, except that you were too late for the best strawberries. I was a kinder friend than you deserved. But you were humble. You begged hard to be commanded to come.'

'Don't say I was cross. I was fatigued. The heat overcame me.'

'It is hotter today.'

'Not to my feelings. I am perfectly comfortable today.'

'You are comfortable because you are under command.'

'Your command? Yes.'

'Perhaps I intended you to say so, but I meant self-command. You had, somehow or other, broken bounds yesterday, and run away from your own management; but today you are got back again – and as I cannot be always with you, it is best to believe your temper under your own command rather than mine.'

'It comes to the same thing. I can have no self-command without a motive. You order me, whether you speak or not. And you can be always with me. You are always with me.'

'Dating from three o'clock yesterday. My perpetual influence could not begin earlier, or you would not have been so much out of humour before.'

'Three o'clock yesterday! That is your date. I thought I had seen you first in February.'

'Your gallantry is really unanswerable. But' (lowering her voice) 'nobody speaks except ourselves, and it is rather too much to be talking nonsense for the entertainment of seven silent people.'

'I say nothing of which I am ashamed,' replied he, with lively impudence. 'I saw you first in February. Let everybody on the Hill hear me if they can. Let my accents swell to Mickleham on one side, and Dorking on the other. I saw you first in February.' And then whispering: 'Our companions are excessively stupid. What shall we do to rouse them? Any nonsense will serve. They *shall* talk. Ladies and gentlemen, I am ordered by Miss Woodhouse (who, wherever she is, presides) to say, that she desires to know what you are all thinking of?'

Some laughed, and answered good-humouredly. Miss Bates said a great deal; Mrs Elton swelled at the idea of

Miss Woodhouse's presiding; Mr Knightley's answer was the most distinct.

'Is Miss Woodhouse sure that she would like to hear what we are all thinking of?'

'Oh, no, no!' cried Emma, laughing as carelessly as she could – 'upon no account in the world. It is the very last thing I would stand the brunt of just now. Let me hear anything rather than what you are all thinking of. I will not say quite all. There are one or two perhaps' (glancing at Mr Weston and Harriet), 'whose thoughts I might not be afraid of knowing.'

'It is a sort of thing,' cried Mrs Elton emphatically, 'which *I* should not have thought myself privileged to enquire into. Though, perhaps, as the *chaperon* of the party – *I* never was in any circle – exploring parties – young ladies – married women – '

Her mutterings were chiefly to her husband; and he murmured, in reply, 'Very true, my love, very true. Exactly so, indeed – quite unheard of – but some ladies say anything. Better pass it off as a joke. Everybody knows what is due to you.'

'It will not do,' whispered Frank to Emma, 'they are most of them affronted. I will attack them with more address. Ladies and gentlemen, I am ordered by Miss Woodhouse to say, that she waives her right of knowing exactly what you may all be thinking of, and only requires something very entertaining from each of you, in a general way. Here are seven of you, besides myself (who, she is pleased to say, am very entertaining already), and she only demands from each of you, either one thing very clever, be it prose or verse, original or repeated; or two things moderately clever; or three things very dull indeed; and she engages to laugh heartily at them all.'

'Oh! very well,' exclaimed Miss Bates; 'then I need not be uneasy. "Three things very dull indeed." That will just do for me, you know. I shall be sure to say three dull things as soon as ever I open my mouth, shan't I?' (looking round with the most good-humoured dependence on everybody's assent). 'Do you not all think I shall?'

Emma could not resist.

'Ah! ma'am, but there may be a difficulty. Pardon me, but you will be limited as to number – only three at once.'

Miss Bates, deceived by the mock ceremony of her manner, did not immediately catch her meaning; but when it burst on her, it could not anger, though a slight blush showed that it could pain her.

'Ah! well – to be sure. Yes, I see what she means' (turning to Mr Knightley) 'and I will try to hold my tongue. I must make myself very disagreeable, or she would not have said such a thing to an old friend.'

'I like your plan,' cried Mr Weston. 'Agreed, agreed. I will do my best. I am making a conundrum. How will a conundrum reckon?'

'Low, I am afraid, sir, very low,' answered his son; 'but we shall be indulgent, especially to anyone who leads the way.'

'No, no,' said Emma, 'it will not reckon low. A conundrum of Mr Weston's shall clear him and his next neighbour. Come, sir, pray let me hear it.'

'I doubt its being very clever myself,' said Mr Weston. 'It is too much a matter of fact; but here it is: What two letters of the alphabet are there that express perfection?'

'What two letters – express perfection? I am sure I do not know.'

'Ah! you will never guess. You' (to Emma), 'I am certain, will never guess. I will tell you. M and A: Emma. Do you understand?'

Understanding and gratification came together. It might be a very indifferent piece of wit, but Emma found a great deal to laugh at and enjoy in it: and so did Frank and Harriet. It did not seem to touch the rest of the party equally; some looked very stupid about it, and Mr Knightley gravely said: 'This explains the sort of clever thing that is wanted, and Mr Weston has done very well for himself: but he must have knocked up everybody else. *Perfection* should not have come quite so soon.'

'Oh! for myself, I protest I must be excused,' said Mrs Elton. 'I really cannot attempt – I am not at all fond of the sort of thing. I had an acrostic once sent to me upon my own name which I was not at all pleased with. I knew who it came from. An abominable puppy! You know who I mean' (nodding to her husband). 'These kind of things are very well at Christmas, when one is sitting round the fire; but quite out of place, in my opinion, when one is exploring about the country in summer. Miss Woodhouse must excuse me. I am not one of those who have witty things at everybody's service. I do not pretend to be a wit. I have a great deal of vivacity in my own way, but I really must be allowed to judge when to speak, and when to hold my tongue. Pass us, if you please, Mr Churchill. Pass Mr E., Knightley, Jane, and myself. We have nothing clever to say – not one of us.'

'Yes, yes, pray pass me,' added her husband, with a sort of sneering consciousness; 'I have nothing to say that can entertain Miss Woodhouse, or any other young lady. An old married man – quite good for nothing. Shall we walk, Augusta?'

'With all my heart. I am really tired of exploring so long on one spot. Come, Jane, take my other arm.'

Jane declined it, however, and the husband and wife walked off. 'Happy couple!' said Frank Churchill, as soon as they were out of hearing; 'how well they suit one another! Very lucky – marrying as they did, upon an acquaintance formed only in a public place! They only knew each other, I think, a few weeks in Bath! Peculiarly lucky! for as to any real knowledge of a person's disposition that Bath, or any public place, can give – it is all nothing; there can be no knowledge. It is only by seeing women in their own homes, among their own set, just as they always are, that you can form any just judgement. Short of that, it is all guess and luck – and will generally be ill luck. How many a man has committed himself on a short acquaintance, and rued it all the rest of his life!'

Miss Fairfax, who had seldom spoken before, except among her own confederates, spoke now.

'Such things do occur, undoubtedly.' She was stopped by a cough. Frank Churchill turned towards her to listen. 'You were speaking,' said he gravely. She recovered her voice.

'I was only going to observe, that though such unfortunate circumstances do sometimes occur both to men and women, I cannot imagine them to be very frequent. A hasty and imprudent attachment may arise – but there is generally time to recover from it afterwards. I would be understood to mean, that it can be only weak, irresolute characters (whose happiness must be always at the mercy of chance), who will suffer an unfortunate acquaintance to be an inconvenience, an oppression for ever.'

He made no answer; merely looked, and bowed in submission; and soon afterwards said, in a lively tone: 'Well, I have so little confidence in my own judgement, that whenever I marry, I hope somebody will choose my wife for me. Will you?' (turning to Emma). 'Will you choose a wife for me? I am sure I should like anybody fixed on by you. You provide for the family, you know' (with a smile at his father). 'Find somebody for me. I am in no hurry. Adopt her; educate her.'

'And make her like myself.'

'By all means, if you can.'

'Very well. I undertake the commission. You shall have a charming wife.'

'She must be very lively, and have hazel eyes. I care for nothing else. I shall go abroad for a couple of years – and when I return, I shall come to you for my wife. Remember.'

Emma was in no danger of forgetting. It was a commission to touch every favourite feeling. Would not Harriet be the very creature described? Hazel eyes excepted, two years more might make her all that he wished. He might even have Harriet in his thoughts at the moment; who could say? Referring the education to her seemed to imply it.

'Now, ma'am,' said Jane to her aunt, 'shall we join Mrs Elton?'

'If you please, my dear. With all my heart. I am quite ready. I was ready to have gone with her, but this will do just as well. We shall soon overtake her. There she is – no, that's somebody else. That's one of the ladies in the Irish car party, not at all like her. Well, I declare – '

They walked off, followed in half a minute by Mr Knightley. Mr Weston, his son, Emma, and Harriet only remained; and the young man's spirits now rose to a pitch almost unpleasant. Even Emma grew tired at last of flattery and merriment, and wished herself rather walking quietly about with any of the others, or sitting almost alone, and quite unattended to, in tranquil observation of the beautiful views beneath her. The appearance of the servants looking out for them to give notice of the carriages was a joyful sight; and even the bustle of collecting and preparing to depart, and the solicitude of Mrs Elton to have her carriage first, were gladly endured, in the prospect of the quiet drive home which was to close the very questionable enjoyments of this day of pleasure. Such another scheme, composed of so many ill-assorted people, she hoped never to be betrayed into again.

While waiting for the carriage, she found Mr Knightley by her side. He looked around, as if to see that no one were near, and then said: 'Emma, I must once more speak to you as I have been used to do; a privilege rather endured than allowed, perhaps, but I must still use it. I cannot see you acting wrong, without a remonstrance. How could you be so unfeeling to Miss Bates? How could you be so insolent in your wit to a woman of her character, age, and situation? Emma, I had not thought it possible.'

Emma recollected, blushed, was sorry, but tried to laugh it off.

'Nay, how could I help saying what I did? Nobody could have helped it. It was not so very bad. I dare say she did not understand me.'

'I assure you she did. She felt your full meaning. She has talked of it since. I wish you could have heard how she talked of it – with what candour and generosity. I wish you could have heard her honouring your forbearance, in being able to pay her such attentions, as she was for ever receiving from yourself and your father, when her society must be so irksome.'

'Oh!' cried Emma, 'I know there is not a better creature in the world; but you must allow, that what is good and what is ridiculous are most unfortunately blended in her.'

'They are blended,' said he, 'I acknowledge; and, were she prosperous, I could allow much for the occasional prevalence of the ridiculous over the good. Were she a woman of fortune, I would leave every harmless absurdity to take its chance; I would not quarrel with you for any liberties of manner. Were she your equal in situation – but, Emma, consider how far this is from being the case. She is poor; she has sunk from the comforts she was born to; and if she live to old age must probably sink more. Her situation should secure your compassion. It was badly done, indeed! You, whom she had known from an infant, whom she had seen grow up from a period when her notice was an honour – to have you now, in thoughtless spirits, and the pride of the moment, laugh at her, humble her – and before her niece, too – and before others, many of whom (certainly *some*) would be entirely guided by your treatment of her. This is not pleasant to you, Emma – and it is very far from pleasant to me; but I must, I will – I tell you truths while I can; satisfied with proving myself your friend by very faithful counsel, and trusting that you will some time or other do me greater justice than you can do now.'

While they talked they were advancing towards the carriage; it was ready; and, before she could speak again, he had handed her in. He had misinterpreted the feelings which had kept her face averted, and her tongue motionless. They were combined only of anger against herself, mortification, and deep concern. She had not been able to speak; and, on entering the carriage, sunk back for a moment, overcome; then reproaching herself for having taken no leave, making no acknowledgement, parting in apparent sullenness, she looked out with voice and hand eager to show a difference; but it was just too late. He had turned away, and the horses were in motion. She continued to look back, but in vain; and soon, with what appeared unusual speed, they were half way down the hill, and everything left far behind. She was vexed beyond what could have been expressed – almost beyond what she could conceal. Never had she felt so agitated, mortified, grieved, at any circumstance in her life. She was forcibly struck. The truth of his representation there was no denying. She felt it at her heart. How could she have been so brutal, so cruel to Miss Bates! How could she have exposed herself to such ill opinion in anyone she valued! And how suffer him to leave her without saying one word of gratitude, of concurrence, of common kindness!

Time did not compose her. As she reflected more, she seemed but to feel it more. She never had been so depressed. Happily it was not necessary to speak. There was only Harriet, who seemed not in spirits herself, fagged, and very willing to be silent; and Emma felt the tears running down her cheeks almost all the way home, without being at any trouble to check them, extraordinary as they were.

Chapter 44

The wretchedness of a scheme to Box Hill was in Emma's thoughts all the evening. How it might be considered by the rest of the party she could not tell. They, in their different homes, and their different ways, might be looking back on it with pleasure; but in her view it was a morning more completely misspent, more totally bare of rational satisfaction at the time, and more to be abhorred in recollection, than any she had ever passed. A whole evening of backgammon with her father was felicity to it. *There*, indeed, lay real pleasure, for there she was giving up the sweetest hours of the twenty-four to his comfort; and feeling that, unmerited as might be the degree of his fond affection and confiding esteem, she could not, in her general conduct, be open to any severe reproach. As a daughter, she hoped she was not without a heart. She hoped no one could have said to her, 'How could you be so unfeeling to your father? – I must, I will tell you truths while I can.' Miss Bates should never again – no never! If attention in future could do away the past she might hope to be forgiven. She had been often remiss, for conscience told her so; remiss, perhaps, more in thought than fact; scornful, ungracious. But it should be so no more. In the warmth of true contrition she would call upon her the very next morning, and it should be the beginning, on her side, of a regular, equal, kindly intercourse.

She was just as determined when the morrow came, and went early, that nothing might prevent her. It was not unlikely, she thought, that she might see Mr Knightley in her way; or perhaps he might come in while she were paying her visit. She had no objection. She would not be ashamed of the appearance of the penitence, so justly and truly hers. Her eyes were towards Donwell as she walked, but she saw him not.

'The ladies were all at home.' She had never rejoiced at the sound before, nor ever before entered the passage, nor walked up the stairs, with any wish of giving pleasure, but in conferring obligation, or of deriving it, except in subsequent ridicule.

There was a bustle on her approach; a good deal of moving and talking. She heard Miss Bates's voice, something was to be done in a hurry, the maid looked frightened and awkward; hoped she would be pleased to wait a moment, and then ushered her in too soon. The aunt and niece seemed both escaping into the adjoining room. Jane she had a distinct glimpse of, looking extremely ill; and before the door had shut them out, she heard Miss Bates saying, 'Well, my dear, I shall *say* you are laid down upon the bed, and I am sure you are ill enough.'

Poor old Mrs Bates, civil and humble as usual, looked as if she did not quite understand what was going on.

'I am afraid Jane is not very well,' said she, 'but I do not know; they *tell* me she is well. I dare say my daughter will be here

presently, Miss Woodhouse. I hope you find a chair. I wish Hetty
had not gone. I am very little able – have you a chair, ma'am? Do
you sit where you like? I am sure she will be here presently.'

Emma seriously hoped she would. She had a moment's fear
of Miss Bates keeping away from her. But Miss Bates soon came –
'Very happy and obliged' – but Emma's conscience told her that
there was not the same cheerful volubility as before – less ease of
look and manner. A very friendly enquiry after Miss Fairfax, she
hoped, might lead the way to a return of old feelings. The touch
seemed immediate.

'Ah, Miss Woodhouse, how kind you are! I suppose you have
heard – and are come to give us joy. This does not seem much
like joy, indeed, in me' (twinkling away a tear or two); 'but it will
be very trying for us to part with her, after having had her so
long; and she has a dreadful headache just now, writing all the
morning; such long letters, you know, to be written to Colonel
Campbell and Mrs Dixon. "My dear," said I, "you will blind
yourself," for tears were in her eyes perpetually. One cannot
wonder, one cannot wonder. It is a great change; and though she
is amazingly fortunate – such a situation, I suppose, as no young
woman before ever met with on first going out; do not think us
ungrateful, Miss Woodhouse, for such surprising good fortune'
(again dispersing her tears) – 'but, poor dear soul! if you were to
see what a headache she has. When one is in great pain, you
know, one cannot feel any blessing quite as it may deserve. She
is as low as possible. To look at her nobody would think how
delighted and happy she is to have secured such a situation. You
will excuse her not coming to you; she is not able, she is gone
into her own room. I want her to lie down upon the bed. "My
dear," said I, "I shall say you are laid down upon the bed"; but,
however, she is not; she is walking about the room. But, now that
she has written her letters, she says she shall soon be well. She
will be extremely sorry to miss seeing you, Miss Woodhouse, but
your kindness will excuse her. You were kept waiting at the door;
I was quite ashamed; but somehow there was a little bustle; for it

so happened that we had not heard the knock; and, till you were on the stairs, we did not know anybody was coming. "It is only Mrs Cole," said I, "depend upon it; nobody else would come so early." – "Well," said she, "it must be borne some time or other, and it may as well be now." But then Patty came in, and said it was you. "Oh," said I, "it is Miss Woodhouse, I am sure you will like to see her" – "I can see nobody," said she, and up she got, and would go away; and that was what made us keep you waiting; and extremely sorry and ashamed we were. "If you must go, my dear," said I, "you must, and I will say you are laid down upon the bed." '

Emma was most sincerely interested. Her heart had been long growing kinder towards Jane; and this picture of her present sufferings acted as a cure of every former ungenerous suspicion, and left her nothing but pity; and the remembrance of the less just and less gentle sensations of the past obliged her to admit that Jane might very naturally resolve on seeing Mrs Cole, or any other steady friend, when she might not bear to see herself. She spoke as she felt, with earnest regret and solicitude – sincerely wishing that the circumstances which she collected from Mrs Bates to be now actually determined on, might be as much for Miss Fairfax's advantage and comfort as possible.

'It must be a severe trial to them all. She had understood it was to be delayed until Colonel Campbell's return.'

'So very kind!' replied Miss Bates; 'but you are always kind.'

There was no bearing such an 'always;' and to break through her dreadful gratitude Emma made to direct enquiry of: 'Where, may I ask, is Miss Fairfax going?'

'To a Mrs Smallridge – charming woman – most superior – to have the charge of her three little girls – delightful children! Impossible that any situation could be more replete with comfort; if we except, perhaps, Mrs Suckling's own family, and Mrs Bragge's, but Mrs Smallridge is intimate with both, and in the very same neighbourhood – lives only four miles from Maple Grove. Jane will be only four miles from Maple Grove.'

'Mrs Elton, I suppose, has been the person to whom Miss Fairfax owes – '

'Yes, our good Mrs Elton. The most indefatigable, true friend. She would not take a denial. She would not let Jane say "No;" for when Jane first heard of it (it was the day before yesterday, the very morning we were at Donwell), when Jane first heard of it, she was quite decided against accepting the offer, and for the reasons you mention; exactly as you say, she had made up her mind to close with nothing till Colonel Campbell's return, and nothing should induce her to enter into any engagement at present – and so she told Mrs Elton over and over again – and I am sure I had no more idea that she would change her mind! – but that good Mrs Elton, whose judgement never fails her, saw farther than I did. It is not everybody that would have stood out in such a kind way as she did, and refuse to take Jane's answer; but she positively declared she would not write any such denial yesterday, as Jane wished her; she would wait – and, sure enough, yesterday evening, it was all settled that Jane should go. Quite a surprise to me! I had not the least idea. Jane took Mrs Elton aside, and told her at once, that, upon thinking over the advantages of Mrs Smallridge's situation, she had come to the resolution of accepting it. I did not know a word of it till it was all settled.'

'You spent the evening with Mrs Elton?'

'Yes, all of us; Mrs Elton would have us come. It was settled so, upon the hill, while we were walking about with Mr Knightley. "You *must all* spend your evening with us," said she – "I positively must have you *all* come." '

'Mr Knightley was there too, was he?'

'No, not Mr Knightley; he declined it from the first; and though I thought he would come, because Mrs Elton declared she would not let him off, he did not; but my mother, and Jane, and I, were all there, and a very agreeable evening we had. Such kind friends, you know, Miss Woodhouse, one must always find agreeable, though everybody seemed rather fagged after the morning's party. Even pleasure, you know, is fatiguing –

and I cannot say that any of them seemed very much to have enjoyed it. However, I shall always think it a very pleasant party, and feel extremely obliged to the kind friends who included me in it.'

'Miss Fairfax, I suppose, though you were not aware of it, had been making up her mind the whole day?'

'I dare say she had.'

'Whenever the time may come it must be unwelcome to her and all her friends – but I hope her engagement will have every alleviation that is possible – I mean, as to character and manners of the family.'

'Thank you, dear Miss Woodhouse. Yes, indeed, there is everything in the world that can make her happy in it. Except the Sucklings and Bragges, there is not such another nursery estab-lishment, so liberal and elegant, in all Mrs Elton's acquaintance. Mrs Smallridge, a most delightful woman! A style of living almost equal to Maple Grove – and as to the children, except the little Sucklings and little Bragges, there are not such elegant sweet children anywhere. Jane will be treated with such regard and kindness! It will be nothing but pleasure – a life of pleasure. And her salary. I really cannot venture to name her salary to you, Miss Woodhouse. Even you, used as you are to great sums, would hardly believe that so much could be given to a young person like Jane.'

'Ah, madam,' cried Emma, 'if other children are at all like what I remember to have been myself, I should think that five times the amount of what I have ever yet heard named as a salary on such occasions dearly earned.'

'You are so noble in your ideas.'

'And when is Miss Fairfax to leave you?'

'Very soon, very soon, indeed; that's the worst of it. Within a fortnight. Mrs Smallridge is in a great hurry. My poor mother does not know how to bear it. So, then, I try to put it out of her thoughts, and say, "Come, ma'am, do not let us think about it any more."'

'Her friends must all be sorry to lose her; and will not Colonel and Mrs Campbell be sorry to find that she has engaged herself before their return?'

'Yes; Jane says she is sure they will; but yet this is such a situation that she cannot feel herself justified in declining. I was so astonished when she first told me what she had been saying to Mrs Elton, and when Mrs Elton at the same moment came congratulating me upon it! It was before tea – stay – no, it could not be before tea, because we were just going to cards – and yet it was before tea, because I remember thinking – oh, no, now I recollect, now I have it; something happened before tea, but not that. Mr Elton was called out of the room before tea, old John Abdy's son wanted to speak with him. Poor old John – I have a great regard for him; he was clerk to my poor father twenty-seven years; and now, poor old man, he is bedridden, and very poorly with the rheumatic gout in his joints – I must go and see him today; and so will Jane, I am sure, if she gets out at all. And poor John's son came to talk to Mr Elton about relief from the parish; he is very well-to-do himself, you know, being head man at the Crown – ostler, and everything of that sort – but still he cannot keep his father without some help; and so, when Mr Elton came back, he told us what John ostler had been telling him, and then it came out about the chaise having been sent to Randalls to take Mr Frank Churchill to Richmond. That was what happened before tea. It was after tea that Jane spoke to Mrs Elton.'

Miss Bates would hardly give Emma time to say how perfectly new this circumstance was to her; but as without supposing it possible that she could be ignorant of any of the particulars of Mr Frank Churchill's going, she proceeded to give them all, it was of no consequence.

What Mr Elton had learned from the ostler on the subject, being the accumulation of the ostler's own knowledge, and the knowledge of the servants at Randalls, was, that a messenger had come over from Richmond soon after the return of the party from Box Hill – which messenger, however, had been no more than was expected; and that Mr Churchill had sent his nephew a few lines containing, upon the whole, a tolerable account of Mrs Churchill, and only wishing him not to delay coming back beyond the next morning early; but that Mr Frank Churchill, having resolved to go home directly, without waiting at all, and his horse seeming to have got a cold, Tom had been sent off immediately for the Crown chaise, and the ostler had stood out and seen it pass by, the boy going a good pace, and driving very steady.

There was nothing in all this either to astonish or interest, and it caught Emma's attention only as it united with the subject which already engaged her mind. The contrast between Mrs Churchill's importance in the world and Jane Fairfax's struck her; one was everything, the other nothing – and she sat musing on the difference of woman's destiny, and quite unconscious on what her eyes were fixed, till roused by Miss Bates saying: 'Ay, I see what you are thinking of, the pianoforte. What is to become of that? Very true. Poor dear Jane was talking of it just now. "You must go," said she. "You and I must part. You will have no business here. Let it stay, however," said she; "give it house-room till Colonel Campbell comes back; I shall talk about it to him; he will settle for me; he will help me out of all my difficulties." And to this day, I do believe, she knows not whether it was his present or his daughter's.'

Now Emma was obliged to think of the pianoforte; and the remembrance of all her former fanciful and unfair conjectures was so little pleasing that she soon allowed herself to believe her visit had been long enough; and, with a repetition of everything that she could venture to say of the good wishes which she really felt, took leave.

Chapter 45

Emma's pensive meditations, as she walked home, were not interrupted; but on entering the parlour, she found those who must rouse her. Mr Knightley and Harriet had arrived during her absence, and were sitting with her father. Mr Knightley immediately got up, and, in a manner decidedly graver than usual, said: 'I would not go away without seeing you, but I have no time to spare, and therefore must now be gone directly. I am going to London, to spend a few days with John and Isabella. Have you anything to send or say, besides the "love", which nobody carries?'

'Nothing at all. But is not this a sudden scheme!'

'Yes – rather – I have been thinking of it some little time.'

Emma was sure he had not forgiven her; he looked unlike himself. Time, however, she thought, would tell him that they ought to be friends again. While he stood, as if meaning to go, but not going – her father began his enquiries.

'Well, my dear, and did you get there safely? – And how did you find my worthy old friend and her daughter? – I dare say they must have been very much obliged to you for coming. Dear Emma has been to call on Mrs and Miss Bates, Mr Knightley, as I told you before. She is always so attentive to them.'

Emma's colour was heightened by this unjust praise; and with a smile and shake of the head, which spoke much, she looked at Mr Knightley. It seemed as if there were an instantaneous impression in her favour, as if his eyes received the truth from hers, and all that had passed of good in her feelings were at once caught and honoured. He looked at her with a glow of regard. She was warmly gratified – and in another moment still more so, by a little movement of more than common friendliness on his part. He took her hand; whether she had not herself made the first motion, she could not say – she might, perhaps, have rather offered it; but he took her hand, pressed it, and certainly was on the point of carrying it to his lips, when, from some fancy or other, he suddenly let it go. Why he should feel such a scruple, why he should change his mind when it was all but done, she could not perceive. He would have judged better, she thought, if he had not stopped. The intention, however, was indubitable; and whether it was that his manners had in general so little gallantry, or however else it happened, but she thought nothing became him more. It was with him of so simple, yet so dignified a nature. She could not but recall the attempt with great satisfaction. It spoke such perfect amity. He left them immediately afterwards – gone in a moment. He always moved with the alertness of a mind which could neither be undecided nor dilatory, but now he seemed more sudden than usual in his disappearance.

Emma could not regret her having gone to Miss Bates, but she wished she had left her ten minutes earlier; it would have been a great pleasure to talk over Jane Fairfax's situation with Mr Knightley. Neither would she regret that he should be going to Brunswick Square, for she knew how much his visit would be enjoyed – but it might have happened at a better time – and to have had longer notice of it would have been pleasanter. They parted thorough friends, however; she could not be deceived as to the meaning of his countenance, and his unfinished gallantry; it was all done to assure her that she had fully recovered his good opinion. He had been sitting with them half an hour she found. It was a pity that she had not come back earlier.

In the hope of diverting her father's thoughts from the disagreeableness of Mr Knightley's going to London, and going so suddenly, and going on horseback, which she knew would be all very bad, Emma communicated her news of Jane Fairfax, and her dependence on the effect was justified; it supplied a very useful check – interested, without disturbing him. He had long made up his mind to Jane Fairfax's going out as governess, and could talk of it cheerfully, but Mr Knightley's going to London had been an unexpected blow.

'I am very glad, indeed, my dear, to hear she is to be so comfortably settled. Mrs Elton is very good-natured and agreeable, and I dare say her acquaintance are just what they ought to be. I hope it is a dry situation, and that her health will be taken good care of. It ought to be a first object, as I am sure poor Miss Taylor's always was with me. You know, my dear, she is going to be to this new lady what Miss Taylor was to us. And I hope she will be better off in one respect, and not be induced to go away after it has been her home so long.'

The following day brought news from Richmond to throw everything else into the background. An express arrived at Randalls to announce the death of Mrs Churchill. Though her nephew had had no particular reason to hasten back on her account, she had not lived above six-and-thirty hours after his return. A sudden seizure of a different nature from anything foreboded by her general state, had carried her off after a short struggle. The great Mrs Churchill was no more.

It was felt as such things must be felt. Everybody had a degree of gravity and sorrow; tenderness towards the departed, solicitude for the surviving friends, and, in a reasonable time, curiosity to know where she would be buried. Goldsmith tells us, that when lovely woman stoops to folly, she has nothing to do but to die; and when she stoops to be disagreeable, it is equally to be recommended as a clearer of ill-fame. Mrs Churchill, after being disliked at least twenty-five years, was now spoken of with compassionate allowances. In one point she was fully justified. She had never been admitted before to be seriously ill. The event acquitted her of all the fancifulness, and all the selfishness of imaginary complaints.

'Poor Mrs Churchill! no doubt she had been suffering a great deal; more than anybody had ever supposed – and continual pain would try the temper. It was a sad event – a great shock – with all her faults, what would Mr Churchill do without her? Mr

Churchill's loss would be dreadful, indeed. Mr Churchill would never get over it.' Even Mr Weston shook his head, and looked solemn, and said, 'Ah, poor woman, who would have thought it!' and resolved that his mourning should be as handsome as possible; and his wife sat sighing and moralising over her broad hems with a commiseration and good sense true and steady. How it would affect Frank, was among the earliest thoughts of both. It was also a very early speculation with Emma. The character of Mrs Churchill, the grief of her husband – her mind glanced over them both with awe and compassion – and then rested with lightened feelings on how Frank might be affected by the event, how benefited, how freed. She saw in a moment all the possible good. Now an attachment to Harriet Smith would have nothing to encounter. Mr Churchill, independent of his wife, was feared by nobody; an easy, guidable man, to be persuaded into anything by his nephew. All that remained to be wished was that the nephew should form the attachment, as, with all her goodwill in the cause, Emma could feel no certainty of its being already formed.

Harriet behaved extremely well on the occasion – with great self-command. Whatever she might feel of brighter hope, she betrayed nothing. Emma was gratified to observe such a proof in her of strengthened character, and refrained from any allusion that might endanger its maintenance. They spoke, therefore, of Mrs Churchill's death with mutual forbearance.

Short letters from Frank were received at Randalls, communicating all that was immediately important of their state and plans. Mr Churchill was better than could be expected; and their first removal, on the departure of the funeral for Yorkshire, was to be to the house of a very old friend in Windsor, to whom Mr Churchill had been promising a visit the last ten years. At present, there was nothing to be done for Harriet; good wishes for the future were all that could yet be possible on Emma's side.

It was a more pressing concern to show attention to Jane Fairfax, whose prospects were closing while Harriet's opened, and whose engagements now allowed of no delay in anyone at

Highbury who wished to show her kindness; and with Emma it
was grown into a first wish. She had scarcely a stronger regret
than for her past coldness; and the person, whom she had been so
many months neglecting, was now the very one on whom she
would have lavished every distinction of regard or sympathy. She
wanted to be of use to her; wanted to show a value for her society,
and testify respect and consideration. She resolved to prevail on
her to spend a day at Hartfield. A note was written to urge it. The
invitation was refused and by a verbal message. 'Miss Fairfax was
not well enough to write;' and when Mr Perry called at Hartfield
the same morning, it appeared that she was so much indisposed
as to have been visited, though against her own consent, by
himself, and that she was suffering under severe headaches, and a
nervous fever to a degree which made him doubt the possibility of
her going to Mrs Smallridge's at the time proposed. Her health
seemed for the moment completely deranged – appetite quite
gone; and though there were no absolutely alarming symptoms,
nothing touching the pulmonary complaint which was the
standing apprehension of the family, Mr Perry was uneasy about
her. He thought she had undertaken more than she was equal to,
and that she felt it so herself, though she would not own it. Her
spirits seemed overcome. Her present home, he could not but
observe, was unfavourable to a nervous disorder; – confined
always to one room – he could have wished it otherwise; and her
good aunt, though his very old friend, he must acknowledge to be
not the best companion for an invalid of that description. Her care
and attention could not be questioned; they were, in fact, only too
great. He very much feared that Miss Fairfax derived more evil
than good from them. Emma listened with the warmest concern;
grieved for her more and more, and looked around eager to
discover some way of being useful. To take her – be it only an hour
or two – from her aunt, to give her change of air and scene, and
quiet, rational conversation, even for an hour or two, might do her
good; and the following morning she wrote again to say, in the
most feeling language she could command, that she would call

for her in the carriage at any hour that Jane would name – mentioning that she had Mr Perry's decided opinion in favour of such exercise for his patient. The answer was only in this short note: 'Miss Fairfax's compliments and thanks, but is quite unequal to any exercise.'

Emma felt that her own note had deserved something better; but it was impossible to quarrel with words, whose tremulous inequality showed indisposition so plainly, and she thought only of how she might best counteract this unwillingness to be seen or assisted. In spite of the answer, therefore, she ordered the carriage, and drove to Mrs Bates's, in the hope that Jane would be induced to join her – but it would not do; Miss Bates came to the carriage door, all gratitude, and agreeing with her most earnestly in thinking an airing might be of the greatest service – and everything that message could do was tried – but all in vain. Miss Bates was obliged to return without success; Jane was quite unpersuadable; the mere proposal of going out seemed to make her worse. Emma wished she could have seen her, and tried her own powers; but, almost before she could hint the wish, Miss Bates made it appear that she had promised her niece on no account to let Miss Woodhouse in. 'Indeed, the truth was, that poor dear Jane could not bear to see anybody – anybody at all – Mrs Elton, indeed, could not be denied – and Mrs Cole had made such a point – and Mrs Perry had said so much – but, except them, Jane would really see nobody.'

Emma did not want to be classed with the Mrs Eltons, the Mrs Perrys, and the Mrs Coles, who would force themselves anywhere; neither could she feel any right of preference herself – she submitted, therefore, and only questioned Miss Bates further as to her niece's appetite and diet, which she longed to be able to assist. On that subject poor Miss Bates was very unhappy, and very communicative; Jane would hardly eat anything. Mr Perry recommended nourishing food; but everything they could command (and never had anybody such good neighbours) was distasteful.

Emma, on reaching home, called the housekeeper directly to an examination of her stores; and some arrowroot of very superior quality was speedily despatched to Miss Bates, with a most friendly note. In half an hour the arrowroot was returned, with a thousand thanks from Miss Bates, but 'dear Jane would not be satisfied without its being sent back; it was a thing she could not take – and, moreover, she insisted on her saying that she was not at all in want of anything.'

When Emma afterwards heard that Jane Fairfax had been seen wandering about the meadows at some distance from Highbury, on the afternoon of the very day on which she had, under the plea of being unequal to any exercise, so peremptorily refused to go out with her in the carriage, she could have no doubt – putting everything together – that Jane was resolved to receive no kindness from her. She was sorry, very sorry. Her heart was grieved for a state which seemed but the more pitiable from this sort of irritation of spirits, inconsistency of action, and inequality of powers; and it mortified her that she was given so little credit for proper feeling, or esteemed so little worthy as a friend; but she had the consolation of knowing that her intentions were good, and of being able to say to herself, that could Mr Knightley have been privy to all her attempts of assisting Jane Fairfax, could he even have seen into her heart, he would not, on this occasion, have found anything to reprove.

Chapter 46

One morning, about ten days after Mrs Churchill's decease, Emma was called downstairs to Mr Weston, who 'could not stay five minutes, and wanted particularly to speak with her.' He met her at the parlour door, and hardly asking her how she did, in the natural key of his voice, sunk it immediately, to say, unheard by her father: 'Can you come to Randalls at any time this morning? Do, if it be possible. Mrs Weston wants to see you. She must see you.'

'Is she unwell?'

'No, no; not at all; only a little agitated. She would have ordered the carriage and come to you, but she must see you *alone,* and that you know' (nodding towards her father). 'Humph! can you come?'

'Certainly. This moment, if you please. It is impossible to refuse what you ask in such a way, but what can be the matter? is she really not ill?'

'Depend upon me; but ask no more questions. You will know it all in time. The most unaccountable business! But, hush, hush!'

To guess what all this meant was impossible even for Emma. Something really important seemed announced by his looks; but, as her friend was well, she endeavoured not to be uneasy, and settling it with her father, that she would take her walk now, she and Mr Weston were soon out of the house together, and on their way at a quick pace for Randalls.

'Now,' said Emma, when they were fairly beyond the sweep gates – 'now, Mr Weston, do let me know what has happened.'

'No, no,' he gravely replied. 'Don't ask me. I promised my wife to leave it all to her. She will break it to you better than I can. Do not be impatient, Emma; it will all come out too soon.'

'Break it to me!' cried Emma, standing still with terror. 'Good God! Mr Weston, tell me at once. Something has happened in Brunswick Square. I know it has. Tell me, I charge you, tell me this moment what it is.'

'No, indeed, you are mistaken.'

'Mr Weston, do not trifle with me. Consider how many of my dearest friends are now in Brunswick Square. Which of them is it? I charge you by all that is sacred not to attempt concealment.'

'Upon my word, Emma – '

'Your word! Why not your honour! why not say upon your honour, that it has nothing to do with any of them? Good Heavens! What can be to be *broke* to me, that does not relate to one of that family?'

'Upon my honour,' said he very seriously, 'it does not. It is not in the smallest degree connected with any human being of the name of Knightley.'

Emma's courage returned, and she walked on.

'I was wrong,' he continued, 'in talking of its being *broke* to you. I should not have used the expression. In fact, it does not concern you, it concerns only myself; that is, we hope. Humph! In short, my dear Emma, there is no occasion to be so uneasy about it. I don't say that it is not a disagreeable business, but things might be much worse. If we walk fast, we shall soon be at Randalls.'

Emma found that she must wait; and now it required little effort. She asked no more questions therefore, merely employed her own fancy, and that soon pointed out to her the probability of its being some money concern – something just come to light, of a disagreeable nature, in the circumstances of the family; something which the late event at Richmond had brought forward. Her fancy was very active. Half a dozen natural children, perhaps, and poor Frank cut off! This, though very undesirable, would be no matter of agony to her. It inspired little more than an animating curiosity.

'Who is that gentleman on horseback?' said she, as they proceeded; speaking more to assist Mr Weston in keeping his secret than with any other view.

'I do not know. One of the Otways – not Frank; it is not Frank, I assure you. You will not see him. He is half-way to Windsor by this time.'

'Has your son been with you, then?'

'Oh, yes! did not you know? Well, well, never mind.'

For a moment he was silent; and then added, in a tone much more guarded and demure: 'Yes, Frank came over this morning, just to ask us how we did.'

They hurried on and were speedily at Randalls. 'Well, my dear,' said he, as they entered the room, 'I have brought her, and now I hope you will soon be better. I shall leave you together. There is no use in delay. I shall not be far off, if you want me.' And Emma distinctly heard him add, in a lower tone, before he quitted the room – 'I have been as good as my word. She has not the least idea.'

Mrs Weston was looking so ill, and had an air of so much perturbation, that Emma's uneasiness increased; and the moment they were alone, she eagerly said: 'What is it, my dear friend? Something of a very unpleasant nature, I find, has occurred; do let me know directly what it is. I have been walking all this way in complete suspense. We both abhor suspense. Do not let mine continue longer. It will do you good to speak of your distress, whatever it may be.'

'Have you indeed, no idea?' said Mrs Weston in a trembling voice. 'Cannot you, my dear Emma – cannot you form a guess as to what you are to hear?'

'So far as that it relates to Mr Frank Churchill, I do guess.'

'You are right. It does relate to him, and I will tell you directly' (resuming her work, and seeming resolved against looking up). 'He has been here, this very morning, on a most extraordinary errand. It is impossible to express our surprise. He came to speak to his father on a subject – to announce an attachment – '

She stopped to breathe. Emma thought first of herself, and then of Harriet.

'More than an attachment, indeed,' resumed Mrs Weston; 'an engagement – a positive engagement. What will you say, Emma – what will anybody say – when it is known that Frank Churchill and Miss Fairfax are engaged – nay, that they have been long engaged?'

Emma even jumped with surprise; and, horrorstruck, exclaimed: 'Jane Fairfax! Good God! You are not serious? You do not mean it?'

'You may well be amazed,' returned Mrs Weston, still averting her eyes, and talking on with eagerness, that Emma might have time to recover – 'you may well be amazed. But it is even so. There has been a solemn engagement between them ever since October – formed at Weymouth, and kept a secret from everybody. Not a creature knowing it but themselves – neither the Campbells, nor her family, nor his. It is so wonderful, that though perfectly convinced of the fact, it is yet almost incredible to myself. I can hardly believe it. I thought I knew him.'

Emma scarcely heard what was said. Her mind was divided between two ideas. Her own former conversations with him about Miss Fairfax, and poor Harriet; and for some time she could only exclaim, and require confirmation, repeated confirmation.

'Well!' said she at last, trying to recover herself, 'this is a circumstance which I must think of at least half a day before I can at all comprehend it. What! – engaged to her all the winter – before either of them came to Highbury?'

'Engaged since October – secretly engaged. It has hurt me, Emma, very much. It has hurt his father equally. *Some part* of his conduct we cannot excuse.'

Emma pondered a moment, and then replied: 'I will not pretend not to understand you; and to give you all the relief in my power, be assured that no such effect has followed his attentions to me as you are apprehensive of.'

Mrs Weston looked up, afraid to believe; but Emma's countenance was as steady as her words.

'That you may have less difficulty in believing this boast of my present perfect indifference,' she continued, 'I will further tell you that there was a period in the early part of our acquaintance when I did like him – when I was very much disposed to be attached to him; nay, was attached – and how it came to cease is perhaps the wonder. Fortunately, however, it did cease. I have really for some time past – for at least these three months – cared nothing about him. You may believe me, Mrs Weston. This is the simple truth.'

Mrs Weston kissed her with tears of joy; and when she could find utterance, assured her that this protestation had done her more good than anything else in the world could do.

'Mr Weston will be almost as much relieved as myself,' said she. 'On this point we have been wretched. It was our darling wish that you might be attached to each other, and we were persuaded that it was so. Imagine what we have been feeling on your account.'

'I have escaped; and that I should escape may be a matter of grateful wonder to you and myself. But this does not acquit him, Mrs Weston; and I must say that I think him greatly to blame. What right had he to come among us with affection and faith engaged, and with manner so very disengaged? What right had he to endeavour to please, as he certainly did – to distinguish any one young woman with persevering attention, as he certainly did, while he really belonged to another? How could he tell what mischief he might be doing? How could he tell that he might not be making me in love with him? Very wrong, very wrong, indeed.'

'From something that he said, my dear Emma, I rather imagine – '

'And how could *she* bear such behaviour? Composure with a witness! to look on, while repeated attentions were offering to another woman before her face, and not resent it. That is a degree of placidity which I can neither comprehend nor respect.'

'There were misunderstandings between them, Emma; he said so expressly. He had not time to enter into much explanation. He was here only a quarter of an hour, and in a state of agitation which did not allow the full use even of the time he could stay – but that there had been misunderstandings, he decidedly said. The present crisis, indeed, seemed to be brought on by them; and those misunderstandings might very possibly arise from the impropriety of his conduct.'

'Impropriety! Oh! Mrs Weston, it is too calm a censure. Much, much beyond impropriety! It has sunk him – I cannot say how it has sunk him in my opinion. So unlike what a man should be. None of that upright integrity, that strict adherence to truth and principle, that disdain of trick and littleness, which a man should display in every transaction of his life.'

'Nay, dear Emma, now I must take his part; for though he has been wrong in this instance, I have known him long enough to answer for his having many, very many good qualities; and – '

'Good God!' cried Emma, not attending to her, 'Mrs Smallridge, too! Jane actually on the point of going as governess! What could he mean by such horrible indelicacy? To suffer her to engage herself – to suffer her even to think of such a measure!'

'He knew nothing about it, Emma. On this article I can fully acquit him. It was a private resolution of hers, not communicated to him, or at least not communicated in a way to carry conviction. Till yesterday, I know, he said he was in the dark as to her plans. They burst on him, I do not know how, but by some letter or message – and it was the discovery of what she was doing, of this very project of hers, which determined him to come forward at once, own it all to his uncle, throw himself on his kindness, and, in short, put an end to the miserable state of concealment that had been carrying on so long.'

Emma began to listen better.

'I am to hear from him soon,' continued Mrs Weston. 'He told me at parting that he should soon write; and he spoke in a manner which seemed to promise me many particulars that could not be given now. Let us wait, therefore, for this letter. It may bring many extenuations. It may make many things intelligible and excusable which now are not to be understood. Don't let us be severe; don't let us be in a hurry to condemn him. Let us have patience. I must love him; and now that I am satisfied on one point, the one material point, I am sincerely anxious for its all turning out well, and ready to hope that it may. They must both have suffered a great deal under such a system of secrecy and concealment.'

'*His* sufferings,' replied Emma, dryly, 'do not appear to have done him much harm. Well, and how did Mr Churchill take it?'

'Most favourably for his nephew – gave his consent with scarcely a difficulty. Conceive what the events of a week have done in that family! While poor Mrs Churchill lived, I suppose there could not have been a hope, a chance, a possibility; but scarcely are her remains at rest in the family vault, than her husband is persuaded to act exactly opposite to what she would have required. What a blessing it is, when undue influence does not survive the grave! He gave his consent with very little persuasion.'

'Ah!' thought Emma, 'he would have done as much for Harriet.'

'This was settled last night, and Frank was off with the light this morning. He stopped at Highbury, at the Bates's, I fancy, some time, and then came on hither; but was in such a hurry to get back to his uncle, to whom he is just now more necessary than ever, that, as I tell you, he could stay with us but a quarter of an hour. He was very much agitated – very much indeed – to a degree that made him appear quite a different creature from anything I had ever seen him before. In addition to all the rest, there had been the shock of finding her so very unwell, which he had had no previous suspicion of, and there was every appearance of his having been feeling a great deal.'

'And do you really believe the affair to have been carrying on with such perfect secrecy? The Campbells, the Dixons – did none of them know of the engagement?'

Emma could not speak the name of Dixon without a little blush.

'None; not one. He positively said that it had been known to no being in the world but their two selves.'

'Well,' said Emma, 'I suppose we shall gradually grow reconciled to the idea, and I wish them very happy. But I shall always think it a very abominable sort of proceeding. What has it been but a system of hypocrisy and deceit, espionage and treachery? To come among us with professions of openness and simplicity; and such a league in secret to judge us all! Here have we been the whole winter and spring, completely duped, fancying ourselves all on an equal footing of truth and honour, with two people in the midst of us who may have been carrying round, comparing and sitting in judgement on sentiments and words that were never meant for both to hear. They must take the consequence, if they have heard each other spoken of in a way not perfectly agreeable.'

'I am quite easy on that head,' replied Mrs Weston. 'I am very sure that I never said anything of either to the other which both might not have heard.'

'You are in luck. Your only blunder was confined to my ear, when you imagined a certain friend of ours in love with the lady.'

'True. But as I have always had a thoroughly good opinion of Miss Fairfax, I never could, under any blunder, have spoken ill of her; and as to speaking ill of him, there I must have been safe.'

At this moment Mr Weston appeared at a little distance from the window, evidently on the watch. His wife gave him a look which invited him in; and, while he was coming round, added: 'Now, dearest Emma, let me entreat you to say and look everything that may set his heart at ease, and incline him to be satisfied with the match. Let us make the best of it – and, indeed, almost everything may be fairly said in her favour. It is not a connection to gratify; but if Mr Churchill does not feel that, why should we? and it may be a very fortunate circumstance for him – for Frank, I mean – that he should have attached himself to a girl of such steadiness of character and good judgement as I have always given her credit for, and still am disposed to give her credit for, in spite of this one great deviation from the strict rule of right. And how much may be said, in her situation, for even that error?'

'Much, indeed!' cried Emma feelingly. 'If a woman can ever be excused for thinking only of herself, it is in a situation like Jane Fairfax's. Of such, one may almost say, that "the world is not theirs, nor the world's law".'

She met Mr Weston on his entrance with a smiling countenance, exclaiming: 'A very pretty trick you have been playing me,
upon my word! This was a device, I suppose, to sport with my
curiosity, and exercise my talent of guessing. But you really frightened me. I thought you had lost half your property at least. And
here, instead of its being a matter of condolence, it turns out to be
one of congratulation. I congratulate you, Mr Weston, with all my
heart, on the prospect of having one of the most lovely and accomplished young women in England for your daughter.'

A glance or two between him and his wife convinced him that
all was as right as this speech proclaimed; and its happy effect on
his spirits was immediate. His air and voice recovered their usual
briskness; he shook her heartily and gratefully by the hand, and
entered on the subject in a manner to prove that he now only
wanted time and persuasion to think the engagement no very bad
thing. His companions suggested only what could palliate imprudence or smooth objections; and by the time they had talked it all
over together, and he had talked it all over again with Emma, in
their walk back to Hartfield, he was become perfectly reconciled,
and not far from thinking it the very best thing that Frank could
possibly have done.

Chapter 47

'Harriet, poor Harriet!' – Those were the words; in them lay the
tormenting ideas which Emma could not get rid of, and which
constituted the real misery of the business to her. Frank Churchill
had behaved very ill by herself – very ill in many ways – but it was
not so much *his* behaviour as her *own* which made her so angry

with him. It was the scrape which he had drawn her into on Harriet's account, that gave the deepest hue to his offence. Poor Harriet! to be a second time the dupe of her misconceptions and flattery. Mr Knightley had spoken prophetically when he once said, 'Emma, you have been no friend to Harriet Smith.' She was afraid she had done her nothing but disservice. It was true that she had not to charge herself in this instance, as in the former, with being the sole and original author of the mischief; with having suggested such feelings as might otherwise never have entered Harriet's imagination; for Harriet had acknowledged her admiration and preference of Frank Churchill before she had ever given her a hint on the subject; but she felt completely guilty of having encouraged what she might have repressed. She might have prevented the indulgence and increase of such sentiments. Her influence would have been enough. And now she was very conscious that she ought to have prevented them. She felt that she had been risking her friend's happiness on most insufficient grounds. Common sense would have directed her to tell Harriet that she must not allow herself to think of him, and that there were five hundred chances to one against his ever caring for her. 'But with common sense,' she added, 'I am afraid I have had little to do.'

She was extremely angry with herself. If she could not have been angry with Frank Churchill too, it would have been dreadful. As for Jane Fairfax, she might at least relieve her feelings from any present solicitude on her account. Harriet would be anxiety enough; she need no longer be unhappy about Jane, whose troubles and whose ill health having, of course, the same origin, must be equally under cure. Her days of insignificance and evil were over. She would soon be well, and happy and prosperous. Emma could now imagine why her own attentions had been slighted. This discovery laid many smaller matters open. No doubt it had been from jealousy. In Jane's eyes she had been a rival; and well might anything she could offer of assistance or regard be repulsed. An airing in the Hartfield carriage would have been the rack, and arrowroot from the Hartfield storeroom must have been poison. She understood it all; and as far as her mind could disengage itself from the injustice and selfishness of angry feelings, she acknowledged that Jane Fairfax would have neither elevation nor happiness beyond her desert. But poor Harriet was such an engrossing charge! There was little sympathy to be spared for anybody else. Emma was sadly fearful that this second disappointment would be more severe than the first. Considering the very superior claims of the object, it ought; and judging by its apparently stronger effect on Harriet's mind, producing reserve and self-command, it would. She must communicate the painful truth, however, and as soon as possible. An injunction of secrecy had been among Mr Weston's parting words. 'For the present the whole affair was to be completely a secret. Mr Churchill had made a point of it, as a token of respect to the wife he had so very recently lost; and everybody admitted it to be no more than due decorum.' Emma had promised; but still Harriet must be excepted. It was her superior duty.

In spite of her vexation, she could not help feeling it almost ridiculous, that she should have the very same distressing and delicate office to perform by Harriet which Mrs Weston had just gone through by herself. The intelligence which had been so anxiously announced to her she was now to be anxiously announcing to another. Her heart beat quick on hearing Harriet's footstep and voice; so, she supposed, had poor Mrs Weston felt when she was approaching Randalls. Could the event of the disclosure bear an equal resemblance! But of that, unfortunately, there could be no chance.

'Well, Miss Woodhouse,' cried Harriet, coming eagerly into the room, 'is not this the oddest news that ever was?'

'What news do you mean?' replied Emma, unable to guess, by look or voice, whether Harriet could indeed have received any hint.

'About Jane Fairfax. Did you ever hear anything so strange? Oh! – you need not be afraid of owning it to me, for Mr Weston has told me himself. I met him just now. He told me it was to be a great secret; and, therefore, I should not think of mentioning it to anybody but you, but he said you knew it.'

'What did Mr Weston tell you?' said Emma, still perplexed.

'Oh! he told me all about it; that Jane Fairfax and Mr Frank Churchill are to be married, and that they have been privately engaged to one another this long while. How very odd!'

It was, indeed, so odd; Harriet's behaviour was so extremely odd, that Emma did not know how to understand it. Her character appeared absolutely changed. She seemed to propose showing no agitation, or disappointment, or peculiar concern in the discovery. Emma looked at her, quite unable to speak.

'Had you any idea,' cried Harriet, 'of his being in love with her? You, perhaps, might. You' (blushing as she spoke) 'who can see into everybody's heart; but nobody else – '

'Upon my word,' said Emma, 'I begin to doubt my having any such talent. Can you seriously ask me, Harriet, whether I imagined him attached to another woman at the very time that I was – tacitly if not openly – encouraging you to give way to your own feelings? I never had the slightest suspicion, till within the last hour, of Mr Frank Churchill's having the least regard for Jane Fairfax. You may be very sure that, if I had, I should have cautioned you accordingly.'

'Me!' cried Harriet, colouring, and astonished. 'Why should you caution me? You do not think I care about Mr Frank Churchill?'

'I am delighted to hear you speak so stoutly on the subject,' replied Emma, smiling; 'but you do not mean to deny that there was a time – and not very distant either – when you gave me reason to understand that you did care about him?'

'Him! – never, never. Dear Miss Woodhouse, how could you so mistake me?' (turning away distressed).

'Harriet,' cried Emma, after a moment's pause, 'what do you mean? – Good Heaven! what do you mean? – Mistake you! – Am I to suppose then?'

She could not speak another word. Her voice was lost; and she sat down, waiting in great terror till Harriet should answer.

Harriet, who was standing at some distance, and with face turned from her, did not immediately say anything; and when she did speak, it was in a voice nearly as agitated as Emma's.

'I should not have thought it possible,' she began, 'that you could have misunderstood me! I know we agreed never to name him – but considering how infinitely superior he is to everybody else, I should not have thought it possible that I could be supposed to mean any other person. Mr Frank Churchill, indeed! I do not know who would ever look at him in the company of the other. I hope I have a better taste than to think of Mr Frank Churchill, who is like nobody by his side. And that you should have been so mistaken is amazing! – I am sure, but for believing that you entirely approved and meant to encourage me in my attachment, I should have considered it at first too great a presumption almost to dare to think of him. At first, if you had not told me that more wonderful things had happened; that there had been matches of greater disparity (those were your very words) – I should not have dared to give way to – I should not have thought it possible; but if *you*, who had been always acquainted with him – '

'Harriet,' cried Emma, collecting herself resolutely, 'let us understand each other now, without the possibility of further mistake. Are you speaking of – Mr Knightley?'

'To be sure I am. I never could have an idea of anybody else; and so I thought you knew. When we talked about him it was as clear as possible.'

'Not quite,' returned Emma, with forced calmness; 'for all that you then said appeared to me to relate to a different person. I could almost assert that you had *named* Mr Frank Churchill. I am sure the service Mr Frank Churchill had rendered you, in protecting you from the gypsies, was spoken of.'

'Oh, Miss Woodhouse, how you do forget.'

'My dear Harriet, I perfectly remember the substance of what I said on the occasion. I told you that I did not wonder at your attachment; that, considering the service he had rendered you, it was extremely natural; and you agreed to it, expressing yourself very warmly as to your sense of that service, and mentioning even what your sensations had been in seeing him come forward to your rescue. The impression of it is strong on my memory.'

'Oh, dear,' cried Harriet, 'now I recollect what you mean; but I was thinking of something very different at the time. It was not the gypsies – it was not Mr Frank Churchill that I meant. No!' (with some elevation) 'I was thinking of a much more precious circumstance – of Mr Knightley coming and asking me to dance, when Mr Elton would not stand up with me, and when there was no other partner in the room. That was the kind action; that was the noble benevolence and generosity; that was the service which made me begin to feel how superior he was to every other being upon earth.'

'Good God!' cried Emma, 'this has been a most unfortunate – most deplorable mistake! What is to be done?'

'You would not have encouraged me, then, if you had understood me? At least, however, I cannot be worse off than I should have been, if the other had been the person; and now – it *is* possible – '

She paused a few moments. Emma could not speak.

'I do not wonder, Miss Woodhouse,' she resumed, 'that you should feel a great difference between the two, as to me or as to anybody. You must think one five hundred million times more above me than the other. But I hope, Miss Woodhouse, that supposing – that if – strange as it may appear – But you know they were your own words, that *more* wonderful things had happened; matches of *greater* disparity had taken place than between Mr Frank Churchill and me; and, therefore, it seems as if such a thing even as this may have occurred before – and if I should be so fortunate, beyond expression, as to – if Mr Knightley should really – if *he* does not mind the disparity, I hope, dear Miss Woodhouse, you will not set yourself against it and try to put difficulties in the way. But you are too good for that, I am sure.'

Harriet was standing at one of the windows. Emma turned round to look at her in consternation, and hastily said: 'Have you any idea of Mr Knightley returning your affection?'

'Yes,' replied Harriet modestly, but not fearfully; 'I must say that I have.'

Emma's eyes were instantly withdrawn; and she sat silently meditating in a fixed attitude, for a few minutes. A few minutes were sufficient for making her acquainted with her own heart. A mind like hers, once opening to suspicion, made rapid progress; she touched, she admitted, she acknowledged the whole truth. Why was it so much worse that Harriet should be in love with Mr Knightley than with Frank Churchill? Why was the evil so dreadfully increased by Harriet's having some hope of a return? It darted through her with the speed of an arrow that Mr Knightley must marry no one but herself!

Her own conduct, as well as her own heart, was before her in the same few minutes. She saw it all with a clearness which had never blessed her before. How improperly had she been acting by Harriet! How inconsiderate, how indelicate, how irrational, how unfeeling, had been her conduct! What blindness, what madness had led her on! It struck her with dreadful force, and she was ready to give it every bad name in the world. Some portion of respect for herself, however, in spite of all these demerits, some concern for her own appearance, and a strong sense of justice by Harriet (there would be no need of *compassion* to the girl who believed herself loved by Mr Knightley – but justice required that she should not be made unhappy by any coldness now) gave Emma the resolution to sit and endure further, with calmness, with even apparent kindness. For her own advantage, indeed, it was fit that the utmost extent of Harriet's hopes should be enquired into; and Harriet had done nothing to forfeit the regard and interest which had been so voluntarily formed and maintained, or to deserve to be slighted by the person whose counsels had never led her right. Rousing from reflection, therefore, and subduing her emotion, she turned to Harriet again, and in a more inviting accent renewed the conversation; for as to the subject which had first introduced it, the wonderful story of Jane Fairfax, that was quite sunk and lost. Neither of them thought but of Mr Knightley and themselves.

Harriet, who had been standing in no unhappy reverie, was yet very glad to be called from it by the now encouraging manner of such a judge, and such a friend as Miss Woodhouse; and only wanted invitation to give the history of her hopes with great, though trembling delight. Emma's tremblings, as she asked, and as she listened, were better concealed than Harriet's, but they were not less. Her voice was not unsteady, but her mind was in all the perturbation that such a development of self, such a burst of threatening evil, such a confusion of sudden and perplexing emotions, must create. She listened with much inward suffering, but with great outward patience, to Harriet's detail. Methodical, or well arranged, or very well delivered, it could not be expected to be; but contained, when separated from all the feebleness and tautology of the narration, a substance to sink her spirit; especially with the corroborating circumstances which her own memory brought in favour of Mr Knightley's most improved opinion of Harriet.

Harriet had been conscious of a difference in his behaviour ever since those two decisive dances. Emma knew that he had, on that occasion, found her much superior to his expectation. From that evening, or at least from the time of Miss Woodhouse's encouraging her to think of him, Harriet had begun to be sensible of his talking to her much more than he had been used to do, and of his having, indeed, quite a different manner towards her; a manner of kindness and sweetness. Latterly, she had been more and more aware of it. When they had been all walking together, he had so often come and walked by her, and talked so very delightfully! He seemed to want to be acquainted with her. Emma knew it to have been very much the case; she had often observed the change, to almost the same extent. Harriet repeated expressions of approbation and praise from him – and Emma felt them to be in the closest agreement with what she had known of his opinion of Harriet. He praised her for being without art or affectation; for having simple, honest, generous feelings. She knew that he saw such recommendations in Harriet; he had dwelt on them to her more than once. Much that lived in Harriet's memory, many little particulars of the notice she had received from him, a look, a speech, a removal from one chair to another, a compliment implied, a preference inferred, had been unnoticed, because unsuspected, by Emma. Circumstances that might swell to half an hour's relation, and contained multiplied proofs to her who had seen them, had passed undiscerned by her who now heard them; but the two latest occurrences to be mentioned – the two of strongest promise to Harriet – were not without some degree of witness from Emma herself. The first was his walking with her apart from the others in the lime-walk at Donwell, where they had been walking some time before Emma came, and he had taken pains (as she was convinced) to draw her from the rest to himself; and at first he had talked to her in a more particular way than he had ever done before – in a very particular way indeed! (Harriet could not recall it without a blush.) He seemed to be almost asking her whether her affections were engaged. But as soon as she (Miss Woodhouse) appeared likely to join them, he changed the subject, and began talking about farming. The second was his having sat talking with her nearly half an hour before Emma came back from her visit, the very last morning of his being at Hartfield – though, when he first came in, he had said that he could not stay five minutes – and his having told her, during their conversation, that though he must go to London, it was very much against his inclination that he left home at all, which was much more (as Emma felt) than he had acknowledged to her. The superior degree of confidence towards Harriet which this one article marked gave her severe pain.

On the subject of the first of the two circumstances, she did, after a little reflection, venture the following question: 'Might he not? – Is not it possible, that, when enquiring, as you thought, into the state of your affections, he might be alluding to Mr Martin – he might have Mr Martin's interest in view?' But Harriet rejected the suspicion with spirit.

'Mr Martin! No, indeed! – There was not a hint of Mr Martin. I hope I know better now than to care for Mr Martin, or to be suspected of it.'

When Harriet had closed her evidence, she appealed to her dear Miss Woodhouse to say whether she had not good ground for hope.

'I never should have presumed to think of it at first,' said she, 'but for you. You told me to observe him carefully, and let his behaviour be the rule of mine – and so I have. But now I seem to feel that I may deserve him; and that if he does choose me, it will not be anything so very wonderful.'

The bitter feelings occasioned by this speech, the many bitter feelings, made the utmost exertion necessary on Emma's side to enable her to say on reply: 'Harriet, I will only venture to declare that Mr Knightley is the last man in the world who would intentionally give any woman the idea of his feeling for her more than he really does.'

Harriet seemed ready to worship her friend for a sentence so satisfactory; and Emma was only saved from raptures and fondness, which at that moment would have been dreadful penance, by the sound of her father's footsteps. He was coming through the hall. Harriet was too much agitated to encounter him. 'She could not compose herself – Mr Woodhouse would be alarmed – she had better go;' with most ready encouragement from her friend, therefore, she passed off through another door – and the moment she was gone, this was the spontaneous burst of Emma's feelings: 'O God! that I had never seen her!'

The rest of the day, the following night, were hardly enough for her thoughts. She was bewildered amidst the confusion of all that had rushed on her within the last few hours. Every moment had brought a fresh surprise; and every surprise must be matter of humiliation to her. How to understand it all! How to understand the deceptions she had been thus practising on herself, and living under! The blunders, the blindness of her own head and heart! She sat still, she walked about, she tried her own room, she tried the shrubbery – in every place, every posture, she perceived that she had acted most weakly; that she had been imposed on by others in a most mortifying degree; that she had been imposing on herself in a degree yet more mortifying; that she was wretched, and should probably find this day but the beginning of wretchedness.

To understand, thoroughly understand her own heart, was the first endeavour. To that point went every leisure moment which her father's claims on her allowed, and every moment of involuntary absence of mind.

How long had Mr Knightley been so dear to her, as every feeling declared him now to be? When had his influence, such influence begun? When had he succeeded to that place in her affection which Frank Churchill had once, for a short period, occupied? – She looked back, she compared the two – compared them, as they had always stood in her estimation, from the time of the latter's becoming known to her – and as they must at any time have been compared by her, had it – oh! had it, by any blessed felicity, occurred to her to institute the comparison. She saw that there never had been a time when she did not consider Mr Knightley as infinitely the superior, or when his regard for her had not been infinitely the most dear. She saw, that in persuading herself, in fancying, in acting to the contrary, she had been entirely under a delusion, totally ignorant of her own heart – and, in short, that she had never really cared for Frank Churchill at all!

This was the conclusion of the first series of reflections. This was the knowledge of herself, on the first question of enquiry, which she reached; and without being long in reaching it. She was most sorrowfully indignant; ashamed of every sensation but the one revealed to her – her affection for Mr Knightley. Every other part of her mind was disgusting.

With insufferable vanity had she believed herself in the secret of everybody's feelings; with unpardonable arrogance proposed to arrange everybody's destiny. She was proved to have been universally mistaken; and she had not quite done nothing – for she had done mischief. She had brought evil on Harriet, on herself, and, she too much feared, on Mr Knightley. Were this most unequal of all connections to take place, on her must rest all the reproach of having given it a beginning; for his attachment she must believe to be produced only by a consciousness of Harriet's; and even were this not the case, he would never have known Harriet at all but for her folly.

Mr Knightley and Harriet Smith! It was a union to distance every wonder of the kind. The attachment of Frank Churchill and Jane Fairfax became commonplace, threadbare, stale in comparison, exciting no surprise, presenting no disparity, affording nothing to be said or thought. Mr Knightley and Harriet Smith! Such an elevation on her side! Such a debasement on his! It was horrible to Emma to think how it must sink him in the general opinion, to foresee the smiles, the sneers, the merriment it would prompt at his expense; the mortification and disdain of his brother, the thousand inconveniences to himself. Could it be? No; it was impossible. And yet it was far, very far, from impossible. Was it a new circumstance for a man of first-rate abilities to be captivated by very inferior powers? Was it new for one, perhaps too busy to seek, to be the prize of a girl who would seek him? Was it new for anything in this world to be unequal, inconsistent, incongruous – or for chance and circumstance (as second causes) to direct the human fate?

Oh! had she never brought Harriet forward! Had she left her where she ought, and where he had told her she ought! Had she not, with a folly which no tongue could express, prevented her marrying the unexceptionable young man who would have madeher happy and respectable in the line of life to which she ought to belong, all would have been safe; none of this dreadful sequel would have been.

How Harriet could ever have had the presumption to raise her thoughts to Mr Knightley! How she could dare to fancy herself the chosen of such a man till actually assured of it! But Harriet was less humble, had fewer scruples than formerly. Her inferiority, whether of mind or situation, seemed little felt. She had seemed more sensible of Mr Elton's being to stoop in marrying her, than she now seemed of Mr Knightley's. Alas! was not that her own doing too? Who had been at pains to give Harriet notions of self-consequence but herself? Who but herself had taught her that she was to elevate herself, if possible, and that her claims were great to a high worldly establishment? If Harriet, from being humble, were grown vain, it was her doing too.

Chapter 48

Till now that she was threatened with its loss, Emma had never known how much of her happiness depended on being *first* with Mr Knightley, first in interest and affection. Satisfied that it was so, and feeling it her due, she had enjoyed it without reflection; and only, in the dread of being supplanted, found how inexpressibly important it had been. Long, very long, she felt she had been first; for, having no female connections of his own, there had been only Isabella whose claims could be compared with hers, and she had always known exactly how far he loved and esteemed Isabella. She had herself been first with him for many years past. She had not deserved it; she had often been negligent or perverse, slighting his advice, or even wilfully opposing him, insensible of half his merits, and quarrelling with him because he would not acknowledge her false and insolent estimate of her own – but still, from family attachment and habit, and thorough excellence of mind, he had loved her, and watched over her from a girl, with an endeavour to improve her, and an anxiety for her doing right, which no other creature had at all shared. In spite of all her faults, she knew she was dear to him; might she not say very dear? When the suggestions of hope, however, which must follow here, presented themselves, she could not presume to indulge them. Harriet Smith might think herself not unworthy of being peculiarly, exclusively, passionately loved by Mr Knightley. *She* could not. She could not flatter herself with any idea of blindness in his attachment to *her*. She had received a very recent proof of its impartiality. How shocked had he been by her behaviour to Miss Bates! How directly, how strongly, had he expressed himself to her on the subject! Not too strongly for the offence – but far, far too strongly to issue from any feeling softer than upright justice and clear-sighted goodwill. She had no hope, nothing to deserve the name of hope, that he could have that sort of affection for herself which was now in question; but there was a hope (at times a slight one, at times much stronger) that Harriet might have deceived herself, and be overrating his regard for *her*. Wish it she must, for his sake – be the consequence nothing to herself, but his remaining single all his life. Could she be secure of that, indeed, of his never marrying at all she believed she should be perfectly satisfied. Let him but continue the same Mr Knightley to her and her father, the same Mr Knightley to all the world; let Donwell and Hartfield lose none of their precious intercourse of friendship and confidence, and her peace would be fully secured. Marriage, in fact, would not do for her. It would be incompatible with what she owed to her father, and with what she felt for him. Nothing should separate her from her father. She would not marry, even if she were asked by Mr Knightley.

It must be her ardent wish that Harriet might be disappointed; and she hoped, that when able to see them together again, she might at least be able to ascertain what the chances for it were. She should see them henceforward with the closest observance; and wretchedly as she had hitherto misunderstood even those she was watching, she did not know how to admit that she could be blinded here! He was expected back every day. The power of observation would be soon given; frightfully soon it appeared when her thoughts were in one course. In the meanwhile, she resolved against seeing Harriet. It would do neither of them good, it would do the subject no good, to be talking of it further. She was resolved not to be convinced, as long as she could doubt, and yet had no authority for opposing Harriet's confidence. To talk would be only to irritate. She wrote to her, therefore, kindly, but decisively, to beg that she would not, at present, come to Hartfield; acknowledging it to be her conviction that all further confidential discussion of *one* topic had better be avoided; and hoping, that if a few days were allowed to pass before they met again, except in the company of others – she objected only to a tête-à-tête – they might be able to act as if they had forgotten the conversation of yesterday. Harriet submitted, and approved, and was grateful.

This point was just arranged when a visitor arrived to tear Emma's thoughts a little from the one subject which had engrossed them, sleeping or waking, the last twenty-four hours – Mrs Weston, who had been calling on her daughter-in-law elect, and took Hartfield in her way home, almost as much in duty to Emma as in pleasure to herself, to relate all the particulars of so interesting an interview.

Mr Weston had accompanied her to Mrs Bates's, and gone through his share of this essential attention most handsomely. But she having then induced Miss Fairfax to join her in an airing, was now returned with much more to say, and much more to say with satisfaction, than a quarter of an hour spent in Mrs Bates's parlour, with all the encumbrance of awkward feelings, could have afforded.

A little curiosity Emma had, and she made the most of it while her friend related. Mrs Weston had set off to pay the visit in a good deal of agitation herself; and in the first place had wished not to go at all at present, to be allowed merely to write to

Miss Fairfax instead, and to defer this ceremonious call till a little time had passed, and Mr Churchill could be reconciled to the engagement's becoming known; as, considering everything, she thought such a visit could not be paid without leading to reports; but Mr Weston had thought differently; he was extremely anxious to show his approbation to Miss Fairfax and her family, and did not conceive that any suspicion could be excited by it; or, if it were, that it would be of any consequence; for 'such things,' he observed, 'always got about.' Emma smiled, and felt that Mr Weston had very good reason for saying so. They had gone, in short; and very great had been the evident distress and confusion of the lady. She had hardly been able to speak a word, and every look and action had shown how deeply she was suffering from consciousness. The quiet, heartfelt satisfaction of the old lady, and the rapturous delight of her daughter, who proved even too joyous to talk as usual, had been a gratifying, yet almost an affecting, scene. They were both so truly respectable in their happiness, so disinterested in every sensation; thought so much of Jane; so much of everybody, and so little of themselves, that every kindly feeling was at work for them. Miss Fairfax's recent illness had offered a fair plea for Mrs Weston to invite her to an airing; she had drawn back and declined at first, but, on being pressed, had yielded; and, in the course of their drive, Mrs Weston had, by gentle encouragement, overcome so much of her embarrassment, as to bring her to converse on the important subject. Apologies for her seemingly ungracious silence in their first reception, and the warmest expressions of the gratitude she was always feeling towards herself and Mr Weston, must necessarily open the cause; but when these effusions were put by, they had talked a good deal of the present and of the future state of the engagement. Mrs Weston was convinced that such conversation must be the greatest relief to her companion, pent up within her own mind as everything had so long been, and was very much pleased with all that she had said on the subject.

'On the misery of what she had suffered, during the conceal-ment of so many months,' continued Mrs Weston, 'she was ener-getic. This was one of her expressions: "I will not say that since I entered into the engagement I have not had some happy moments; but I can say, that I have never known the blessing of one tranquil hour" – and the quivering lip, Emma, which uttered it was an attestation that I felt at my heart.'

'Poor girl!' said Emma. 'She thinks herself wrong, then, for having consented to a private engagement?'

'Wrong! No one, I believe, can blame her more than she is disposed to blame herself. "The consequence," said she, "has been a state of perpetual suffering to me; and so it ought. But after all the punishment that misconduct can bring, it is still not less misconduct. Pain is no expiation. I never can be blameless. I have been acting contrary to all my sense of right; and the fortunate turn that everything has taken, and the kindness I am now receiving is what my conscience tells me ought not to be. Do not imagine, madam," she continued, "that I was taught wrong. Do not let any reflection fall on the principles or the care of the friends who brought me up. The error has been all my own; and I do assure you that, with all the excuse that present circumstances may appear to give, I shall yet dread making the story known to Colonel Campbell." '

'Poor girl!' said Emma, again. 'She loves him, then, exces-sively, I suppose. It must have been from attachment only that she could be led to form the engagement. Her affection must have overpowered her judgement.'

'Yes, I have no doubt of her being extremely attached to him.'

'I am afraid,' returned Emma, sighing, 'that I must often have contributed to make her unhappy.'

'On your side, my love, it was very innocently done. But she probably had something of that in her thoughts, when alluding to the misunderstandings which he had given us hints of before. One natural consequence of the evil she had involved herself in she said, was that of making her *unreasonable*. The consciousness of having done amiss had exposed her to a thousand inquietudes and made her captious and irritable to a degree, that must have been – that had been – hard for him to bear. "I did not make the allowances," said she, "which I ought to have done, for his temper and spirits – his delightful spirits, and that gaiety, that playfulness of disposition, which, under any other circumstances would, I am sure, have been as constantly bewitching to me as they were at first." She then began to speak of you, and of the great kindness you had shown her during her illness; and, with a blush, which showed me how it was all connected, desired me, whenever I had an opportunity, to thank you – I could not thank you too much – for every wish and every endeavour to do her good. She was sensible that you had never received any proper acknowledgement from herself.'

'If I did not know her to be happy now,' said Emma seriously, 'which in spite of every little drawback from her scrupulous conscience, she must be, I could not bear these thanks; for, oh! Mrs Weston, if there were an account drawn up of the evil and the good I have done Miss Fairfax – Well' (checking herself and trying to be more lively), 'this is all to be forgotten. You are very kind to bring me these interesting particulars; they show her to the greatest advantage. I am sure she is very good; I hope she will be very happy. It is fit that the fortune should be on his side, for I think the merit will be all on hers.'

Such a conclusion could not pass unanswered by Mrs Weston. She thought well of Frank in almost every respect; and, what was more, she loved him very much, and her defence was, therefore earnest. She talked with a great deal of reason, and at least equal affection; but she had too much to urge for Emma's attention; it was soon gone to Brunswick Square or to Donwell; she forgot to attempt to listen; and when Mrs Weston ended with, 'We have not yet had the letter we are so anxious for, you know, but I hope it will soon come,' she was obliged to pause before she answered, and at last obliged to answer at random, before she could at all recollect what letter it was which they were so anxious for.

'Are you well, my Emma?' was Mrs Weston's parting question.

'Oh, perfectly. I am always well, you know. Be sure to give me intelligence of the letter as soon as possible.'

Mrs Weston's communications furnished Emma with more food for unpleasant reflection, by increasing her esteem and compassion, and her sense of past injustice towards Miss Fairfax. She bitterly regretted not having sought a closer acquaintance with her, and blushed for the envious feelings which had certainly been, in some measure, the cause. Had she followed Mr Knightley's known wishes, in paying that attention to Miss Fairfax which was every way her due; had she tried to know her better; had she done her part towards intimacy; had she endeavoured to find a friend there instead of in Harriet Smith; she must, in all probability, have been spared from every pain which pressed on her now. Birth, abilities, and education had been equally marking one as an associate for her, to be received with gratitude; and the other – what was she? Supposing even that they had never become intimate friends; that she had never been admitted into Miss Fairfax's confidence on this important matter – which was most probable – still, in knowing her as she ought, and as she might, she must have been preserved from the abominable suspicions of an improper attachment to Mr Dixon, which she had not only so foolishly fashioned and harboured herself, but had so unpardonably imparted; an idea which she greatly feared had been made a subject of material distress to the delicacy of Jane's feelings, by the levity or carelessness of Frank Churchill's. Of all the sources of evil surrounding the former, since her coming to Highbury, she was persuaded that she must herself have been the worst. She must have been a perpetual enemy. They never could have been all three together, without her having stabbed Jane Fairfax's peace in a thousand instances;

and on Box Hill, perhaps, it had been the agony of a mind that would bear no more.

The evening of this day was very long and melancholy at Hartfield. The weather added what it could of gloom. A cold stormy rain set in, and nothing of July appeared but in the trees and shrubs, which the wind was despoiling, and the length of the day, which only made such cruel sights the longer visible.

The weather affected Mr Woodhouse; and he could only be kept tolerably comfortable by almost ceaseless attention on his daughter's side, and by exertions which had never cost her half so much before. It reminded her of their first forlorn tête-à-tête, on the evening of Mrs Weston's wedding-day. But Mr Knightley had walked in then, soon after tea, and dissipated every melancholy fancy. Alas! such delightful proofs of Hartfield's attractions, as those sort of visits conveyed, might shortly be over. The picture which she had then drawn of the privations of the approaching winter had proved erroneous; no friends had deserted them, no pleasures had been lost. But her present forebodings she feared would experience no similar contradictions. The prospect before her now was threatening to a degree that could not be entirely dispelled – that might not be even partially brightened. If all took place that might take place among the circle of her friends, Hartfield must be comparatively deserted; and she left to cheer her father with the spirits only of ruined happiness.

The child to be born at Randalls must be a tie there even dearer than herself; and Mrs Weston's heart and time would be occupied by it. They should lose her; and probably, in great measure, her husband also. Frank Churchill would return among them no more; and Miss Fairfax, it was reasonable to suppose, would soon cease to belong to Highbury. They would be married, and settled either at or near Enscombe. All that were good would be withdrawn; and if to these losses the loss of Donwell were to be added, what would remain of cheerful or of rational society within their reach? Mr Knightley to be no longer coming there for his evening comfort! No longer walking in at all hours, as if ever willing to change his own home for theirs! How was it to be endured? And if he were to be lost to them for Harriet's sake; if he were to be thought of hereafter, as finding in Harriet's society all that he wanted! if Harriet were to be the chosen, the first, the dearest, the friend, the wife to whom he looked for all the best blessings of existence; what could be increasing Emma's wretchedness but the reflection, never far distant from her mind, that it had been all her own work?

When it came to such a pitch as this, she was not able to refrain from a start, or a heavy sigh, or even from walking about the room for a few seconds; and the only source whence anything like consolation or composure could be drawn, was in the resolution of her own better conduct, and the hope that, however inferior in spirit and gaiety might be the following and every future winter of her life to the past, it would yet find her more rational, more acquainted with herself, and leave her less to regret when it were gone.

Chapter 49

The weather continued much the same all the following morning; and the same loneliness, and the same melancholy, seemed to reign at Hartfield; but in the afternoon it cleared; the wind changed into a softer quarter; the clouds were carried off; the sun appeared; it was summer again. With all the eagerness which such a transition gives, Emma resolved to be out of doors as soon as possible. Never had the exquisite sight, smell, sensation of nature, tranquil, warm, and brilliant after a storm, been more attractive to her. She longed for the serenity they might gradually introduce; and, on Mr Perry's coming in soon after dinner, with a disengaged hour to give her father, she lost no time in hurrying into the shrubbery. There, with spirits freshened, and thoughts a little relieved, she had taken a few turns, when she saw Mr Knightley passing through the garden door and coming towards her. It was the first intimation of his being returned from London. She had been thinking of him the moment before, as unquestionably sixteen miles distant. There was time only for the quickest arrangement of mind. She must be collected and calm. In half a minute they were together. The 'How-d'ye-do's' were quiet and constrained on each side. She asked after their mutual friends; they were all well. When had he left them? Only that morning. He must have had a wet ride. – Yes! – He meant to walk with her, she found. 'He had just looked into the dining-room, and as he was not wanted there, preferred being out-of-doors.' She thought he neither looked nor spoke cheerfully; and the first possible cause for it, suggested by her fears, was, that he had perhaps been communicating his plans to his brother, and was pained by the manner in which they had been received.

They walked together. He was silent. She thought he was often looking at her, and trying for a fuller view of her face than it suited her to give. And this belief produced another dread. Perhaps he wanted to speak to her of his attachment to Harriet, he might be watching for encouragement to begin. She did not, could not, feel equal to lead the way to any such subject. He must do it all himself. Yet she could not bear this silence. With him it was most unnatural. She considered, resolved, and trying to smile, began: 'You have some news to hear, now you are come back, that will rather surprise you.'

'Have I?' said he quietly, and looking at her; 'of what nature?'

'Oh, the best nature in the world – a wedding.'

After waiting a moment, as if to be sure she intended to say no more, he replied: 'If you mean Miss Fairfax and Frank Churchill, I have heard that already.'

'How is it possible?' cried Emma, turning her glowing cheeks towards him; for, while she spoke, it occurred to her that he might have called at Mrs Goddard's in his way.

'I had a few lines on parish business from Mr Weston this morning, and at the end of them he gave me a brief account of what had happened.'

Emma was quite relieved, and could presently say, with a little more composure: '*You* probably have been less surprised than any of us, for you have had your suspicions. I have not forgotten that you once tried to give me a caution. I wish I had attended to it – but' (with a sinking voice and a heavy sigh) 'I seem to have been doomed to blindness.'

For a moment or two nothing was said, and she was unsuspicious of having excited any particular interest, till she found her arm drawn within his, and pressed against his heart, and heard him thus saying, in a tone of great sensibility, speaking low: 'Time, my dearest Emma, time will heal the wound. Your own excellent sense; your exertions for your father's sake; I know you will not allow yourself – ' Her arm was pressed again, as he added, in a more broken and subdued accent, 'The feelings of the warmest friendship – indignation – abominable scoundrel!' And in a louder, steadier tone, he concluded with, 'He will soon be gone. They will soon be in Yorkshire. I am sorry for her. She deserves a better fate.'

Emma understood him; and as soon as she could recover from the flutter of pleasure, excited by such tender consideration, replied: 'You are very kind, but you are mistaken, and I must set you right. I am not in want of that sort of compassion. My blindness to what was going on led me to act by them in a way that I must always be ashamed of, and I was very foolishly tempted to say and do many things which may well lay me open to unpleasant conjectures, but I have no other reason to regret that I was not in the secret earlier.'

'Emma,' cried he, looking eagerly at her, 'are you indeed?' – but checking himself – 'No, no, I understand you – forgive me; I am pleased that you can say even so much. He is no object of regret, indeed! and it will not be very long, I hope, before that becomes the acknowledgement of more than your reason. Fortunate that your affections were not further entangled! I could never, I confess, from your manners, assure myself as to the degree of what you felt – I could only be certain that there was a preference – and a preference which I never believed him to deserve. He is a disgrace to the name of man. And is he to be rewarded with that sweet young woman? Jane! Jane! you will be a miserable creature.'

'Mr Knightley,' said Emma, trying to be lively, but really confused – 'I am in a very extraordinary situation. I cannot let you continue in your error; and yet, perhaps, since my manners gave such an impression, I have as much reason to be ashamed of confessing that I never have been at all attached to the person we are speaking of, as it might be natural for a woman to feel in confessing exactly the reverse. But I never have.'

He listened in perfect silence. She wished him to speak, but he would not. She supposed she must say more before she was entitled to his clemency; but it was a hard case to be obliged still to lower herself in his opinion. She went on, however.

'I have very little to say for my own conduct. I was tempted by his attentions, and allowed myself to appear pleased. An old story, probably – a common case – and no more than has happened to hundreds of my sex before; and yet it may not be the more excusable in one who sets up as I do for understanding. Many circumstances assisted the temptation. He was the son of Mr Weston – he was continually here – I always found him very pleasant – and in short, for' (with a sigh) 'let me swell out the causes ever so ingeniously, they all centre in this at last – my vanity was flattered, and I allowed his attentions. Latterly, however – for some time, indeed – I have had no idea of their meaning anything. I thought them a habit, a trick, nothing that called for seriousness on my side. He has imposed on me, but he has not injured me. I have never been attached to him. And now I can tolerably comprehend his behaviour. He never wished to attach me. It was merely a blind to conceal his real situation with another. It was his object to blind all about him; and no one, I am sure, could be more effectually blinded than myself – except that I was *not* blinded – that it was my good fortune – that, in short, I was somehow or other safe from him.'

She had hoped for an answer here – for a few words to say that her conduct was at least intelligible; but he was silent; and, as far as she could judge, deep in thought. At last, and tolerably in his usual tone, he said: 'I have never had a high opinion of Frank Churchill. I can suppose, however, that I may have underrated him. My acquaintance with him has been but trifling. And even if I have not underrated him hitherto, he may yet turn out well. With such a woman he has a chance. I have no motive for wishing him ill – and for her sake, whose happiness will be involved in his good character and conduct, I shall certainly wish him well.'

'I have no doubt of their being happy together,' said Emma; 'I believe them to be very mutually and very sincerely attached.'

'He is a most fortunate man,' returned Mr Knightley, with energy. 'So early in life – at three-and-twenty – a period when, if a man chooses a wife, he generally chooses ill. At three-and-twenty to have drawn such a prize! What years of felicity that man in all human calculation has before him! Assured of the love of such a woman – the disinterested love – for Jane Fairfax's character vouches for her disinterestedness; everything in his favour – equality of situation – I mean, as far as regards society, and all the habits and manners that are important; equality in every point but one – and that one, since the purity of her heart is not to be doubted, such as must increase his felicity, for it will be his to bestow the only advantages she wants. A man would always wish to give a woman a better home than the one he takes her from; and he who can do it, where there is no doubt of her regard, must, I think, be the happiest of mortals. Frank Churchill is, indeed, the favourite of fortune. Everything turns out for his good. He meets with a young woman at a watering-place, gains her affection, cannot even weary her by negligent treatment – and had he and all his family sought round the world for a perfect wife for him, they could not have found her superior. His aunt is in the way. His aunt dies. He has only to speak. His friends are eager to promote his happiness. He has used everybody ill – and they are all delighted to forgive him. He is a fortunate man, indeed!'

'You speak as if you envied him.'

'And I do envy him, Emma. In one respect he is the object of my envy.'

Emma could say no more. They seemed to be within half a sentence of Harriet, and her immediate feeling was to avert the subject, if possible. She made her plan; she would speak of something totally different – the children in Brunswick Square; and she only waited for breath to begin, when Mr Knightley startled her by saying: 'You will not ask me what is the point of envy. You are determined, I see, to have no curiosity. You are wise – but I cannot be wise. Emma, I must tell what you will not ask, though I may wish it unsaid the next moment.'

'Oh, then, don't speak it, don't speak it,' she eagerly cried. 'Take a little time, consider, do not commit yourself.'

'Thank you,' said he, in an accent of deep mortification, and not another syllable followed.

Emma could not bear to give him pain. He was wishing to confide in her – perhaps to consult her; cost her what it would, she would listen. She might assist his resolution, or reconcile him to it; she might give just praise to Harriet, or, by representing to him his own independence, relieve him from that state of indecision which must be more intolerable than any alternative to such a mind as his. They had reached the house.

'You are going in, I suppose?' said he.

'No,' replied Emma, quite confirmed by the depressed manner in which he still spoke, 'I should like to take another turn. Mr Perry is not gone.' And, after proceeding a few steps, she added – 'I stopped you ungraciously, just now, Mr Knightley, and, I am afraid, gave you pain. But if you have any wish to speak openly to me as a friend, or to ask my opinion of anything that you may have in contemplation – as a friend, indeed, you may command me. I will hear whatever you like. I will tell you exactly what I think.'

'As a friend!' repeated Mr Knightley. 'Emma, that, I fear, is a word – no, I have no wish. Stay, yes, why should I hesitate? I have gone too far already for concealment. Emma, I accept your offer, extraordinary as it may seem, I accept it, and refer myself to you as a friend. Tell me, then, have I no chance of ever succeeding?'

He stopped in his earnestness to look the question, and the expression of his eyes overpowered her.

'My dearest Emma,' said he, 'for dearest you will always be, whatever the event of this hour's conversation, my dearest, most beloved Emma – tell me at once. Say "No," if it is to be said.' She could really say nothing. 'You are silent,' he cried, with great animation; 'absolutely silent! at present I ask no more.'

Emma was almost ready to sink under the agitation of this moment. The dread of being awakened from the happiest dream was perhaps the most prominent feeling.

'I cannot make speeches, Emma,' he soon resumed, and in a tone of such sincere, decided, intelligible tenderness as was tolerably convincing. 'If I loved you less, I might be able to talk about it more. But you know what I am. You hear nothing but truth from me. I have blamed you, and lectured you, and you have borne it as no other woman in England would have borne it. Bear with the truths I would tell you now, dearest Emma, as well as you have borne with them. The manner, perhaps, may have as little to recommend them. God knows, I have been a very indifferent lover. But you understand me. Yes, you see, you understand my feelings – and will return them if you can. At present, I ask only to hear – once to hear your voice.'

While he spoke, Emma's mind was most busy, and, with all the wonderful velocity of thought, had been able – and yet without losing a word – to catch and comprehend the exact truth of the whole; to see that Harriet's hopes had been entirely groundless, a

mistake, a delusion, as complete a delusion as any of her own –
that Harriet was nothing; that she was everything herself; that
what she had been saying relative to Harriet had been all taken as
the language of her own feelings; and that her agitation, her
doubts, her reluctance, her discouragement, had been all received
as discouragement from herself. And not only was there time for
these convictions, with all their glow of attendant happiness,
there was time also to rejoice that Harriet's secret had not escaped
her, and to resolve that it need not, and should not. It was all the
service she could now render her poor friend; for as to any of that
heroism of sentiment which might have prompted her to entreat
him to transfer his affection from herself to Harriet, as infinitely
the most worthy of the two – or even the more simple sublimity of
resolving to refuse him at once and for ever, without vouchsafing
any motive because he could not marry them both – Emma had it
not. She felt for Harriet, with pain and with contrition; but no
flight of generosity run mad, opposing all that could be probable
or reasonable, entered her brain. She had led her friend astray,
and it would be a reproach to her for ever; but her judgement was
as strong as her feelings, and as strong as it had ever been before,
in reprobating any such alliance for him, as most unequal and
degrading. Her way was clear, though not quite smooth. She
spoke then, on being so entreated. What did she say? Just what
she ought, of course. A lady always does. She said enough to show
there need not be despair – and to invite him to say more himself.
He *had* despaired at one period; he had received such an injunction to caution and silence, as for the time crushed every hope –
she had begun by refusing to hear him. The change had perhaps
been somewhat sudden – her proposal of taking another turn, her
renewing the conversation which she had just put an end to,
might be a little extraordinary. She felt its inconsistency; but Mr
Knightley was so obliging as to put up with it, and seek no further
explanation.

Seldom, very seldom, does complete truth belong to any
human disclosure; seldom can it happen that something is not a

little disguised, or a little mistaken; but where, as in this case, though the conduct is mistaken, the feelings are not, it may not be very material. Mr Knightley could not impute to Emma a more relenting heart than she possessed, or a heart more disposed to accept of his.

He had, in fact, been wholly unsuspicious of his own influence. He had followed her into the shrubbery with no idea of trying it. He had come, in his anxiety to see how she bore Frank Churchill's engagement, with no selfish view, no view at all, but of endeavouring, if she allowed him an opening, to soothe or to counsel her. The rest had been the work of the moment, the immediate effect of what he heard, on his feelings. The delightful assurance of her total indifference towards Frank Churchill, of her having a heart completely disengaged from him, had given birth to the hope that, in time, he might gain her affection himself; but it had been no present hope; he had only, in the momentary conquest of eagerness over judgement, aspired to be told that she did not forbid his attempt to attach her. The superior hopes which gradually opened were so much the more enchanting. The affection which he had been asking to be allowed to create, if he could, was already his. Within half an hour he had passed from a thoroughly distressed state of mind, to something so like perfect happiness, that it could bear no other name.

Her change was equal. This one half-hour had given to each the same precious certainty of being beloved, had cleared from each the same degree of ignorance, jealousy, or distrust. On his side, there had been a long-standing jealousy, old as the arrival or even the expectation of Frank Churchill. He had been in love with Emma, and jealous of Frank Churchill, from about the same period, one sentiment having probably enlightened him as to the other. It was his jealousy of Frank Churchill that had taken him from the country. The Box Hill party had decided him on going away. He would save himself from witnessing again such permitted, encouraged attentions. He had gone to learn to be indifferent. But he had gone to a wrong place. There was too much domestic happiness in his brother's house; woman wore too amiable a form in it. Isabella was too much like Emma – differing only in those striking inferiorities which always brought the other in brilliancy before him, for much to have been done even had his time been longer. He had stayed on, however, vigorously, day after day – till this very morning's post had conveyed the history of Jane Fairfax. Then, with the gladness which must be felt, nay, which he did not scruple to feel, having never believed Frank Churchill to be at all deserving Emma, was there so much fond solicitude, so much keen anxiety for her, that he could stay no longer. He had ridden home through the rain; and had walked up directly after dinner, to see how this sweetest and best of all creatures, faultless in spite of all her faults, bore the discovery.

He had found her agitated and low. Frank Churchill was a villain. He heard her declare that she had never loved him. Frank Churchill's character was not desperate. She was his own Emma, by hand and word, when they returned into the house; and if he could have thought of Frank Churchill then, he might have deemed him a very good sort of fellow.

Chapter 50

What totally different feelings did Emma take back into the house from what she had brought out! She had then been only daring to hope for a little respite of suffering; she was now in an exquisite flutter of happiness – and such happiness, moreover, as she believed must still be greater when the flutter should have passed away.

They sat down to tea – the same party round the same table – how often it had been collected! and how often had her eyes fallen on the same shrubs in the lawn, and observed the same beautiful effect of the western sun! But never in such a state of spirits, never in anything like it; and it was with difficulty that she could summon enough of her usual self to be the attentive lady of the house, or even the attentive daughter.

Poor Mr Woodhouse little suspected what was plotting against him in the breast of that man whom he was so cordially welcoming, and so anxiously hoping might not have taken cold from his ride. Could he have seen the heart, he would have cared very little for the lungs; but without the most distant imagination of the impending evil, without the slightest perception of anything extraordinary, in the looks or ways of either, he repeated to them very comfortably all the articles of news he had received from Mr Perry, and talked on with much self-contentment, totally unsuspicious of what they could have told him in return.

As long as Mr Knightley remained with them, Emma's fever continued; but when he was gone she began to be a little tranquillised and subdued, and in the course of the sleepless night, which was the tax for such an evening, she found one or two such very serious points to consider, as made her feel, that even her happiness must have some alloy. Her father – and Harriet. She could not be alone without feeling the full weight of their separate claims; and how to guard the comfort of both to the utmost was the question. With respect to her father, it was a question soon answered. She hardly knew yet what Mr Knightley would ask; but a very short parley with her own heart produced the most solemn resolution of never quitting her father. She even wept over the idea of it, as a sin of thought. While he lived, it must be only an engagement; but she flattered herself, that if divested of the danger of drawing her away, it might become an increase of comfort to him. How to do her best by Harriet was of more difficult decision; how to spare her from any unnecessary pain; how to make her any possible atonement; how to appear least her enemy? On these subjects her perplexity and distress were very great – and her mind had to pass again and again through every bitter reproach and sorrowful regret that had ever surrounded it. She could only resolve at last that she would still avoid a meeting with her and communicate all that need be told by letter; that it would be inexpressibly desirable to have her removed just now for a time from Highbury, and – indulging in one scheme more – nearly resolve that it might be practicable to get an invitation for her to Brunswick Square. Isabella had been pleased with Harriet; and a few weeks spent in London must give her some amusement. She did not think it in Harriet's nature to escape being benefited by novelty and variety, by the streets, the shops, and the children. At any rate, it would be a proof of attention and kindness in herself, from whom everything was due; a separation for the present; an averting of the evil day, when they must all be together again.

She rose early, and wrote her letter to Harriet: an employment which left her so very serious, so nearly sad, that Mr Knightley, in walking up to Hartfield to breakfast, did not arrive at all too soon; and half an hour stolen afterwards to go over the same ground again with him, literally and figuratively, was quite necessary to reinstate her in a proper share of the happiness of the evening before.

He had not left her long – by no means long enough for her to have the slightest inclination for thinking of anybody else – when a letter was brought her from Randalls – a very thick letter; she guessed what it must contain, and deprecated the necessity of reading it. She was now in perfect charity with Frank Churchill: she wanted no explanations, she wanted only to have her thoughts to herself – and as for understanding anything he wrote, she was sure she was incapable of it. It must be waded through, however. She opened the packet; it was too surely so; a note from Mrs Weston to herself, ushered in the letter from Frank to Mrs Weston:

I have the greatest pleasure, my dear Emma, in forwarding to you the enclosed. I know what thorough justice you will do it, and have scarcely a doubt of its happy effect. I think we shall never materially disagree about the writer again; but I will not delay you by a long preface. We are quite well. This letter has been the cure of all the little nervousness I have been feeling lately. I did not quite like your looks on Tuesday, but it was an ungenial morning; and though you will never own being affected by weather, I think everybody feels a north-east wind. I felt for your dear father very much in the storm of Tuesday afternoon and yesterday morning, but had the comfort of hearing last night, by Mr Perry, that it had not made him ill. – Yours ever,

    A. W.

                               [To Mrs Weston]
                                 Windsor – July

MY DEAR MADAM – If I made myself intelligible yesterday, this letter will be expected; but expected or not, I know it will be read with candour and indulgence. You are all goodness, and I believe there will be need of even all your goodness to allow for some parts of my past conduct. But I have been forgiven by one who had still more to resent. My courage rises while I write. It is very difficult for the prosperous to be humble. I have already met with such success in two applications for pardon, that I may be in danger of thinking myself too sure of yours, and of those among your friends who have had any ground of offence. You must all endeavour to comprehend the exact nature of my situation when I first arrived at Randalls; you must consider me as having a secret which was to be kept at all hazards. This was the fact. My right to place myself in a situation requiring such concealment is another question. I shall not discuss it here. For my temptation to *think* it a right, I refer every caviller to a brick house, sashed windows below, and casements above, in

Highbury. I dared not address her openly; my difficulties in the then state of Enscombe must be too well known to require definition; and I was fortunate enough to prevail, before we parted at Weymouth, and to induce the most upright female mind in the creation to stoop in charity to a secret engagement. Had she refused, I should have gone mad. But you will be ready to say, What was your hope in doing this? What did you look forward to? To anything, everything – to time, chance, circumstance, slow effects, sudden bursts, perseverance, and weariness, health, and sickness. Every possibility of good was before me, and the first of blessings secured, in obtaining her promises of faith and correspondence. If you need further explanation, I have the honour, my dear madam, of being your husband's son, and the advantage of inheriting a disposition to hope for good, which no inheritance of houses or lands can ever equal the value of. See me, then, under these circumstances, arriving on my first visit to Randalls; and here I am conscious of wrong, for that visit might have been sooner paid. You will look back, and see that I did not come till Miss Fairfax was in Highbury; and as you were the person slighted, you will forgive me instantly; but I must work on my father's compassion, by reminding him, that so long as I absented myself from his house, so long I lost the blessing of knowing you. My behaviour, during the very happy fortnight which I spent with you, did not, I hope, lay me open to reprehension, excepting on one point. And now I come to the principal, the only important part of my conduct, while belonging to you, which excites my own anxiety, or requires very solicitous explanation. With the greatest respect, and the warmest friendship, do I mention Miss Woodhouse; my father, perhaps, will think I ought to add, with the deepest humiliation. A few words which dropped from him yesterday spoke his opinion, and some censure I acknowledge myself liable to. My behaviour to Miss Woodhouse indicated, I believe, more than it ought. In order to assist a concealment so essential to me, I was led on to make more than an allowable use of the sort of intimacy into which we were immediately thrown. I cannot deny that Miss Woodhouse was my ostensible object; but I am sure you will believe the declaration, that had I not been convinced of her indifference, I would not have been induced by any selfish views to go on. Amiable and delightful as Miss Woodhouse is, she never gave me the idea of a young woman likely to be attached; and that she was perfectly free from any tendency to being attached to me, was as much my conviction as my wish. She received my attention with an easy, friendly, good-humoured playfulness which exactly suited me. We seemed to understand each other. From our relative situation, those attentions were her due, and were felt to be so. Whether Miss Woodhouse began really to understand me before the expiration of that fortnight I cannot say; when I called to take leave of her, I remember that I was within a moment of confessing the truth, and I then fancied she was not without suspicion; but I have no doubt of her having since detected me – at least in some degree. She may not have surmised the whole, but her quickness must have penetrated a part. I cannot doubt it. You will find, whenever the subject becomes freed from its present restraints, that it did not take her wholly by surprise. She frequently gave me hints of it. I remember her telling me at the ball that I owed Mrs Elton gratitude for her attentions to Miss Fairfax. I hope this history of my conduct towards her will be admitted by you and my father as great extenuation of what you saw amiss. While you considered me as having sinned against Emma Woodhouse, I could deserve nothing from either. Acquit me here, and procure for me, when it is allowable, the acquittal and good wishes of that said Emma Woodhouse, whom I regard with so much brotherly affection as to long to have her as deeply and as happily in love as myself. Whatever strange things I said or did during that fortnight you have now a key to. My heart was in Highbury, and my business was to get my body thither as often as might be, and with the least suspicion. If you remember any queernesses set them all to the right account. Of the pianoforte so much talked of, I feel it only neccssary to say, that its being ordered was absolutely unknown to Miss F—, who would never have allowed me to send it had any choice been given her. The delicacy of her mind throughout the whole engagement, my dear madam, is much beyond my power of doing justice to. You will soon, I earnestly hope, know her thoroughly yourself. No description can describe her. She must tell you herself what she is; yet not by word, for never was there a human creature who would so designedly suppress her own merit. Since I began this letter, which will be longer than I foresaw, I have heard from her. She gives a good account of her own health; but as she never complains, I dare not depend. I want to have your opinion of her looks. I know you will soon call on her; she is living in dread of the visit. Perhaps it is paid already. Let me hear from you without delay; I am impatient for a thousand particulars. Remember how few minutes I was at Randalls, and in how bewildered, how mad a state: and I am not much better yet; still insane either from happiness or misery. When I think of the kindness and favour I have met with, of her excellence and patience, and my uncle's generosity, I am mad with joy: but when I recollect all the uneasiness I occasioned her, and how little I deserve to be forgiven, I am mad with anger. If I could but see her again! But I must not propose it yet; my uncle has been too good for me to encroach. I must still add to this long letter. You have not heard all that you ought to hear. I could not give any connected detail yesterday; but the suddenness and, in one light, the unseasonableness with which the affair burst out, needs explanation; for though the event of the 26th *ult.*, as you will conclude, immediately opened to me the happiest prospects, I should not have presumed on such early measures, but from the very particular circumstances which left me not an hour to lose. I should myself have shrunk from anything so hasty, and she would have felt every scruple of mine with multiplied strength and refinement: but I had no choice. The hasty engagement she had entered into with that woman – here, my dear madam, I was obliged to leave off abruptly, to recollect and compose myself. I have been walking over the country, and am now, I hope, rational enough to make the rest of my letter what it ought to be. It is, in fact, a most mortifying retrospect for me. I behaved shamefully. And here I can admit that my manners to Miss W., in being unpleasant to Miss F., were highly blamable. *She* disapproved them, which ought to have been enough. My plea of concealing the truth she did not think sufficient. She was displeased: I thought unreasonably so; I thought her, on a thousand occasions, unnecessarily scrupulous and cautious; I thought her even cold. But she was always right. If I had followed her judgement, and subdued my spirits to the level of what she deemed proper, I should have escaped the greatest unhappiness I have ever known. We quarrelled. Do you remember the morning spent at Donwell? *There* every little dissatisfaction that had occurred before came to a crisis. I was late: I met her walking home by herself, and wanted to walk with her, but she would not suffer it. She absolutely refused to allow me, which I then thought most unreasonable. Now, however, I see nothing in it but a very natural and consistent degree of discretion. While I, to blind the world to our engagement, was behaving one hour with objectionable particularity to another woman, was she to be consenting the next to a proposal which might have made every previous caution useless? Had we been met walking together between Donwell and Highbury, the truth must have been suspected. I was mad enough, however, to resent. I doubted her affection. I doubted it more the next day on Box Hill; when, provoked by such conduct on my side, such shameful, insolent, neglect of her, and such apparent devotion to Miss W., as it would have been impossible for any woman of sense to endure, she spoke her resentment in a form of words perfectly intelligible to me. In short, my dear madam, it was a quarrel blameless on her side, abominable on mine; and I returned the same evening to Richmond, though I might have stayed with you till the next morning, merely because I would be as angry with her as possible. Even then I was not such a fool as not to mean to be reconciled in time; but I was the injured person – injured by her coldness – and I went away determined that she should make the first advances. I shall always congratulate myself that you were not of the Box Hill party. Had you witnessed my behaviour there, I can hardly suppose you would ever have thought well of me again. Its effect upon her appears in the immediate resolution it produced. As soon as she found I was really gone from Randalls, she closed with the offer of that officious Mrs Elton; the whole system of whose treatment of her, by the by, has ever filled me with indignation and hatred. I must not quarrel with a spirit of forbearance which has been so richly extended towards myself; but, otherwise, I should loudly protest against the share of it which that woman has known. 'Jane', indeed! You will observe that I have not yet indulged myself in calling her by that name, even to you. Think, then, what I must have endured in hearing it bandied between the Eltons, with all the vulgarity of needless repetition, and all the insolence of imaginary superiority. Have patience with me, I shall soon have done. She closed with this offer, resolving to break with me entirely, and wrote the next day to tell me that we never were to meet again. *She felt the engagement to be a source of repentance and misery to each: she dissolved it.* This letter reached me on the very morning of my poor aunt's death. I answered it within an hour; but from the confusion of my mind, and the multiplicity of business falling on me at once, my answer, instead of being sent with all the many other letters of that day, was locked up in my writing-desk, and I, trusting that I had written enough, though but a few lines, to satisfy her, remained without any uneasiness. I was rather disappointed that I did not hear from her again speedily; but I made excuses for her, and was too busy, and (may I add?) too cheerful in my views to be captious. We removed to Windsor; and two days afterwards I received a parcel from her – my own letters all returned! and a few lines at the same time by the post, stating her extreme surprise at not having had the smallest reply to her last; and adding that as silence on such a point could not be misconstrued, and as it must be equally desirable to both to have every subordinate arrangement concluded as soon as possible, she now sent me, by a safe conveyance, all my letters, and requested that if I could not directly command hers, so as to send them to Highbury within a week, I would forward them after that period to her at —: in short, the full direction to Mr Smallridge's, near Bristol, stared me in the face. I knew the name, the place, I knew all about it, and instantly saw what she had been doing. It was perfectly accordant with that resolution of character which I knew her to possess; and the secrecy she had maintained as to any such design in her former letter, was equally descriptive of its anxious delicacy. For the world would not she have seemed to threaten me. Imagine the shock; imagine how, till I had actually detected my own blunder, I raved at the blunders of the post. What was to be done? One thing only. I must speak to my uncle. Without his sanction, I could not hope to be listened to again. I spoke; circumstances were in my favour; the late event had softened away his pride, and he was, earlier than I could have anticipated, wholly reconciled and complying; and could say at last, poor man! with a deep sigh, that he wished I might find as much happiness in the marriage state as he had done. I felt that it would be of a different sort. Are you disposed to pity me for what I must have suffered in opening the cause to him, for my suspense while all was at stake? No; do not pity me till I reached Highbury, and saw how ill I had made her. Do not pity me till I saw her wan, sick looks. I reached Highbury at the time of day when, from my knowledge of their late breakfast-hour, I was certain of a good chance of finding her alone. I was not disappointed; and at last I was not disappointed either in the object of my journey. A great deal of very reasonable, very just displeasure I had to persuade away. But it is done; we are reconciled, dearer, much dearer, than ever, and no moment's uneasiness can ever occur between us again. Now, my dear madam, I will release you; but I could not conclude before. A thousand and a thousand thanks for all the kindness you have ever shown me, and ten thousand for the attentions your heart will dictate towards her. If you think me in a way to be happier than I deserve, I am quite of your opinion. Miss W. calls me the child of good fortune. I hope she is right. In one respect my good fortune is undoubted, that of being able to subscribe myself, your obliged and affectionate son,

F. C. WESTON CHURCHILL

Chapter 51

This letter must make its way to Emma's feelings. She was obliged, in spite of her previous determination to the contrary, to do it all the justice that Mrs Weston foretold. As soon as she came to her own name, it was irresistible; every line relating to herself was interesting, and almost every line agreeable; and when this charm ceased, the subject could still maintain itself by the natural return of her former regard for the writer, and the very strong attraction which any picture of love must have for her at that moment. Shenever stopped till she had gone through the whole: and though it was impossible not to feel that he had been wrong, yet he had been less wrong than she had supposed; and he had suffered and was very sorry; and he was so grateful to Mrs Weston, and so much in love with Miss Fairfax, and she was so happy herself, that there was no being severe; and could he have entered the room, she must have shaken hands with him as heartily as ever.

She thought so well of the letter, that when Mr Knightley came again she desired him to read it. She was sure of Mrs Weston's wishing it to be communicated; especially to one who, like Mr Knightley, had seen so much to blame in his conduct.

'I shall be very glad to look it over,' said he; 'but it seems long. I will take it home with me at night.'

But that would not do. Mr Weston was to call in the evening, and she must return it by him.

'I would rather be talking to you,' he replied; 'but as it seems a matter of justice, it shall be done.'

He began – stopping, however, almost directly to say: 'Had I been offered the sight of one of this gentleman's letters to his mother-in-law a few months ago, Emma, it would not have been taken with such indifference.'

He proceeded a little farther, reading to himself; and then, with a smile, observed, 'Humph! a fine complimentary opening: but it is his way. One man's style must not be the rule of another's. We will not be severe.'

'It will be natural for me,' he added shortly afterwards, 'to speak my opinion aloud as I read. By doing it, I shall feel that I am near you. It will not be so great a loss of time; but if you dislike it – '

'Not at all. I should wish it.'

Mr Knightley returned to his reading with greater alacrity.

'He trifles here,' said he, 'as to the temptation. He knows he is wrong, and has nothing rational to urge. Bad. He ought not to have formed the engagement. "His father's disposition" – he is unjust, however, to his father. Mr Weston's sanguine temper was a blessing on all his upright and honourable exertions; but Mr Weston earned every present comfort before he endeavoured to gain it. Very true; he did not come till Miss Fairfax was here.'

'And I have not forgotten,' said Emma, 'how sure you were that he might have come sooner if he would. You pass it over very handsomely; but you were perfectly right.'

'I was not quite impartial in my judgement, Emma; but yet, I think, had *you* not been in the case, I should still have distrusted him.'

When he came to Miss Woodhouse, he was obliged to read the whole of it aloud – all that related to her – with a smile, a look, a shake of the head, a word or two of assent, or disapprobation, or merely of love, as the subject required; concluding, however, seriously, and, after steady reflection, thus: 'Very bad – though it might have been worse. Playing a most dangerous game. Too much indebted to the event for his acquittal. No judge of his own manners by you. Always deceived, in fact, by his own wishes, and regardless of little besides his own convenience. Fancying you to have fathomed his secret! Natural enough! his own mind full of intrigue, that he should suspect it in others. Mystery – finesse – how they pervert the understanding! My Emma, does not everything serve to prove more and more the beauty of truth and sincerity in all our dealings with each other?'

Emma agreed to it, and with a blush of sensibility on Harriet's account, which she could not give any sincere explanation of.

'You had better go on,' said she.

He did so, but very soon stopped again to say: 'The pianoforte! Ah! that was the act of a very, very young man, one too young to consider whether the inconvenience of it might not very much exceed the pleasure. A boyish scheme, indeed! I cannot comprehend a man's wishing to give a woman any proof of affection which he knows she would rather dispense with: and he did know that she would have prevented the instrument's coming if she could.'

After this, he made some progress without any pause. Frank Churchill's confession of having behaved shamefully was the first thing to call for more than a word in passing.

'I perfectly agree with you, sir,' was then his remark. 'You did behave very shamefully. You never wrote a truer line.' And having gone through what immediately followed of the basis of their disagreement, and his persisting to act in direct opposition to Jane Fairfax's sense of right, he made a fuller pause to say: 'This is very bad. He had induced her to place herself, for his sake, in a situation of extreme difficulty and uneasiness, and it should have been his first object to prevent her from suffering unnecessarily. She must have had much more to contend with in carrying on the correspondence than he could. He should have respected even unreasonable scruples, had there been such; but hers were all reasonable. We must look to her one fault, and remember that she had done a wrong thing in consenting to the engagement, to bear that she should have been in such a state of punishment.'

Emma knew that he was now getting to the Box Hill party, and grew uncomfortable. Her own behaviour had been so very improper! She was deeply ashamed, and a little afraid of his next look. It was all read, however, steadily, attentively, and without the smallest remark; and, excepting one momentary glance at her, instantly withdrawn, in the fear of giving pain, no remembrance of Box Hill seemed to exist.

'There is no saying much for the delicacy of our good friends, the Eltons,' was his next observation. 'His feelings are natural. What? actually resolve to break with him entirely! She felt the engagement to be a source of repentance and misery to each: she dissolved it. What a view this gives of her sense of his behaviour! Well, he must be a most extraordinary – '

'Nay, nay, read on. You will find how very much he suffers.'

'I hope he does,' replied Mr Knightley coolly, and resuming the letter. ' "Smallridge!" What does this mean? What is all this?'

'She had engaged to go as governess to Mrs Smallridge's children – a dear friend of Mrs Elton's – a neighbour of Maple Grove; and, by the by, I wonder how Mrs Elton bears the disappointment?'

'Say nothing, my dear Emma, while you oblige me to read – not even of Mrs Elton. Only one page more. I shall soon have done. What a letter the man writes!'

'I wish you would read it with a kinder spirit towards him.'

'Well, there *is* feeling here. He does seem to have suffered in finding her ill. Certainly, I can have no doubt of his being fond of her. "Dearer, much dearer, than ever." I hope he may long continue to feel all the value of such a reconciliation. He is a very liberal thanker, with his thousands and tens of thousands. "Happier than I deserve." Come, he knows himself there. "Miss Woodhouse calls me the child of good fortune." Those were Miss Woodhouse's words, were they? And a fine ending – and there is the letter. "The child of good fortune!" That was your name for him, was it?'

'You do not appear so well satisfied with his letter as I am; but still you must, at least I hope you must, think the better of him for it. I hope it does him some service with you.'

'Yes, certainly it does. He has had great faults – faults of inconsideration and thoughtlessness; and I am very much of his opinion in thinking him likely to be happier than he deserves: but, still, as he is, beyond a doubt, really attached to Miss Fairfax, and will soon, it may be hoped, have the advantage of being constantly with her, I am very ready to believe his character will improve, and acquire from hers the steadiness and delicacy of principle that it wants. And now, let me talk to you of something else. I have another person's interest at present so much at heart, that I cannot think any longer about Frank Churchill. Ever since I left you this morning, Emma, my mind has been hard at work on one subject.'

The subject followed; it was in plain, unaffected, gentlemanlike English, such as Mr Knightley used even to the woman he was in love with, how to be able to ask her to marry him without attacking the happiness of her father. Emma's answer was ready at the first word. 'While her dear father lived, any change of condition must be impossible for her. She could never quit him.' Part only of this answer, however, was admitted. The impossibility of her quitting her father Mr Knightley felt as strongly as herself; but the inadmissibility of any other change he could not agree to. He had been thinking it over most deeply, most intently; he had at first hoped to induce Mr Woodhouse to remove with her to Donwell; he had wanted to believe it feasible but his knowledge of Mr Woodhouse would not suffer him to deceive himself long; and now he confessed his persuasion that such a transplantation would be a risk of her father's comfort, perhaps even of his life, which must not be hazarded. Mr Woodhouse taken from Hartfield! No, he felt that it ought not to be attempted. But the plan which had arisen on the sacrifice of this, he trusted his dearest Emma would not find in any respect objectionable; it was, that he should be received at Hartfield! that so long as her father's happiness – in other words, his life – required Hartfield to continue her home, it should be his likewise.

Of their all removing to Donwell, Emma had already had her own passing thoughts. Like him, she had tried the scheme and rejected it; but such an alternative as this had not occurred to her. She was sensible of all the affection it evinced. She felt that, in quitting Donwell, he must be sacrificing a great deal of independence of hours and habits; that in living constantly with her father, and in no house of his own, there would be much, very much, to be borne with. She promised to think of it, and advised him to think of it more; but he was fully convinced that no reflection could alter his wishes or his opinion on the subject. He had given it, he could assure her, very long and calm consideration; he had been walking away from William Larkins the whole morning to have his thoughts to himself.

'Ah! there is one difficulty unprovided for,' cried Emma. 'I am sure William Larkins will not like it. You must get his consent before you ask mine.'

She promised, however, to think of it; and pretty nearly promised, moreover, to think of it with the intention of finding it a very good scheme.

It is remarkable that Emma, in the many, very many, points of view in which she was now beginning to consider Donwell Abbey, was never struck with any sense of injury to her nephew Henry, whose rights as heir expectant had formerly been so tenaciously regarded. Think she must of the possible difference to the poor little boy; and yet she only gave herself a saucy conscious smile about it, and found amusement in detecting the real cause of that violent dislike of Mr Knightley's marrying Jane Fairfax, or anybody else, which at the time she had wholly imputed to the amiable solicitude of the sister and the aunt.

This proposal of his, this plan of marrying and continuing at Hartfield – the more she contemplated it the more pleasing it became. His evils seemed to lessen, her own advantages to increase, their mutual good to outweight every drawback. Such a companion for herself in the periods of anxiety and cheerlessness before her! Such a partner in all those duties and cares to which time must be giving increase of melancholy!

She would have been too happy but for poor Harriet; but every blessing of her own seemed to involve and advance the sufferings of her friend, who must now be even excluded from Hartfield. The delightful family party which Emma was securing for herself, poor Harriet must, in mere charitable caution, be kept at a distance from. She would be a loser in every way. Emma could not deplore her future absence as any deduction from her own enjoyment. In such a party, Harriet would be rather a dead weight than otherwise; but for the poor girl herself, it seemed a peculiarly cruel necessity that was to be placing her in such a state of unmerited punishment.

In time, of course, Mr Knightley would be forgotten, that is, supplanted; but this could not be expected to happen very early. Mr

Knightley himself would be doing nothing to assist the cure; not like Mr Elton. Mr Knightley, always so kind, so feeling, so truly considerate for everybody, would never deserve to be less worshipped than now; and it really was too much to hope even of Harriet, that she could be in love with more than *three* men in one year.

Chapter 52

It was a very great relief to Emma to find Harriet as desirous as herself to avoid a meeting. Their intercourse was painful enough by letter. How much worse had they been obliged to meet!

Harriet expressed herself very much, as might be supposed, without reproaches, or apparent sense of ill usage; and yet Emma fancied there was a something of resentment, a something bordering on it in her style, which increased the desirableness of their being separate. It might be only her own consciousness; but it seemed as if an angel only could have been quite without resentment under such a stroke.

She had no difficulty in procuring Isabella's invitation; and she was fortunate in having a sufficient reason for asking it, without resorting to invention. There was a tooth amiss. Harriet really wished, and had wished some time, to consult a dentist. Mrs John Knightley was delighted to be of use; anything of ill health was a recommendation to her; and though not so fond of a dentist as of a Mr Wingfield, she was quite eager to have Harriet under her care. When it was thus settled on her sister's side, Emma proposed it to her friend, and found her very persuadable. Harriet was to go; she was invited for at least a fortnight. She was to be conveyed in Mr Woodhouse's carriage. It was all arranged, it was all completed, and Harriet was safe in Brunswick Square.

Now Emma could, indeed, enjoy Mr Knightley's visits; now she could talk, and she could listen with true happiness, unchecked by that sense of injustice, of guilt, of something most painful, which had haunted her when remembering how disappointed a heart was near her, how much might at that moment, and at a little distance, be enduring by the feelings which she had led astray herself.

The difference of Harriet at Mrs Goddard's, or in London made, perhaps, an unreasonable difference in Emma's sensations; but she could not think of her in London without objects of curiosity and employment, which must be averting the past, and carrying her out of herself.

She would not allow any other anxiety to succeed directly to the place in her mind which Harriet had occupied. There was a communication before her, one which *she* only could be competent to make – the confession of her engagement to her father; but she would have nothing to do with it at present. She had resolved to defer the disclosure till Mrs Weston were safe and well. No additional agitation should be thrown at this period among those she loved – and the evil should not act on herself by anticipation before the appointed time. A fortnight, at least, of leisure and peace of mind, to crown every warmer, but more agitating, delight, should be hers.

She soon resolved, equally as a duty and a pleasure, to employ half an hour of this holiday of spirits in calling on Miss Fairfax. She ought to go – and she was longing to see her; the resemblance of their present situations increasing every other motive of goodwill. It would be a *secret* satisfaction; but the consciousness of a similiarity of prospect would certainly add to the interest with which she should attend to anything Jane might communicate.

She went – she had driven once unsuccessfully to the door, but had not been into the house since the morning after Box Hill, when poor Jane had been in such distress as had filled her with compassion, though all the worst of her sufferings had been unsuspected. The fear of being still unwelcome determined her, though assured of their being at home, to wait in the passage, and send up her name. She heard Patty announcing it; but no such bustle succeeded as poor Miss Bates had before made so happily intelligible. No; she heard nothing but the instant reply of: 'Beg her to walk up'; and a moment afterwards she was met on the stairs by Jane herself coming eagerly forward, as if no other reception of her were felt sufficient. Emma had never seen her look so well, so lovely, so engaging. There was consciousness, animation, and warmth; there was everything which her countenance or manner could ever have wanted. She came forward with an offered hand; and said, in a low, but very feeling tone: 'This is most kind, indeed! Miss Woodhouse, it is impossible for me to express – I hope you will believe – Excuse me for being so entirely without words.'

Emma was gratified, and would soon have shown no want of words, if the sound of Mrs Elton's voice from the sitting-room had not checked her, and made it expedient to compress all her friendly and all her congratulatory sensations into a very, very earnest shake of the hand.

Mrs Bates and Mrs Elton were together. Miss Bates was out, which accounted for the previous tranquillity. Emma could have wished Mrs Elton elsewhere; but she was in a humour to have patience with everybody; and as Mrs Elton met her with unusual graciousness, she hoped the rencontre would do them no harm.

She soon believed herself to penetrate Mrs Elton's thoughts, and understand why she was, like herself, in happy spirits; it was being in Miss Fairfax's confidence, and fancying herself acquainted with what was still a secret to other people. Emma saw symptoms of it immediately in the expression of her face; and while paying her own compliments to Mrs Bates, and appearing to attend to the good old lady's replies, she saw her with a sort of anxious parade of mystery fold up a letter which she had apparently been reading aloud to Miss Fairfax, and return it into the purple and gold reticule by her side, saying, with significant nods: 'We can finish this some other time, you know. You and I shall not want opportunities; and, in fact, you have heard all the essential already. I only wanted to prove to you that Mrs S. admits our apology, and is not offended. You see how delightfully she writes. Oh, she is a sweet creature! You would have doted on her, had you gone. But not a word more. Let us be discreet – quite on our good behaviour. Hush! You remember those lines – I forget the poem at this moment:

> For when a lady's in the case,
> You know, all other things give place.

Now I say, my dear, in our case, for *lady*, read – mum! a word to the wise. I am in a fine flow of spirits, ain't I? But I want to see your heart at ease as to Mrs S. *My* representation, you see, has quite appeased her.'

And again, on Emma's merely turning her head to look at Mrs Bates's knitting, she added, in a half whisper: 'I mentioned no *names*, you will observe. Oh no! cautious as a minister of state. I managed it extremely well.'

Emma could not doubt. It was a palpable display, repeated on every possible occasion. When they had all talked a little while in harmony of the weather and Mrs Weston, she found herself abruptly addressed with: 'Do not you think, Miss Woodhouse, our saucy little friend here is charmingly recovered? Do not you think her cure does Perry the highest credit?' (here was a side glance of great meaning at Jane). 'Upon my word, Perry has restored her in a wonderful short time! Oh, if you had seen her, as I did, when she was at the worst!' And when Mrs Bates was saying something to Emma, whispered further: 'We do not say a word of any *assistance* that Perry might have; not a word of a certain young physician from Windsor. Oh! no, Perry shall have all the credit.'

'I have scarce had the pleasure of seeing you, Miss Woodhouse,' she shortly afterwards began, 'since the party to Box Hill. Very pleasant party. But yet I think there was something wanting.

Things did not seem – that is, there seemed a little cloud upon the spirits of some. So it appeared to me, at least, but I might be mistaken. However, I think it answered so far as to tempt one to go again. What say you both to our collecting the same party, and exploring to Box Hill again, while the fine weather lasts? It must be the same party, you know – quite the same party, not one exception.'

Soon after this Miss Bates came in, and Emma could not help being diverted by the perplexity of her first answer to herself, resulting, she supposed, from doubt of what might be said, and impatience to say everything.

'Thank you, dear Miss Woodhouse, you are all kindness. It is impossible to say – yes, indeed, I quite understand – dearest Jane's prospects – that is, I do not mean. But she is charmingly recovered. How is Mr Woodhouse? I am so glad. Quite out of my power. Such a happy little circle as you find us here. Yes, indeed. Charming young man! that is, so very friendly; I mean good Mr Perry! such attention to Jane!' And from her great, her more than commonly thankful delight towards Mrs Elton for being there, Emma guessed that there had been a little show of resentment towards Jane, from the Vicarage quarter, which was now graciously overcome. After a few whispers, indeed, which placed it beyond a guess, Mrs Elton, speaking louder, said: 'Yes, here I am, my good friend; and here I have been so long, that anywhere else I should think it necessary to apologise; but, the truth is, that I am waiting for my lord and master. He promised to join me here, and pay his respects to you.'

'What! are we to have the pleasure of a call from Mr Elton? That will be a favour indeed. for I know gentlemen do not like morning visits, and Mr Elton's time is so engaged.'

'Upon my word it is, Miss Bates. He really is engaged from morning to night. There is no end of people's coming to him, on some pretence or other. The magistrates, and overseers, and church-wardens, are always wanting his opinion. They seem not able to do anything without him. "Upon my word, Mr E.," I often say, "rather you than I. I do not know what would become of my crayons and my instrument if I had half so many applicants." Bad enough as it is, for I absolutely neglect them both to an unpardonable degree. I believe I have not played a bar this fortnight. However, he is coming, I assure you: yes, indeed, on purpose to wait on you all.' And putting up her hand to screen her words from Emma: 'A congratulatory visit, you know. Oh! yes, quite indispensable.'

Miss Bates looked about her, so happily!

'He promised to come to me as soon as he could disengage himself from Knightley; but he and Knightley are shut up together in deep consultation. Mr E. is Knightley's right hand.'

Emma would not have smiled for the world, and only said: 'Is Mr Elton gone on foot to Donwell? He will have a hot walk.'

'Oh no, it is a meeting at the Crown – a regular meeting. Weston and Cole will be there too; but one is apt to speak only of those who lead. I fancy Mr E. and Knightley have everything their own way.'

'Have you not mistaken the day?' said Emma. 'I am almost certain that the meeting at the Crown is not till tomorrow. Mr Knightley was at Hartfield yesterday, and spoke of it as for Saturday.'

'Oh no, the meeting is certainly today,' was the abrupt answer, which denoted the impossibility of any blunder on Mrs Elton's side. 'I do believe,' she continued, 'this is the most troublesome parish that ever was. We never heard of such things at Maple Grove.'

'Your parish there was small,' said Jane.

'Upon my word, my dear, I do not know, for I never heard the subject talked of.'

'But it is proved by the smallness of the school, which I have heard you speak of, as under the patronage of your sister and Mrs Bragge; the only school, and not more than five-and-twenty children.'

'Ah! you clever creature, that's very true. What a thinking brain you have! I say, Jane, what a perfect character you and I should make, if we could be shaken together. My liveliness and your solidity would produce perfection. Not that I presume to insinuate, however, that *some* people may not think *you* perfection already. But hush – not a word, if you please.'

It seemed an unneccessary caution; Jane was wanting to give her words, not to Mrs Elton, but to Miss Woodhouse, as the latter plainly saw. The wish of distinguishing her, as far as civility permitted, was very evident, though it could not often proceed beyond a look.

Mr Elton made his appearance. His lady greeted him with some of her sparkling vivacity.

'Very pretty, sir, upon my word; to send me on here, to be an encumbrance to my friends, so long before you vouchsafe to come. But you knew what a dutiful creature you had to deal with. You knew I should not stir till my lord and master appeared. Here have I been sitting this hour, giving these young ladies a sample of true conjugal obedience; for who can say; you know, how soon it may be wanted?'

Mr Elton was so hot and tired, that all this wit seemed thrown away. His civilities to the other ladies must be paid; but his subsequent object was to lament over himself, for the heat he was suffering, and the walk he had had for nothing.

'When I got to Donwell,' said he, 'Knightley could not be found. Very odd! very unaccountable! after the note I sent him this morning, and the message he returned, that he should certainly be at home till one.'

'Donwell!' cried his wife. 'My dear Mr E., you have not been to Donwell! you mean the Crown; you come from the meeting at the Crown.'

'No, no, that's tomorrow; and I particularly wanted to see Knightley today on that very account. Such a dreadful broiling morning! I went over the fields too' (speaking in a tone of great ill usage), 'which made it so much the worse. And then not to find him at home! I assure you I am not at all pleased. And no apology left, no message for me. The housekeeper declared she knew nothing of my being expected. Very extraordinary! And nobody knew at all which way he was gone. Perhaps to Hartfield, perhaps to the Abbey Mill, perhaps into his woods. Miss Woodhouse, this is not like our friend Knightley! Can you explain it?'

Emma amused herself by protesting that it was very extraordinary indeed, and that she had not a syllable to say for him.

'I cannot imagine,' said Mrs Elton (feeling the indignity as a wife ought to do), 'I cannot imagine how he could do such a thing by you, of all people in the world! The very last person whom one should expect to be forgotten! My dear Mr E., he must have left a message for you, I am sure he must. Not even Knightley could be so very eccentric; and his servants forgot it. Depend upon it that was the case; and very likely to happen with the Donwell servants, who are all, I have often observed, extremely awkward and remiss. I am sure I would not have such a creature as his Harry stand at our sideboard for any consideration. And as for Mrs Hodges, Wright holds her very cheap indeed. She promised Wright a receipt, and never sent it.'

'I met William Larkins,' continued Mr Elton, 'as I got near the house, and he told me I should not find his master at home but I did not believe him. William seemed rather out of humour. He did not know what was come to his master lately, he said, but he could hardly ever get the speech of him. I have nothing to do with William's wants, but it really is of very great importance that *I* should see Knightley today; and it becomes a matter, therefore, of very serious inconvenience that I should have had this hot walk to no purpose.'

Emma felt that she could not do better than go home directly. In all probability she was at this very time waited for there; and Mr Knightley might be preserved from sinking deeper in aggression towards Mr Elton, if not towards William Larkins.

She was pleased, on taking leave, to find Miss Fairfax determined to attend her out of the room, to go with her even downstairs; it gave her an opportunity, which she immediately made use of, to say: 'It is as well, perhaps, that I have not had the possibility.

Had you not been surrounded by other friends, I might have been tempted to introduce a subject, to ask questions, to speak more openly than might have been strictly correct. I feel that I should certainly have been impertinent.'

'Oh!' cried Jane, with a blush and a hesitation which Emma thought more becoming to her than all the elegance of all her usual composure – 'there would have been no danger. The danger would have been of my wearying you. You could not have gratified me more than by expressing an interest – Indeed, Miss Wood-house' (speaking more collectedly), 'with the consciousness which I have of misconduct – very great misconduct – it is particularly consoling to me to know that those of my friends whose good opinion is most worth preserving, are not disgusted to such a degree as to – I have not time for half that I could wish to say. I long to make apologies, excuses, to urge something for myself. I feel it so very due. But, unfortunately – in short, if your compassion does not stand my friend – '

'Oh! you are too scrupulous, indeed you are,' cried Emma warmly, and taking her hand. 'You owe me no apologies; and everybody to whom you might be supposed to owe them is so perfectly satisfied, so delighted even – '

'You are very kind, but I know what my manners were to you. So cold and artificial! I had always a part to act. It was a life of deceit! I know that I must have disgusted you.'

'Pray say no more. I feel that all the apologies should be on my side. Let us forgive each other at once. We must do whatever is to be done quickest, and I think our feelings will lose no time there. I hope you have pleasant accounts from Windsor?'

'Very.'

'And the next news, I suppose, will be, that we are to lose you – just as I begin to know you.'

'Oh! as to all that, of course nothing can be thought of yet. I am here till claimed by Colonel and Mrs Campbell.'

'Nothing can be actually settled yet, perhaps,' replied Emma, smiling – 'but, excuse me, it must be thought of.'

The smile was returned as Jane answered: 'You are very right; it has been thought of. And I will own to you (I am sure it will be safe), that so far as our living with Mr Churchill at Enscombe, it is settled. There must be three months, at least, of deep mourning; but when they are over, I imagine there will be nothing more to wait for.'

'Thank you, thank you. This is just what I wanted to be assured of. Oh! if you knew how much I love everything that is decided and open! Goodbye, goodbye.'

Chapter 53

Mrs Weston's friends were all made happy by her safety; and if the satisfaction of her well-doing could be increased to Emma, it was by knowing her to be the mother of a little girl. She had been decided in wishing for a Miss Weston. She would not acknowledge that it was with any view of making a match for her, hereafter, with either of Isabella's sons; but she was convinced that a daughter would suit both father and mother best. It would be a great comfort to Mr Weston, as he grew older – and even Mr Weston might be growing older ten years hence – to have his fireside enlivened by the sports and the nonsense, the freaks and the fancies of a child never banished from home; and Mrs Weston – no one could doubt that a daughter would be most to her; and it would be quite a pity that anyone who so well knew how to teach, should not have their powers in exercise again.

'She has had the advantage, you know, of practising on me,' she continued – 'like La Baronne d'Almane on La Comtesse d'Ostalis, in Madame de Genlis's *Adelaide and Theodore*, and we shall now see her own little Adelaide educated on a more perfect plan.'

'That is,' replied Mr Knightley, 'she will indulge her even more than she did you, and believe that she does not indulge her at all. It will be the only difference.'

'Poor child!' cried Emma; 'at that rate, what will become of her?'

'Nothing very bad. The fate of thousands. She will be disagreeable in infancy, and correct herself as she grows older. I am losing all my bitterness against spoilt children, my dearest Emma. I, who am owing all my happiness to *you*, would not it be horrible ingratitude in me to be severe on them?'

Emma laughed, and replied: 'But I had the assistance of all your endeavours to counteract the indulgence of other people. I doubt whether my own sense would have corrected me without it.'

'Do you? I have no doubt. Nature gave you understanding: Miss Taylor gave you principles. You must have done well. My interference was quite as likely to do harm as good. It was very natural for you to say: "What right has he to lecture me?" and I am afraid very natural for you to feel that it was done in a disagreeable manner. I do not believe I did you any good. The good was all to myself, by making you an object of the tenderest affection to me. I could not think about you so much without doting on you, faults and all; and by dint of fancying so many errors, have been in love with you ever since you were thirteen at least.'

'I am sure you were of use to me,' cried Emma. 'I was very often influenced rightly by you – oftener than I would own at the time. I am very sure you did me good. And if poor little Anna Weston is to be spoiled, it will be the greatest humanity in you to do as much for her as you have done for me, except falling in love with her when she is thirteen.'

'How often, when you were a girl, have you said to me, with one of your saucy looks: "Mr Knightley, I am going to do so-and-so; papa says I may," or, "I have Miss Taylor's leave" – something which, you knew, I did not approve. In such cases my interference was giving you two bad feelings instead of one.'

'What an amiable creature I was! No wonder you should hold my speeches in such affectionate remembrance.'

' "Mr Knightley," you always called me. "Mr Knightley"; and, from habit, it has not so very formal a sound. And yet it is formal. I want you to call me something else, but I do not know what.'

'I remember once calling you "George," in one of my amiable fits, about ten years ago. I did it because I thought it would offend you; but, as you made no objection, I never did it again.'

'And cannot you call me "George" now?'

'Impossible! I never can call you anything but "Mr Knightley". I will not promise even to equal the elegant terseness of Mrs Elton, by calling you Mr K. But I will promise,' she added presently, laughing and blushing, 'I will promise to call you once by your Christian name. I do not say when, but perhaps you may guess where – in the building in which N. takes M. for better, for worse.'

Emma grieved that she could not be more openly just to one important service which his better sense would have rendered her, to the advice which would have saved her from the worst of all her womanly follies – her wilful intimacy with Harriet Smith; but it was too tender a subject. She could not enter on it. Harriet was very seldom mentioned between them. This, on his side, might merely proceed from her not being thought of; but Emma was rather inclined to attribute it to delicacy, and a suspicion, from some appearances, that their friendship was declining. She was aware herself that, parting under any other circumstances, they certainly should have corresponded more, and that her intelligence would not have rested, as it now almost wholly did, on Isabella's letters. He might observe that it was so. The pain of being obliged to practise concealment towards him was very little inferior to the pain of having made Harriet unhappy.

Isabella sent quite as good an account of her visitor as could be expected; on her first arrival she had thought her out of spirits, which appeared perfectly natural, as there was a dentist to be consulted; but since that business had been over, she did not appear to find Harriet different from what she had known her before. Isabella, to be sure, was no very quick observer; yet if Harriet had not been equal to playing with the children, it would not have escaped her. Emma's comforts and hopes were most agreeably carried on, by Harriet's being to stay longer; her fortnight was likely to be a month at least. Mr and Mrs John Knightley were to come down in August, and she was invited to remain till they could bring her back.

'John does not even mention your friend,' said Mr Knightley. 'Here is his answer, if you like to see it.' It was the answer to the communication of his intended marriage. Emma accepted it with a very eager hand, with an impatience all alive to know what he would say about it, and not at all checked by hearing that her friend was unmentioned.

'John enters like a brother into my happiness,' continued Mr Knightley, 'but he is no complimenter; and though I well know him, to have likewise a most brotherly affection for you, he is so far from making flourishes, that any other young woman might think him rather cool in her praise. But I am not afraid of your seeing what he writes.'

'He writes like a sensible man,' replied Emma, when she had read the letter. 'I honour his sincerity. It is very plain that he considers the good fortune of the engagement as all on my side, but that he is not without hope of my growing, in time, as worthy of your affection as you think me already. Had he said anything to bear a different construction, I should not have believed him.'

'My Emma, he means no such thing. He only means – '

'He and I should differ very little in our estimation of the two' – interrupted she, with a sort of serious smile – 'much less, perhaps, than he is aware of, if we could enter without ceremony or reserve on the subject.'

'Emma, my dear Emma – '

'Oh!' she cried, with more thorough gaiety, 'if you fancy your brother does not do me justice, only wait till my dear father is in the secret, and hear his opinion. Depend upon it, he will be much further from doing you justice. He will think all the happiness, all the advantage, on your side of the question; all the merit on mine. I wish I may not sink into "poor Emma" with him at once. His tender compassion towards oppressed worth can go no further.'

'Ah!' he cried, 'I wish your father might be half as easily convinced as John will be, of our having every right that equal worth can give, to be happy together. I am amused by one part of John's letter – did you notice it? – where he says that my information did not take him wholly by surprise, that he was rather in expectation of hearing something of the kind.'

'If I understand your brother, he only means so far as your having some thoughts of marrying. He had no idea of me. He seems perfectly unprepared for that.'

'Yes, yes – but I am amused that he should have seen so far into my feelings. What has he been judging by? I am not conscious of any difference in my spirits or conversation that could prepare him at this time for my marrying any more than at another. But it was so, I suppose. I dare say there was a difference when I was staying with them the other day. I believe I did not play with the children quite so much as usual. I remember one evening the poor boys saying, "Uncle seems always tired now." '

The time was coming when the news must be spread further, and other persons' reception of it tried. As soon as Mrs Weston was sufficiently recovered to admit Mr Woodhouse's visits, Emma having it in view that her gentle reasonings should be employed in the cause, resolved first to announce it at home, and then at Randalls. But how to break it to her father at last! She had bound herself to do it, in such an hour of Mr Knightley's absence, or when it came to the point her heart would have failed her, and she must have put it off; but Mr Knightley was to come at such a time, and follow up the beginning she was to make. She was forced to speak, and to speak cheerfully too. She must not make it a more decided subject of misery to him, by a melancholy tone herself. She must not appear to think it a misfortune. With all the spirits she could command, she prepared him first for something strange, and then, in a few words, said, that if his consent and approbation could be obtained – which, she trusted, would be attended with no difficulty, since it was a plan to promote the happiness of all – she and Mr Knightley meant to marry; by which means Hartfield would receive the constant addition of that person's company, whom she knew he loved, next to his daughters and Mrs Weston, best in the world.

Poor man! it was at first a considerable shock to him, and he tried earnestly to dissuade her from it. She was reminded, more than once, of having always said she would never marry, and assured that it would be a great deal better for her to remain single; and told of poor Isabella, and poor Miss Taylor. But it would not do. Emma hung about him affectionately, and smiled, and said it must be so; and that he must not class her with Isabella and Mrs Weston, whose marriages taking them from Hartfield had, indeed, made a melancholy change: but she was not going from Hartfield; she should be always there; she was introducing no change in their numbers or their comforts but for the better. and she was very sure that he would be a great deal the happier for having Mr Knightley always at hand, when he were once got used to the idea. Did he not love Mr Knightley very much? He would not deny that he did, she was sure. Whom did he ever want to consult on business but Mr Knightley? Who was so useful to him, who so ready to write his letters, who so glad to assist him? Who so cheerful, so attentive, so attached to him? Would not he like to have him always on the spot? Yes. That was all very true. Mr Knightley could not be there too often; he should be glad to see him every day; but they did see him every day as it was. Why could not they go on as they had done?

Mr Woodhouse could not be soon reconciled; but the worst was overcome, the idea was given; time and continual repetition must do the rest. To Emma's entreaties and assurances succeeded Mr Knightley's, whose fond praise of her gave the subject even a kind of welcome; and he was soon used to be talked to by each on every fair occasion. They had all the assistance which Isabella could give, by letters of the strongest approbation; and Mrs Weston was ready, on the first meeting, to consider the subject in the most serviceable light; first as a settled, and, secondly, as a good one – well aware of the nearly equal importance of the two recommendations to Mr Woodhouse's mind. It was agreed upon, as what was to be; and everybody by whom he was used to be guided assuring him that it would be for his happiness, and having some feelings himself which almost admitted it, he began to think that some time or other, in another year or two, perhaps, it might not be so very bad if the marriage did take place.

Mrs Weston was acting no part, feigning no feelings in all that she said to him in favour of the event. She had been extremely surprised, never more so than when Emma first opened the affair to her; but she saw in it only increase of happiness to all, and had no scruple in urging him to the utmost. She had such a regard for Mr Knightley, as to think he deserved even her dearest Emma; and it was in every respect so proper, suitable, and unexceptionable a connection, and in one respect, one point of the highest importance, so peculiarly eligible, so singularly fortunate, that now it seemed as if Emma could not safely have attached herself to any other creature, and that she had herself been the stupidest of beings in not having thought of it, and wished it long ago. How very few of those men in a rank of life to address Emma would have renounced their own home for Hartfield! And who but Mr Knightley could know and bear with Mr Woodhouse, so as to make such an arrangement desirable! The difficulty of disposing of poor Mr Woodhouse had been always felt in her husband's plans and her own, for a marriage between Frank and Emma. How to settle the claims of Enscombe and Hartfield had been a continual impediment – less acknowledged by Mr Weston than by herself – but even he had never been able to finish the subject better than by saying: 'Those matters will take care of themselves; the young people will find a way.' But here there was nothing to be shifted off in a wild speculation of the future. It was all right, all open, all equal. No sacrifice on any side worth the name. It was a union of the highest promise of felicity in itself, and without one real, rational difficulty to oppose or delay it.

Mrs Weston, with her baby on her knee, indulging in such reflections as these, was one of the happiest women in the world. If anything could increase her delight, it was perceiving that the baby would soon have outgrown its first set of caps.

The news was universally a surprise wherever it spread; and Mr Weston had his five minutes' share of it; but five minutes were enough to familiarise the idea to his quickness of mind. He saw the advantages of the match, and rejoiced in them with all the constancy of his wife; but the wonder of it was very soon nothing; and by the end of an hour he was not far from believing that he had always foreseen it.

'It is to be a secret, I conclude,' said he. 'These matters are always a secret till it is found out that everybody knows them. Only let me be told when I may speak out. I wonder whether Jane has any suspicion?'

He went to Highbury the next morning, and satisfied himself on that point. He told her the news. Was not she like a daughter, his eldest daughter? he must tell her; and Miss Bates being present, it passed, of course, to Mrs Cole, Mrs Perry, and Mrs Elton, immediately afterwards. It was no more than the principals were prepared for; they had calculated from the time of its being known at Randalls how soon it would be over Highbury; and were thinking of themselves, as the evening wonder in many a family circle, with great sagacity.

In general, it was a very well approved match. Some might think him, and others might think her, the most in luck. One set might recommend their all removing to Donwell, and leaving Hartfield for the John Knightleys; and another might predict disagreements among their servants; but yet, upon the whole, there was no serious objection raised, except in one habitation – the Vicarage. There, the surprise was not softened by any satisfaction. Mr Elton cared little about it, compared with his wife; he only hoped 'the young lady's pride would now be contented'; and supposed 'she had always meant to catch Knightley if she could'; and, on the point of living at Hartfield, could daringly exclaim, 'Rather he than I!' But Mrs Elton was very much discomposed indeed. 'Poor Knightley! poor fellow! sad business for him. She was extremely concerned; for though very eccentric, he had a thousand good qualities. How could he be so taken in? Did not think him at all in love – not in the least. Poor Knightley! There would be an end of all pleasant intercourse with him. How happy he had been to come and dine with them whenever they asked him! But that would be all over now. Poor fellow! No more exploring parties to Donwell made for *her*. Oh no; there would be a Mrs Knightley to throw cold water on everything. Extremely disagreeable; but she was not at all sorry that she had abused the housekeeper the other day. Shocking plan, living together. It would never do. She knew a family near Maple Grove who had tried it, and been obliged to separate before the end of the first quarter.'

Chapter 54

Time passed on. A few more tomorrows, and the party from London would be arriving. It was an alarming change; and Emma was thinking of it one morning, as what must bring a great deal to agitate and grieve her, when Mr Knightley came in, and distressing thoughts were put by. After the first chat of pleasure, he was silent; and then, in a graver tone, began with: 'I have something to tell you, Emma; some news.'

'Good or bad?' said she, quickly, looking up in his face.

'I do not know which it ought to be called.'

'Oh, good, I am sure. I see it in your countenance. You are trying not to smile.'

'I am afraid,' said he, composing his features, 'I am very much afraid, my dear Emma, that you will not smile when you hear it.'

'Indeed! but why so? I can hardly imagine that anything which pleases or amuses you should not please and amuse me too.'

'There is one subject,' he replied, 'I hope but one, on which we do not think alike.' He paused a moment, again smiling, with his eyes fixed on her face. 'Does nothing occur to you? Do not you recollect? Harriet Smith.'

Her cheeks flushed at the name, and she felt afraid of something, though she knew not what.

'Have you heard from her yourself this morning?' cried he. 'You have, I believe, and know the whole.'

'No, I have not; I know nothing; pray tell me.'

'You are prepared for the worst, I see; and very bad it is. Harriet Smith marries Robert Martin.'

Emma gave a start, which did not seem like being prepared; and her eyes, in eager gaze, said, 'No, this is impossible!' but her lips were closed.

'It is so, indeed! continued Mr Knightley; 'I have it from Robert Martin himself. He left me not half an hour ago.'

She was still looking at him with the most speaking amazement.

'You like it, my Emma, as little as I feared – I wish our opinions were the same. But in time they will. Time, you may be sure, will make one or the other of us think differently; and in the meanwhile, we need not talk much on the subject.'

'You mistake me, you quite mistake me,' she replied, exerting herself. 'It is not that such a circumstance would now make me unhappy, but I cannot believe it. It seems an impossibility! You cannot mean to say that Harriet Smith has accepted Robert Martin! You cannot mean that he has even proposed to her again – yet! You only mean that he intends it.'

'I mean that he has done it,' answered Mr Knightley, with smiling but determined decision, 'and been accepted.'

'Good God!' she cried. 'Well!' Then having recourse to her work-basket, in excuse for leaning down her face, and concealing all the exquisite feelings of delight and entertainment which she knew she must be expressing, she added, 'Well, now tell me everything; make this intelligible to me. How, where, when? Let me know it all. I never was more surprised – but it does not make me unhappy, I assure you. How – how has it been possible?'

'It is a very simple story. He went to town on business three days ago, and I got him to take charge of some papers which I was wanting to send to John. He delivered these papers to John, at his chambers, and was asked by him to join their party the same evening to Astley's. They were going to take the two eldest boys to Astley's. The party was to be our brother and sister, Henry, John – and Miss Smith. My friend Robert could not resist. They called for him in their way; were all extremely amused: and my brother asked him to dine with them the next day, which he did, and in the course of that visit (as I understand) he found an opportunity of speaking to Harriet; and certainly did not speak in vain. She made him, by her acceptance, as happy even as he is deserving. He came down by yesterday's coach, and was with me this morning, immediately after breakfast, to report his proceedings, first on my affairs, and then on his own. This is all that I can relate of the how, where, and when. Your friend Harriet will make a much longer history when you see her. She will give you all the minute particulars, which only woman's language can make interesting. In our communications we deal only in the great. However, I must say, that Robert Martin's heart seemed for *him*, and to *me*, very overflowing; and that he did mention, without its being much to the purpose, that on quitting their box at Astley's, my brother took charge of Mrs John Knightley and Little John, and he followed, with Miss Smith and Henry; and that at one time they were in such a crowd as to make Miss Smith rather uneasy.'

He stopped. Emma dared not attempt any immediate reply. To speak, she was sure, would be to betray a most unreasonable degree of happiness. She must wait a moment, or he would think her mad. Her silence disturbed him; and after observing her a little while, he added: 'Emma, my love, you said that this circumstance would not now make you unhappy; but I am afraid it gives you more pain than you expected. His situation is an evil; but you must consider it as what satisfies your friend; and I will answer for your thinking better and better of him as you know him more; his good sense and good principles would delight you. As far as the man is concerned, you could not wish your friend in better hands. His rank in society I would alter if I could, which is saying a great deal, I assure you, Emma. You laugh at me about William Larkins; but I could quite as ill spare Robert Martin.'

He wanted her to look up and smile; and having now brought herself not to smile too broadly, she did, cheerfully answering: 'You need not be at any pains to reconcile me to the match. I think Harriet is doing extremely well. *Her* connections may be worse than *his*: in respectability of character, there can be no doubt that they are. I have been silent from surprise, merely – excessive surprise. You cannot imagine how suddenly it has come on me, how peculiarly unprepared I was! – for I had reason to believe her very lately more determined against him, much more than she was before.'

'You ought to know your friend best,' replied Mr Knightley. 'but I should say she was a good-tempered, soft-hearted girl, not likely to be very, very determined against any young man who told her he loved her.'

Emma could not help laughing as she answered, 'Upon my word, I believe you know her quite as well as I do. But, Mr Knightley, are you perfectly sure that she has absolutely and downright *accepted* him? I could suppose she might in time, but can she already? Did not you misunderstand him? You were both talking of other things; of business, shows of cattle, or new drills; and might not you, in the confusion of so many subjects, mistake him? It was not Harriet's hand that he was certain of – it was the dimensions of some famous ox.'

The contrast between the countenance and air of Mr Knightley and Robert Martin was, at this moment, so strong to Emma's feelings, and so strong was the recollection of all that had so recently passed on Harriet's side, so fresh the sound of those words spoken with such emphasis, 'No, I hope I know better than to think of Robert Martin,' that she was really expecting the intelligence to prove, in some measure, premature. It could not be otherwise.

'Do you dare say this?' cried Mr Knightley. 'Do you dare to suppose me so great a blockhead as not to know what a man is talking of? What do you deserve?'

'Oh! I always deserve the best treatment, because I never put up with any other; and, therefore, you must give me a plain, direct answer. Are you quite sure that you understand the terms on which Mr Martin and Harriet now are?'

'I am quite sure,' he replied, speaking very distinctly, 'that he told me she had accepted him; and that there was no obscurity, nothing doubtful, in the words he used; and I think I can give you a proof that it must be so. He asked my opinion as to what he was now to do. He knew of no one but Mrs Goddard to whom he could apply for information of her relations or friends. Could I mention anything more fit to be done than to go to Mrs Goddard? I assured him that I could not. Then, he said, he would endeavour to see her in the course of this day.'

'I am perfectly satisfied,' replied Emma, with the brightest smiles, 'and most sincerely wish them happy.'

'You are materially changed since we talked on this subject before.'

'I hope so – for at that time I was a fool.'

'And I am changed also; for I am now very willing to grant you all Harriet's good qualities. I have taken some pains for your sake, and for Robert Martin's sake (whom I have always had reason to believe as much in love with her as ever), to get acquainted with her. I have often talked to her a good deal. You must have seen that I did. Sometimes, indeed, I have thought you were half suspecting me of pleading poor Martin's cause, which was never the case; but, from all my observations, I am convinced of her being an artless, amiable girl, with very good notions, very seriously good principles, and placing her happiness in the affections and utility of domestic life. Much of this, I have no doubt, she may thank you for.'

'Me!' cried Emma, shaking her head. 'Ah, poor Harriet!'

She checked herself, however, and submitted quietly to a little more praise than she deserved.

Their conversation was soon afterwards closed by the entrance of her father. She was not sorry. She wanted to be alone. Her mind was in a state of flutter and wonder, which made it impossible for her to be collected. She was in dancing, singing, exclaiming spirits; and till she had moved about, and talked to herself, and laughed and reflected, she could be fit for nothing rational.

Her father's business was to announce James's being gone out to put the horses to, preparatory to their now daily drive to Randalls; and she had, therefore, an immediate excuse for disappearing.

The joy, the gratitude, the exquisite delight of her sensations may be imagined. The sole grievance and alloy thus removed in the prospect of Harriet's welfare, she was really in danger of becoming too happy for security. What had she to wish for? Nothing, but to grow more worthy of him, whose intentions and judgement had been ever so superior to her own. Nothing but that the lessons of her past folly might teach her humility and circumspection in future.

Serious she was, very serious, in her thankfulness and in her resolutions; and yet there was no preventing a laugh, sometimes in the very midst of them. She must laugh at such a close – such an end of the doleful disappointment of five weeks back – such a heart – such a Harriet!

Now there would be pleasure in her returning; everything would be a pleasure; it would be a great pleasure to know Robert Martin.

High in the rank of her most serious and heartfelt felicities was the reflection that all necessity of concealment from Mr Knightley would soon be over. The disguise, equivocation, mystery, so hateful to her to practise, might soon be over. She could now look forward to giving him that full and perfect confidence which her disposition was most ready to welcome as a duty.

In the gayest and happiest spirits, she set forward with her father, not always listening, but always agreeing, to what he said; and, whether in speech or silence, conniving at the comfortable persuasion of his being obliged to go to Randalls every day, or poor Mrs Weston would be disappointed.

They arrived. Mrs Weston was alone in the drawing-room. But hardly had they been told of the baby, and Mr Woodhouse received the thanks for coming, which he asked for, when a glimpse was caught through the blind of two figures passing near the window.

'It is Frank and Miss Fairfax,' said Mrs Weston. 'I was just going to tell you of our agreeable surprise in seeing him arrive this morning. He stays till tomorrow, and Miss Fairfax has been persuaded to spend the day with us. They are coming in, I hope.'

In half a minute they were in the room. Emma was extremely glad to see him; but there was a degree of confusion, a number of embarrassing recollections, on each side. They met readily and smiling, but with a consciousness which at first allowed little to be said; and having all sat down again, there was for some time such a blank in the circle that Emma began to doubt whether the wish now indulged, which she had long felt, of seeing Frank Churchill once more, and of seeing him with Jane, would yield its proportion of pleasure. When Mr Weston joined the party, however, and when the baby was fetched, there was no longer a want of subject or animation, or of courage and opportunity for Frank Churchill to draw near her and say: 'I have to thank you, Miss Woodhouse, for a very kind, forgiving message, in one of Mrs Weston's letters. I hope time has not made you less willing to pardon; I hope you do not retract what you then said.'

'No, indeed,' cried Emma, most happy to begin; 'not in the least. I am particularly glad to see and shake hands with you, and to give you joy in person.'

He thanked her with all his heart, and continued some time to speak with serious feeling of his gratitude and happiness.

'Is not she looking well?' said he, turning his eyes towards Jane – 'better than she ever used to do? You see how my father and Mrs Weston dote upon her.'

But his spirits were soon rising again; and, with laughing eyes, after mentioning the expected return of the Campbells, he named the name of Dixon. Emma blushed, and forbade its being pronounced in her hearing.

'I can never think of it,' she cried, 'without extreme shame.'

'The shame,' he answered, 'is all mine, or ought to be. But is it possible that you had no suspicion? I mean of late: early, I know, you had none.'

'I never had the smallest, I assure you.'

'That appears quite wonderful. I was once very near – and I wish I had; it would have been better. But though I was always doing wrong things, they were very *bad* wrong things, and such as did me no service. It would have been a much better transgression had I broken the bond of secrecy and told you everything.'

'It is not now worth a regret,' said Emma.

'I have some hope,' resumed he, 'of my uncle's being persuaded to pay a visit at Randalls; he wants to be introduced to her. When the Campbells are returned, we shall meet them in London, and continue there, I trust, till we may carry her northward; but now, I am at such a distance from her – is not it hard, Miss Woodhouse? Till this morning, we have not once met since the day of reconciliation. Do not you pity me?'

Emma spoke her pity so very kindly, that with a sudden accession of gay thought, he cried: 'Ah! by the by,' then sinking his

435

voice, and looking demure for the moment, 'I hope Mr Knightley is well?' He paused. She coloured and laughed. 'I know you saw my letter, and think you may remember my wish in your favour. Let me return your congratulations. I assure you that I have heard the news with the warmest interest and satisfaction. He is a man whom I cannot presume to praise.'

Emma was delighted, and only wanted him to go on in the same style; but his mind was the next moment in his own concerns and with his own Jane, and his next words were: 'Did you ever see such a skin? such smoothness! such delicacy! and yet without being actually fair. One cannot call her fair. It is a most uncommon complexion, with her dark eyelashes and hair – a most distinguishing complexion! So peculiarly the lady in it. Just colour enough for beauty.'

'I have always admired her complexion,' replied Emma archly; 'but do not I remember the time when you found fault with her for being so pale? When we first began to talk of her. Have you quite forgotten?'

'Oh, no! what an impudent dog I was! how could I dare – '

But he laughed so heartily at the recollection that Emma could not help saying: 'I do suspect that in the midst of your perplexities at that time, you had very great amusement in tricking us all. I am sure you had. I am sure it was a consolation to you.'

'Oh, no, no, no! how can you suspect me of such a thing? I was the most miserable wretch.'

'Not quite so miserable as to be insensibile to mirth. I am sure it was a source of high entertainment to you, to feel that you were taking us all in. Perhaps I am the readier to suspect, because, to tell you the truth, I think it might have been some amusement to myself in the same situation. I think there is a little likeness between us.'

He bowed.

'If not in our dispositions,' she presently added, with a look of true sensibility, 'there is a likeness in our destiny; the destiny which bids fair to connect us with two characters so much superior to our own.'

'True, true,' he answered warmly. 'No, not true on your side. You can have no superior, but most true on mine. She is a complete angel. Look at her. Is not she an angel in every gesture? Observe the turn of her throat. Observe her eyes, as she is looking up at my father. You will be glad to hear' (inclining his head, and whispering seriously) 'that my uncle means to give her all my aunt's jewels. They are to be new set. I am resolved to have some in an ornament for the head. Will not it be beautiful in her dark hair?'

'Very beautiful, indeed,' replied Emma; and she spoke so kindly that he gratefully burst out: 'How delighted I am to see you again! and to see you in such excellent looks! I would not have missed this meeting for the world. I should certainly have called at Hartfield had you failed to come.'

The others had been talking of the child, Mrs Weston giving an account of a little alarm she had been under the evening before, from the infant's appearing not quite well. She believed she had been foolish, but it had alarmed her, and she had been within half a minute of sending for Mr Perry. Perhaps she ought to be ashamed, but Mr Weston had been almost as uneasy as herself. In ten minutes, however, the child had been perfectly well again. This was her history; and particularly interesting it was to Mr Woodhouse, who commended her very much for thinking of sending for Perry, and only regretted that she had not done it. 'She should always send for Perry, if the child appeared in the slightest degree disordered, were it only for a moment. She could not be too soon alarmed, nor send for Perry too often. It was a pity, perhaps, that he had not come last night; for, though the child seemed well now – very well considering – it would probably have been better if Perry had seen it.'

Frank Churchill caught the name.

'Perry!' said he to Emma, and trying, as he spoke, to catch Miss Fairfax's eye. 'My friend Mr Perry! What are they saying about Mr Perry? Has he been here this morning? And how does he travel now? Has he set up his carriage?'

Emma soon recollected, and understood him; and while she joined in the laugh, it was evident from Jane's countenance, that she too was really hearing him, though trying to seem deaf.

'Such an extraordinary dream of mine!' he cried. 'I can never think of it without laughing. She hears us, she hears us, Miss Wood-house. I see it in her cheek, her smile, her vain attempt to frown. Look at her. Do not you see that, at this instant, the very passage of her own letter, which sent me the report, is passing under her eye; that the whole blunder is spread before her; that she can attend to nothing else, though pretending to listen to the others?'

Jane was forced to smile completely for a moment; and the smile partly remained as she turned towards him, and said in a conscious, low, yet steady voice: 'How you can bear such recollections is astonishing to me. They *will* sometimes obtrude; but how you can *court* them!'

He had a great deal to say in return, and very entertainingly; but Emma's feelings were chiefly with Jane in the argument; and on leaving Randalls, and falling naturally into a comparison of the two men, she felt, that pleased as she had been to see Frank Chur-chill, and really regarding him as she did with friendship, she had never been more sensible of Mr Knightley's high superiority of character. The happiness of this most happy day received its completion in the animated contemplation of his worth which this comparison produced.

Chapter 55

If Emma had still, at intervals, an anxious feeling for Harriet, a momentary doubt of its being possible for her to be really cured of her attachment to Mr Knightley, and really able to accept another man from unbiassed inclination, it was not long that she had to suffer from the recurrence of any such uncertainty. A very few days brought the party from London; and she had no sooner an opportunity of being one hour alone with Harriet, than she became perfectly satisfied, unaccountable as it was, that Robert Martin had thoroughly supplanted Mr Knightley; and was now forming all her views of happiness.

Harriet was a little distressed; – did look a little foolish at first but having once owned that she had been presumptuous and silly, and self-deceived before, her pain and confusion seemed to die away with the words, and leave her without a care for the past, and with the fullest exultation in the present and future: for as to her friend's approbation, Emma had instantly removed every fear of that nature, by meeting her with the most unqualified congratulations. Harriet was most happy to give every particular of the evening at Astley's, and the dinner the next day; she could dwell on it all with the utmost delight. But what did such particulars explain? The fact was, as Emma could now acknowledge, that Harriet had always liked Robert Martin; and that his continuing to love her had been irresistible. Beyond this, it must ever be unintelligible to Emma.

The event, however, was most joyful; and every day was giving her fresh reason for thinking so. Harriet's parentage became known. She proved to be the daughter of a tradesman, rich enough to afford her the comfortable maintenance which had ever been hers, and decent enough to have always wished for concealment. Such was the blood of gentility which Emma had formerly been so ready to vouch for! It was likely to be as untainted, perhaps, as the blood of many a gentleman: but what a connection had she been preparing for Mr Knightley or for the Churchills, or even for Mr Elton! The stain of illegitimacy, unbleached by nobility or wealth, would have been a stain indeed.

No objection was raised on the father's side; the young man was treated liberally; it was all as it should be; and as Emma became acquainted with Robert Martin, who was now introduced at Hartfield, she fully acknowledged in him all the appearance of sense and worth which could bid fairest for her little friend. She had no doubt of Harriet's happiness with any good-tempered man; but with him, and in the home he offered, there would be the hope of more, of security, stability, and improvement. She would be placed in the midst of those who loved her, and who had better sense than herself; retired enough for safety, and occupied enough for cheerfulness. She would be never led into temptation, nor left for it to find her out. She would be respectable and happy; and Emma admitted her to be the luckiest creature in the world, to have created so steady and persevering an affection in such a man; or, if not quite the luckiest, to yield only to herself.

Harriet, necessarily drawn away by her engagements with the Martins, was less and less at Hartfield, which was not to be regretted. The intimacy between her and Emma must sink; their friendship must change into a calmer sort of goodwill; and, fortunately, what ought to be, and must be, seemed already beginning, and in the most gradual, natural manner.

Before the end of September, Emma attended Harriet to church, and saw her hand bestowed on Robert Martin with so complete a satisfaction, as no remembrances, even connected with Mr Elton as he stood before them, could impair. Perhaps indeed, at that time, she scarcely saw Mr Elton, but as the clergyman whose blessing at the altar might next fall on herself. Robert Martin and Harriet Smith, the latest couple engaged of the three, were the first to be married.

Jane Fairfax had already quitted Highbury, and was restored to the comforts of her beloved home with the Campbells. The Mr Churchills were also in town; and they were only waiting for November.

The intermediate month was the one fixed on, as far as they dared, by Emma and Mr Knightley. They had determined that their marriage ought to be concluded, while John and Isabella were still at Hartfield; to allow them the fortnight's absence in a tour to the sea-side, which was the plan. John and Isabella, and every other friend, were agreed in approving it. But Mr Wood-house – how was Mr Woodhouse to be induced to consent? he, who had never yet alluded to their marriage but as a distant event. When first sounded on the subject, he was so miserable that they were almost hopeless. A second allusion, indeed, gave less pain. He began to think it was to be, and that he could not prevent it – a very promising step of the mind on its way to resignation. Still, however, he was not happy. Nay, he appeared so much other-wise that his daughter's courage failed. She could not bear to see him suffering; to know him fancying himself neglected; and though her understanding almost acquiesced in the assurance of both the Mr Knightleys, that when once the event were over, his distress would be soon over too, she hesitated – she could not proceed.

In this state of suspense, they were befriended, not by any sudden illumination of Mr Woodhouse's mind, or any wonderful change of his nervous system, but by the operation of the same system in another way. Mrs Weston's poultry-house was robbed one night of all her turkeys – evidently by the ingenuity of man. Other poultry-yards in the neighbourhood also suffered. Pilfering was *house-breaking* to Mr Woodhouse's fears. He was very uneasy; and but for the sense of his son-in-law's protection, would have been under wretched alarm every night of his life. The strength, resolution, and presence of mind of the Mr Knightleys commanded his fullest dependence. While either of them protected him and his, Hartfield was safe. But Mr John Knightley must be in London again by the end of the first week in November.

The result of this distress was, that, with a much more volun-tary, cheerful consent than his daughter had ever presumed to hope for at the moment, she was able to fix her wedding-day; and Mr Elton was called on, within a month from the marriage of Mr and Mrs Robert Martin, to join the hands of Mr Knightley and Miss Woodhouse.

The wedding was very much like other weddings, where the parties have no taste for finery or parade; and Mrs Elton, from the particulars detailed by her husband, thought it all extremely shabby, and very inferior to her own. 'Very little white satin, very few lace veils; a most pitiful business! Selina would stare when she heard of it.' But, in spite of these deficiencies, the wishes, the hopes, the confidence, the predictions of the small band of true friends who witnessed the ceremony, were fully answered in the perfect happiness of the union.